Ultrasensitive and
Rapid Enzyme
Immunoassay

LABORATORY TECHNIQUES IN BIOCHEMISTRY AND MOLECULAR BIOLOGY

Edited by

P.C. van der Vliet — *Department for Physiological Chemistry, University of Utrecht, Utrecht, Netherlands*

Volume 27

ELSEVIER

AMSTERDAM – LAUSANNE – NEW YORK – OXFORD – SHANNON – SINGAPORE – TOKYO

ULTRASENSITIVE AND RAPID ENZYME IMMUNOASSAY

Eiji Ishikawa

Professor of Biochemistry
Department of Biochemistry
Miyazaki Medical College
Miyazaki, Japan

1999
ELSEVIER
AMSTERDAM – LAUSANNE – NEW YORK – OXFORD – SHANNON – SINGAPORE – TOKYO

ELSEVIER SCIENCE B.V.
Sara Burgerhartstraat 25
P.O. Box 211, 1000 AE Amsterdam, The Netherlands

First edition 1999

Library of Congress Cataloging in Publication Data
A catalog record from the Library of Congress has been applied for.

British Library Cataloguing in Publication Data
A catalogue record from the British Library has been applied for.

ISBN: 0-444-50201-7 (library edition)
ISBN: 0-444-50202-5 (pocket edition)
ISBN: 0-7204-4200-1 (series)

Transferred to digital printing 2006

Printed and bound by CPI Antony Rowe, Eastbourne

Preface

During the last 39 years since the development of radioimmuno-assay, or during the last 27 years since the first attempts at enzyme immunoassay, information on immunoassays and related techniques has expanded tremendously, and these techniques have become essential in various fields of pure and applied research. Basic information on these techniques has been summarized in various books to assist not only those who have plans to enter such fields for the first time, but also those who already have some practical experience but are seeking to broaden their knowledge and experience. The aim of this book is to assist those who have plans or are making efforts to perform sensitive or ultrasensitive immunoassays. For this purpose, factors limiting the sensitivity of noncompetitive solid phase enzyme immunoassays are first presented, and some measures to overcome difficulties limiting sensitivities are described. Then, methods are described for performing ultrasensitive immunoassays as rapidly as possible without loss of sensitivity. Finally, some details of protocols for ultrasensitive and rapid enzyme immunoassays and enzyme-labeling, which is an important technique in successful enzyme immunoassays are described.

The author takes this opportunity to thank all the scientists and research assistants, who have worked with me for many years, for their invaluable contributions to development of ultrasensitive and rapid enzyme immunoassays.

Eiji Ishikawa

Contents

xvi

CHAPTER 1

Introduction: classification of immunoassays

The immunoassays that have been developed and used in various fields of research and applications, may be classified as follows (Fig. 1.1).

First, they may be divided into two groups. The group using no labels includes methods such as immunodiffusion and nephelometry and, the other group using labels such as radioisotopes, enzymes, fluorescent and luminescent substances, etc., includes well-known methods such as radioimmunoassay and enzyme immunoassay.

Second, immunoassays using labels may be divided into two groups: homogeneous and heterogeneous immunoassays. In homogeneous immunoassays, signals that can be correlated with the amount or concentration of analytes are obtained directly from reaction mixtures of labeled reagents and samples containing analytes, requiring no bound/free separation steps. Heterogeneous immunoassays require bound/free separation steps but are in general more sensitive than homogenous ones.

Third, both homogeneous and heterogeneous immunoassays may be divided into two groups: competitive and noncompetitive. In general, using identical reacting reagents, noncompetitive immunoassays are more sensitive than competitive ones (Ishikawa et al., 1983a).

In a typical competitive immunoassay, a certain amount of labeled antigen is reacted with a corresponding amount of antibody

1

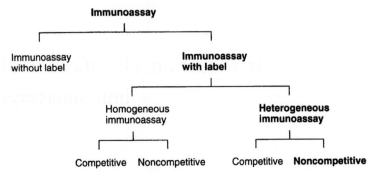

Fig. 1.1. Classification of immunoassay. Boldtype indicates immunoassays described in this book.

in the absence and presence of the antigen to be measured. The amount of antigen to be measured is correlated with the amount of labeled antigen bound to the antibody, which is measured only with a certain range of error (approximately 5%). The sensitivity is higher with lower concentrations of labeled antigen and antibody. However, the concentrations of labeled antigen and antibody should be sufficiently high, so that more than 50% of the labeled antigen and antibody used are in the bound form in the absence of the antigen to be measured. In other words, the minimal concentrations of labeled antigen are limited by the affinities of the antibodies used. Thus, the detection limits of antigens by competitive immunoassays are at femtomole or higher levels in most cases (Fig. 1.2). It makes no difference whether radioisotopes or enzymes are used as labels.

By contrast, in a typical noncompetitive two-site immunoassay, the antigen to be measured is trapped onto antibody-coated solid phase and subsequently allowed to react with labeled antibody. The amount of antigen measured is correlated with the amount of labeled antibody bound to the solid phase. Since excess labeled antibody is effectively eliminated by simple washing, the amount of labeled antibody nonspecifically bound to the solid phase in the absence of antigen (background) can be reduced to a minimum. Thus, attomole sensitivities can be achieved by appropriate techniques,

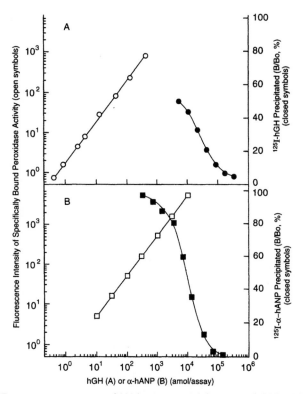

Fig. 1.2. Dose-response curves of (A) human growth hormone (hGH) with a molecular weight of 21 KDa, and (B) human α-atrial natriuretic peptide (α-hANP) of 28 amino acids on competitive radioimmunoassay (closed symbols) and noncompetitive heterogeneous (two-site) solid phase enzyme immunoassay (open symbols).

provided that antibodies with sufficiently high affinity are used (Fig. 1.2) (Ishikawa et al., 1983a).

Thus, noncompetitive immunoassays are more sensitive than competitive ones, when identical antibodies are used in the two immunoassays.

This book deals with noncompetitive heterogeneous solid phase immunoassays using enzymes as labels that can be ultrasensitive.

Fig. 1.2. Dose-response curves of (A) human growth hormone (hGH) with a molecular weight of 21 kDa, and (B) human atrial natriuretic peptide (α-hANP) of 28 amino acids an competitive radioimmunoassay (closed symbols) and non-competitive heterogeneous two-site solid phase enzyme immunoassay (open symbols).

provided that antibodies with sufficiently high affinity are used (Fig. 1.2) (Ishikawa et al., 1983a).

Thus, noncompetitive immunoassays are more sensitive than competitive ones, when identical antibodies are used in the two immunoassays.

This book deals with noncompetitive heterogeneous solid phase immunoassays using enzymes as labels that can be ultrasensitive.

CHAPTER 2

History of ultrasensitive enzyme immunoassay

Radioimmunoassay, developed in 1959 (Berson and Yalow, 1959), made it possible to measure femtomole amounts of peptide hormones in the circulation and was almost generally accepted not to be exceeded in sensitivity by any other method.

However, in 1968, less than a decade later, the use of enzymes as labels in immunoassay was suggested (Miles and Hales, 1968), and the first attempts of enzyme immunoassay were reported in 1971 (Engvall and Perlmann, 1971; van Weemen and Schuurs, 1971). For many years later, the potential of enzyme immunoassay particularly concerning its sensitivity was a focus of discussion by many investigators.

In 1976, a typical view that enzyme immunoassays would replace radioimmunoassays in various fields was published (Editorial, Lancet 1976). One month later, arguments against this view appeared in the same journal. One stated that the suggestion that enzyme-labeling would replace radioisotopic techniques (particularly in assays demanding highest sensitivity) was questionable (Ekins, 1976). The other stated that for analysis of femtomole $(1 \times 10^{-15}$ mol) amounts of steroids, hormones, etc., to aid patient diagnosis and treatment there is only radioimmunoassay (Watson, 1976).

Less than four months after these arguments, detection by a two-site enzyme immunoassay of one attomole $(1 \times 10^{-18}$ mol; 600,000 molecules as calculated from Avogadro's number) of a macromolecular antigen, ornithine δ-aminotransferase from rat liver with a molecular weight of 170 kDa, was reported (Kato et al., 1977). During the ensuing decade, the two-site enzyme immunoassay was successfully applied in measurements of various antigens at attomole levels, which are below those detectable by radioimmunoassay. The human antigens measured at attomole levels were thyroid-stimulating hormone, IgE, ferritin, α-fetoprotein (Ishikawa et al., 1983a), growth hormone (Ishikawa et al., 1987), chorionic gonadotropin, insulin (Ishikawa, 1987), atrial natriuretic peptides, interleukin-1 and luteinizing hormone (Ishikawa et al., 1989a).

For antibodies and haptens, both the assay system and the sensitivity of enzyme immunoassay were fundamentally unchanged for many years after their first reports. In 1987, an ultrasensitive enzyme immunoassay (immune complex transfer enzyme immunoassay) for antibodies was developed (Kohno and Ishikawa, 1987). Later, the sensitivity to antigens was improved to zeptomole $(1 \times 10^{-21}$ mol) levels by the immune complex transfer method (Hashida and Ishikawa, 1990). For some haptens, a noncompetitive method with attomole sensitivity was developed (Tanaka et al., 1989).

Recently, the period required for ultrasensitive enzyme immunoassays has been considerably shortened with even further improvement of the sensitivity not only to antigens (Ishikawa S. et al., 1998b, c) but also to antibodies (Ishikawa S. et al., 1998a, c).

CHAPTER 3

Factors limiting the sensitivity of noncompetitive heterogeneous solid phase enzyme immunoassays

3.1. Factors limiting the sensitivity to antigens and antibodies

There are at least three reasons why one attomole (10^{-18} mol) of a macromolecular antigen with a molecular weight of 170 kDa, ornithine-δ-aminotransferase from rat liver, was first measured by a noncompetitive heterogeneous two-site solid phase enzyme immunoassay in 1976 (Ishikawa and Kato, 1978).

The first reason is that the antibodies used had strong affinity.

The second reason is that β-D-galactosidase from *Escherichia coli* used as a label was detected with attomole sensitivity using a fluorogenic substrate, 4-methylumbelliferyl-β-D-galactoside, while the label enzymes were detected with lower sensitivities by colorimetry in other reports. This fluorometric assay is approximately 1000-fold more sensitive than a colorimetric assay using *o*-nitrophenyl-β-D-galactoside as substrate (Ishikawa et al., 1983a).

The third reason is that Fab' was conjugated to β-D-galactosidase through thiol groups in the hinge of Fab' (the hinge method), while, in other reports, antibody IgG or its fragments were conjugated to enzymes through their amino groups (the nonhinge method) (see Chapters 11 and 13 of this volume for details of the hinge and nonhinge methods) (Kato et al., 1975b). Fab'-β-D-galactosidase conjugates prepared by the hinge method retain the original activities of Fab′ and β-D-galactosidase, and give lower nonspecific and higher specific bindings, resulting in higher sensitivities than IgG, Fab′ and Fab conjugated with β-D-galactosidase through their amino groups by the nonhinge method (Ishikawa et al., 1983b).

As evident from this first example, an obvious first factor limiting the sensitivity of immunoassays is the affinity between antigens and antibodies to be measured and used as reagents. The higher the affinity between antigen and antibody, the higher the ratio of the concentration of their bound forms to that of their free forms at their low concentrations and, therefore, the higher is the ratio of the specific signal to the nonspecific one, since the specific signal is proportional to the concentration of their bound forms, and the nonspecific signal depends on the concentrations of the labeled reagents used.

The second factor limiting the sensitivity of enzyme immunoassays is the detection limit of enzymes used as labels (Ishikawa et al., 1983a). In immunoassays, the detection limit of analytes cannot exceed that of labels. For example, the detection limit of carrier-free radioisotopes can be assessed from their specific radioactivities, which can be calculated from their half-lives. The specific radioactivity of carrier-free ^{125}I, that has been most widely used in radioimmunoassays, is 4.8 dpm/amol and, therefore, its detection limit is approximately 10 amol (Ishikawa et al., 1983b). In contrast, the detection limits of some enzymes used in enzyme immunoassays are much lower at the zeptomole (10^{-21} mol) levels (Ishikawa 1987). This indicates that enzyme immunoassays must have the potential for higher sensitivity than radioimmunoassays.

The third factor limiting the sensitivity of immunoassays is the time used to perform the immunoassays. The lower the concentration of labeled reagents used, the lower is the nonspecific signal and, thus, the higher the sensitivity achieved. However, the lower the concentrations of antibodies and antigens, the longer is the time required for their binding.

A fourth factor limiting the sensitivity of solid phase immunoassays is the reactivity of antigens and antibodies on solid phases. Immunoreactions on solid phases are limited to various extents among different antigens, antibodies, solid phases etc. (Ishikawa S. et al., 1998d).

A fifth factor limiting the sensitivity of immunoassays is serum interference. Samples such as serum and plasma are most frequently subjected to enzyme immunoassays, and substances, probably proteins, in these samples have been reported to reduce the specific binding of labeled reagents to various extents in many cases, limiting their sensitivities (Ishikawa S. et al., 1999). The molecular weights of serum substances causing serum interference were 200–1000 kDa in the two-site enzyme immunoassay for human growth hormone (hGH) using horseradish peroxidase as a label (Fig. 3.1) (Hashida et al., 1983).

In addition to the above factors, which limit the sensitivities in all types of immunoassays, each immunoassay has its own factors limiting its sensitivity.

3.2. Factors limiting the sensitivity to antibodies

In the most widely used conventional enzyme immunoassay for antibodies, an antigen-coated solid phase is incubated with samples such as serum and plasma to trap specific immunoglobulins and, after washing, with anti-immunoglobulin antibody-enzyme conjugates to measure the specific immunoglobulins trapped (Fig. 3.2). The enzyme activity bound to the solid phase is correlated with the amount or concentration of antibodies to be measured. The most serious factor limiting the sensitivity of this assay is the specific binding of the conjugates to the corresponding nonspecific immunoglobulins in the samples nonspecifically bound to the antigen-coated solid phase (Ishikawa and Kohno, 1989).

In the second conventional enzyme immunoassay for antibodies (so-called antibody capture enzyme immunoassay), an anti-

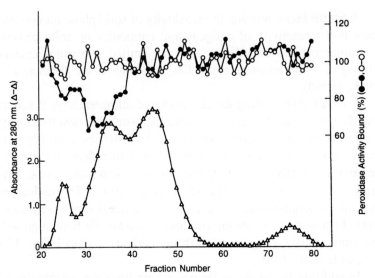

Fig. 3.1. Molecular sizes of substances in human serum causing serum interference in the two-site enzyme immunoassay for hGH. Human serum was subjected to gel filtration on a column of Sephadex G-200, and an aliquot of each fraction was added in the first step of the two-site enzyme immunoassay for hGH (Hashida et al., 1983). Closed and open circles indicate results using 0.1 and 0.4 mol/L NaCl, respectively.

immunoglobulin IgG-coated solid phase is incubated with samples such as serum and plasma to capture both specific and nonspecific immunoglobulins and, after washing, with antigen-enzyme conjugates to measure the specific immunoglobulins captured (Fig. 3.3). In general, this assay is slightly more sensitive than the most widely used conventional enzyme immunoassay described above. However, the most important factor limiting the sensitivity of this assay is the capacity of anti-immunoglobulin IgG-coated solid phase to capture immunoglobulins. The capacity becomes larger with increasing sizes of solid phase surfaces. However, larger sizes of solid phase surfaces show higher nonspecific bindings of the conjugates, enhancing the background and limiting the sensitivity.

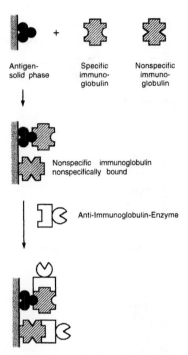

Fig. 3.2. Most widely used conventional enzyme immunoassay of antibodies. Binding of anti-immunoglobulin antibody-enzyme conjugate to nonspecific immunoglobulin nonspecifically bound to the antigen-coated solid phase markedly enhances the nonspecific signal and seriously limits the sensitivity.

In the third conventional enzyme immunoassay for antibodies (two-site or sandwich enzyme immunoassay), an antigen-coated solid phase is incubated with samples such as serum and plasma to trap specific antibodies, and subsequently with antigen-enzyme conjugates to measure the specific antibodies trapped on the solid phase (Fig. 3.4). The enzyme activity bound to the solid phase is correlated with the amount or concentration of the antibodies to be measured.

An important factor limiting the sensitivity of the two-site immunoassay is the nonspecific binding of the conjugates to the solid

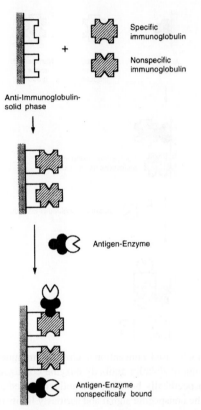

Fig. 3.3. Conventional antibody capture enzyme immunoassay of antibodies. Nonspecific binding of antigen-enzyme conjugate to the anti-immunoglobulin antibody-coated solid phase enhances the nonspecific signal and limits the sensitivity.

phase, but not the presence of nonspecific immunoglobulins which limits the sensitivities of the above two conventional methods.

Another factor limiting the sensitivity of the two-site immunoassay is the concentration of antigens used for coating the solid phase. The sensitivity is improved in proportion to the fraction of specific antibodies trapped on the solid phase, which is increased by

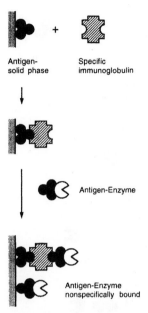

Fig. 3.4. Conventional two-site (sandwich) enzyme immunoassay of antibodies. Nonspecific binding of the antigen-enzyme conjugate to the antigen-coated solid phase enhances the nonspecific signal and limits the sensitivity.

increasing the concentration of antigen used for coating the solid phase.

However, the sensitivity of the two-site immunoassay is lost to various extents with the increase in the concentration of antigen used for coating the solid phase above a certain level. This is probably because the number of free antigen-binding sites in the antibody molecules trapped on the solid phase decreases with the increase in the concentration of antigen used for coating the solid phase, reducing the specific binding of antigen-enzyme conjugates to antigen molecules trapped.

Thus, the optimal concentration of antigens for coating the solid phase has to be determined.

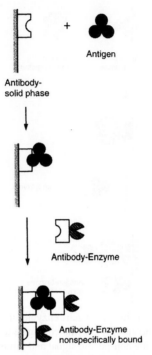

Fig. 3.5. Conventional two-site (sandwich) enzyme immunoassay of antigens. Nonspecific binding of the antibody-enzyme conjugate to the antibody-coated solid phase enhances the nonspecific signal and limits the sensitivity.

The two-site immunoassay is more sensitive than the above two conventional methods, although it does not distinguish between the classes of antibodies.

3.3. Factors limiting the sensitivity to antigens

In the most widely used conventional two-site enzyme immunoassay for antigens, a great obstacle limiting the sensitivity is the nonspecific binding of antibody-enzyme conjugates to antibody-coated solid phases (background noise) (Fig. 3.5).

An easy way to lower the background noise is to reduce the size of the solid phase surface. In fact, a smallscale two-site enzyme immunoassay was developed by using glass beads of 1 mm in diameter and a reaction mixture volume of 5 μL for immunoreactions (Ruan et al., 1987), while, in two-site enzyme immunoassays for antigens described in Chapter 2, solid phases with larger surface areas such as polystyrene beads of 3.2 mm in diameter, and reaction mixture volumes of 150–200 μL, were used for immunoreactions. By this smallscale enzyme immunoassay, one zeptomole (zmol = 1×10^{-21} mol; 600 molecules as calculated from Avogadro's number) of human ferritin was detected. Smaller or microscale two-site enzyme immunoassays may detect even smaller amounts of antigens.

However, the improvement in sensitivity thus achieved is only in terms of mol/assay or g/assay, not mol/L or g/L of samples such as serum, plasma or urine, since the volumes of samples that can be used in smaller or microscale assays are reduced proportionally.

Other important factors limiting the sensitivity of the conventional two-site enzyme immunoassays for antigens are the affinity and concentration of specific antibodies for coating solid phases. In general, the sensitivity is improved in proportion to the fraction of antigens or the immune complexes comprising antigens and antibody-enzyme conjugates trapped onto antibody-coated solid phases, which are increased by increasing the affinity and concentration of specific antibodies for coating solid phases.

However, the sensitivity declines by increasing the concentrations of specific antibodies for coating solid phases above a certain level. This is probably because the number of free epitopes in antigen molecules trapped on the solid phase decreases with the increase in the concentration of specific antibodies used for coating the solid phase reducing the specific binding of antibody-enzyme conjugates to antigen molecules trapped on the solid phase.

Thus, in the two-site enzyme immunoassays for antigens, in which a solid phase coated with polyclonal antibodies is incubated with antigens and, after washing, with enzyme-labeled antibodies, the optimal concentration of specific antibodies for coating the solid phase has to be determined.

Finally, it is well known that antibodies to immunoglobulins present at various concentrations in different serum samples enhance the nonspecific signals by bridging antibodies immobilized on solid phases and labeled with enzymes. Antibodies to mouse IgG present in many human samples seriously limit the sensitivity of two-site enzyme immunoassays for antigens using monoclonal mouse IgG and its fragments (Yone et al., 1990; Hashida et al., 1991b).

CHAPTER 4

Methods to minimize effects of factors limiting the sensitivity

4.1. Methods to minimize the nonspecific bindings of antigen- and antibody-enzyme conjugates

In two-site enzyme immunoassays for antigens and antibodies (see Figs. 3.4 and 3.5), antibody- and antigen-enzyme conjugates are adsorbed nonspecifically (nonimmunologically and physically) to antibody- and antigen-coated solid phases to various extents. This is a major problem in the improvement of the sensitivity of assay, and various attempts have been made to reduce the nonspecific bindings.

4.1.1. Reducing the concentration of antigen- and antibody-enzyme conjugates

The easiest way to reduce the nonspecific bindings of antigen- and antibody-enzyme conjugates is to use lower concentrations of the conjugates for immunoreactions, since, at the concentrations usually used for immunoreactions, their nonspecific bindings increase with their concentrations. However, when there is a decrease in concentrations, the specific bindings of different antibody-enzyme conjugates decrease in different manners, depending on their affinities (Fig. 4.1) (Ishikawa et al., 1982). Therefore, the optimal concentrations of conjugates to obtain the highest specific binding, and the highest ratio of specific binding to nonspecific binding must be determined (Table 4.1) (Imagawa et al., 1984b, c).

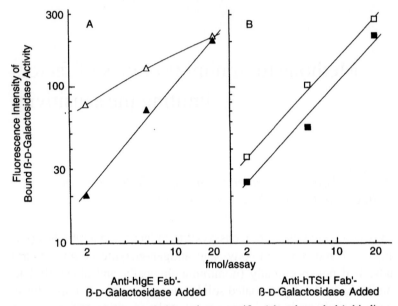

Fig. 4.1. Specific (open symbols) and nonspecific (closed symbols) bindings related to the amount of affinity-purified antibody-enzyme conjugates used in two-site enzyme immunoassays for (A) human IgE (hIgE), and (B) human thyroid-stimulating hormone (hTSH), (Ishikawa et al., 1982).

4.1.2. Use of antibody fragments rather than intact antibodies

In immunoassays, antibody IgG has been most widely used for labeling, but the Fc portion of the IgG molecule (Fig. 4.2) is hydrophobic, causing a high nonspecific binding of enzyme-labeled IgG. This problem can be overcome by using antibody fragments (Ishikawa et al., 1983b). The F(ab')$_2$ fragment is obtained by pepsin digestion of IgG, and the Fab' fragment obtained by reduction of F(ab')$_2$ with 2-mercaptoethylamine. The Fab fragment is obtained by papain digestion of IgG. The nonspecific bindings of these fragments labeled with enzymes are lower than that of enzyme-labeled IgG (Table 4.2 and Fig. 4.3) (Imagawa et al., 1982b).

TABLE 4.1

Ratio of specific binding to nonspecific binding in relation to the amount of antibody-enzyme conjugates used in two-site enzyme immunoassays for human α-fetoprotein and human ferritin

Antigen added	Enzyme label	Affinity-purification of antibodies	Amount of antibody-enzyme conjugate used (fmol/assay)	Ratio of specific binding to nonspecific binding	
				Incubation temperature	
				20°C	37°C
α-Feto-protein (1 fmol per assay)	GAL	No	3.1	11	3.0
			31	14	3.8
			311	18	3.5
			1557	11	1.3
	HRP	No	250	20	5.4
			2500	13	2.6
			6250	9.6	1.2
	GAL	Yes	2.7	151	75
			27	143	58
			274	115	21
	HRP	Yes	63	447	120
			625	125	30
			2500	90	13
Ferritin (0.1 fmol per assay)	GAL	No	2.9	0.98	2.5
			29	0.46	2.2
			290	1.1	1.2
			1400	0.25	0.52
	HRP	No	63	32	35
			625	33	24
			6250	8.2	6.5
	GAL	Yes	0.7	21	67
			6.6	12	64
			66	6.8	11
			660	0.8	2.5
	HRP	Yes	25	474	249
			250	148	61
			2500	26	8

Polystyrene beads coated with rabbit antibody IgG were incubated in the absence and presence of antigens and, after washing, with rabbit antibody Fab'-enzyme conjugates prepared by the hinge method (Chapters 11 and 12) (Imagawa et al., 1984b, c). GAL: β-D-galactosidase from *Escherichia coli*. HRP: horseradish peroxidase.

TABLE 4.2

Specific and nonspecific bindings of rabbit antihuman ferritin antibody-peroxidase conjugates prepared by various methods in the two-site enzyme immunoassay of human ferritin

Enzyme-labeling method	Peroxidase-labeled antibody	Nonspecific binding (N) (%)		Specific binding (S) (%)	S/N ratio
Maleimide hinge method	Fab$'$	A	0.013	1.55	119
Maleimide nonhinge method	Fab$'$	A	0.025	0.86	34
Maleimide nonhinge method	F(ab$'$)$_2$	A	0.045	0.99	22
Maleimide nonhinge method	IgG	A	0.061	1.47	24
Two-step glutaraldehyde method	Fab$'$	A	0.016	0.22	14
	Fab	A	0.033	0.18	5.5
Periodate method	Fab$'$	A	0.070	0.71	10
		B	0.17	0.74	4.4
	Fab	A	0.079	0.59	7.5
		B	0.23	0.81	3.5
	IgG	A	0.20	1.62	8.1
		B	0.57	3.81	6.7

Polystyrene beads coated with rabbit antihuman ferritin IgG were incubated in the absence and presence of human ferritin (1 fmol/assay) and, after washing, with rabbit antihuman ferritin antibody-peroxidase conjugates. Specific and nonspecific bindings are expressed as percentages of the conjugates added. A and B indicate the results obtained with monomeric and polymeric conjugates, respectively.

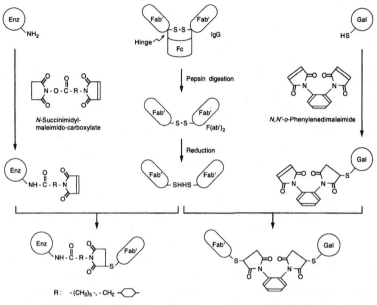

Fig. 4.2. Preparation of Fab′-enzyme conjugates by the hinge method using maleimide derivatives (Ishikawa, 1996). Enz: enzyme. S—S: disulfide bond. Gal: β-D-galactosidase from *E. coli*. See Chapters 11 and 13 for details of the hinge and nonhinge methods.

4.1.3. Hinge method for enzyme-labeling of antibodies

In the hinge methods (Chapters 11 and 13), Fab′ is conjugated to enzymes by selective use of thiol groups in the hinge of Fab′, which is remote from its antigen-binding site (Fig. 4.2). Therefore, the hinge methods preserve the original antigen-binding activity of Fab′, and Fab′ conjugates prepared by the hinge methods provide higher specific bindings than those prepared by other methods (see the nonhinge methods in Chapters 11 and 13), in which Fab′ or Fab is conjugated with enzymes through the amino groups. In addition, the nonspecific bindings of these Fab′ conjugates prepared by the hinge methods are lower than those of conjugates prepared by the nonhinge methods. The nonspecific bindings of polymeric conju-

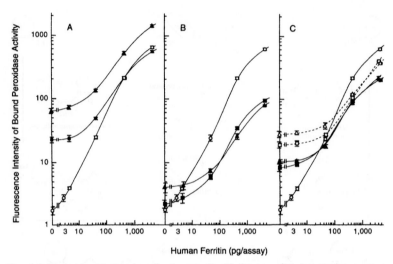

Human Ferritin (pg/assay)

Fig. 4.3. Dose-response curves for human ferritin by two-site enzyme immunoassay using antibody-horseradish peroxidase conjugates prepared by the hinge and nonhinge methods (Imagawa et al., 1982b). Open circles: Fab′-peroxidase conjugate prepared by the hinge method. (A) monomeric (closed squares) and polymeric (closed triangles) IgG-peroxidase conjugates prepared by the periodate method (the nonhinge method); (B) Fab′-(closed squares) and Fab (closed triangles) peroxidase conjugates prepared by the glutaraldehyde method (the nonhinge method); and (C) monomeric Fab′ (closed squares), monomeric Fab (closed triangles), polymeric Fab′ (open squares) and polymeric Fab′ (open triangles) peroxidase conjugates prepared by the periodate method (the nonhinge method). See Chapters 11 and 13 for details of the hinge and nonhinge methods.

gates prepared by the periodate method—a nonhinge method—are high. The specific and nonspecific bindings of various conjugates are shown in Table 4.2 and Fig. 4.3 (Imagawa et al., 1982b).

4.1.4. Purification of antigen- and antibody-enzyme conjugates

IgG in antiserum consists of specific and nonspecific IgG, and the proportion of nonspecific IgG is generally more than 90%. Therefore, preparations of Fab′-enzyme conjugates from IgG without affinity-purification contain more than 90% of nonspecific Fab'-enzyme conjugates, which show no specific binding and cause high nonspecific binding, limiting the sensitivity of two-site enzyme immunoassays for antigens. Theoretically, this problem can be overcome by using affinity-purified Fab'-enzyme conjugates (Ishikawa, 1987).

However, in the two-site enzyme immunoassays for antigens using affinity-purified antibody Fab'-enzyme conjugates, both specific binding and nonspecific binding are considerably enhanced, resulting in little improvement in sensitivity. This is because when antibody $F(ab')_2$, for example, is affinity-purified by elution from a column of antigen-Sepharose 4B (Amersham Pharmacia Biotech, Uppsala, Sweden), a small amount of antigen is released from the column and forms a complex with the affinity-purified antibody $F(ab')_2$, causing high nonspecific binding.

This problem can be overcome by gel filtration of affinity-purified antibody $F(ab')_2$ to eliminate antigens released from the column that form complexes with affinity-purified antibody $F(ab')_2$ (Ruan et al., 1985; Kasai et al., 1990). By use of antigens conjugated to proteins such as bovine serum albumin and nonspecific IgG and immobilized on Sepharose 4B (Amersham Pharmacia Biotech, Uppsala, Sweden) for affinity-purification, it is easy to eliminate antigens released from the column by gel filtration and to improve the sensitivity (Chapter 12).

Use of affinity-purified antibody Fab'-enzyme conjugates containing little antigen improves the sensitivity 10- to 100-fold in most cases (Table 4.3) (Ishikawa et al., 1983a).

Similarly, the purification of enzyme-labeled antigens and antibodies to eliminate unconjugated antigens, antibodies and enzymes after conjugation is effective for improving the sensitivity of solid phase enzyme immunoassays.

TABLE 4.3

Effect of the purity of Fab′-enzyme conjugates on the detection limit of human antigens by the two-site enzyme immunoassay

Antigen	Enzyme label	Affinity-purification of Fab′	Purity of Fab′-enzyme conjugate (%)	Detection limit (amol/assay)
IgE	GAL	No	13	100
		Yes	95	2
Ferritin	GAL	No	14	2
		Yes	93	0.05
Thyroid-stimulating hormone	GAL	No	7	250
		Yes	98	2
Growth hormone	HRP	No	35	200
		Yes	86	3
α-fetoprotein	HRP	No	15	50
		Yes	84	2

Fab′-enzyme conjugates were prepared by the reaction between thiol groups in the hinge of Fab′ and maleimide groups introduced into enzyme molecules (the hinge method) (see Chapter 11) (Ishikawa et al., 1983a). The average number of Fab′ molecules conjugated per β-D-galactosidase molecule was 1.7–2.5. The purities of Fab′-enzyme conjugates are expressed as percentages of the conjugates adsorbed to antigen-Sepharose 4B columns.

GAL: β-D-galactosidase from *E. coli*.

HRP: horseradish peroxidase.

4.1.5. Addition of proteins analogous to antibodies and label enzymes

The nonspecific bindings of antibody Fab′-enzyme conjugates to solid phases can be significantly reduced with only slight decreases in specific binding by addition of nonspecific IgG, F(ab′)$_2$ and related proteins (Fig. 4.4) (Hashida and Ishikawa, 1985). Nonspecific

F(ab′)$_2$ and related proteins such as Fab′-bovine serum albumin conjugate appeared to be more effective than nonspecific IgG. These effects tended to be larger when nonspecific F(ab′)$_2$ and specific antibody Fab′-enzyme conjugates were prepared from the same rather than different species of animals, and when β-D-galactosidase from *E. coli* rather than horseradish peroxidase was used as label.

In some cases, the nonspecific bindings of antibody Fab′-β-D-galactosidase conjugates can be significantly reduced by the presence of both nonspecific F(ab′)$_2$ and inactive β-D-galactosidase (Table 4.4 and Fig. 4.5) (Ishikawa S. et al., 1992).

By these methods, the detection limits of antigens by two-site enzyme immunoassays are lowered approximately 10-fold in many cases.

4.1.6. Immune complex transfer from solid phase to solid phase

The most effective method for reducing the nonspecific signals in noncompetitive heterogeneous solid phase immunoassays is the immune complex transfer method. The immune complex consisting of analytes and labeled reactant(s) is trapped on the first solid phase. After washing the first solid phase, the immune complex is specifically eluted and transferred to a second clean solid phase. This markedly reduces the nonspecific bindings of labeled reactants, greatly improving the sensitivity. These methods are described in detail in Chapters 5–9.

4.1.7. Miscellaneous conditions

The nonspecific bindings of antigen- and antibody-enzyme conjugates are significantly reduced in many but not all cases by changing conditions such as the temperature, pH, aging of antigen- and antibody-coated solid phases, addition of sera from various species

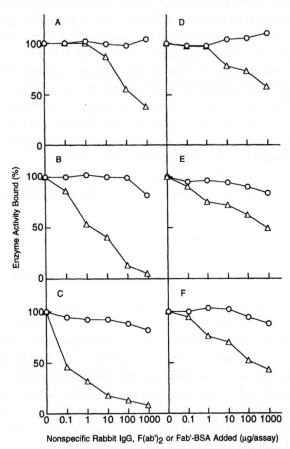

Fig. 4.4. Effects of nonspecific rabbit IgG and related proteins on the specific and nonspecific bindings of affinity-purified rabbit anti-human chorionic gonadotropin (hCG) Fab′-enzyme conjugates in two-site enzyme immunoassay of hCG (Hashida and Ishikawa, 1985). The enzymes used as labels were β-D-galactosidase from *E. coli* (A, B and C), and horseradish peroxidase (D, E and F). The proteins added were nonspecific rabbit IgG (A and D), nonspecific rabbit F(ab′)$_2$ (B and E) and nonspecific rabbit Fab′-bovine serum albumin (BSA) conjugate (C and F). Circles and triangles indicate specific and nonspecific bindings, respectively. The amount of hCG added was 0.1 mU/assay.

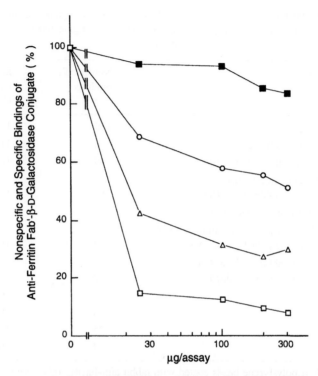

Nonspecific F(ab')$_2$ and Inactive β-D-Galactosidase

Fig. 4.5. Effects of nonspecific F(ab')$_2$ and inactive β-D-galactosidase on the specific and nonspecific bindings of anti-ferritin Fab'-β-D-galactosidase conjugate in two-site enzyme immunoassay of human ferritin. Individual polystyrene beads coated with rabbit (anti-human ferritin) IgG were incubated with and without ferritin (50 amol/assay) and, after washing, with rabbit anti-ferritin Fab'-β-D-galactosidase conjugate in the presence of nonspecific rabbit F(ab')$_2$ (triangles), inactive β-D-galactosidase (circles) or both (squares) (Ishikawa S. et al., 1992). Open and closed symbols indicate nonspecific binding (β-D-galactosidase activity nonspecifically bound to polystyrene beads in the absence of ferritin) and specific binding (the difference between β-D-galactosidase activities bound in the presence and absence of ferritin), respectively.

TABLE 4.4

Specific and nonspecific bindings of anti-ferritin Fab'-β-D-galactosidase conjugate in the presence of nonspecific F(ab')$_2$, inactive β-D-galactosidase and their related substances

Addition	Nonspecific binding (%)	Specific binding (%)
None	100	100
Nonspecific rabbit IgG (I)	66	111
Nonspecific rabbit F(ab')$_2$ (II)	49	103
N-ethylmaleimide-treated nonspecific rabbit Fab' (III)	50	108
Inactive β-D-galactosidase (IV)	63	109
N,N'-1,2-phenylenedimaleimide-treated inactive β-D-galactosidase (V)	64	107
Nonspecific rabbit Fab'-inactive β-D-galactosidase conjugate	32	105
I, IV	53	107
II, IV	25	107
III, IV	25	108
II, V	23	108

Individual polystyrene beads coated with rabbit anti-ferritin IgG were incubated with or without ferritin (50 amol/assay) and, after washing, with rabbit anti-ferritin Fab'-β-D-galactosidase conjugate in the presence of 10 μg/assay of substances indicated (Ishikawa S. et al., 1992). The specific binding is defined as the difference between β-D-galactosidase activities bound in the absence and presence of ferritin.

of animals and use of different solid phase materials and different enzymes as labels.

The nonspecific bindings of antigen- and antibody-enzyme conjugates are in general reduced at lower temperatures, while specific bindings increase faster at higher temperatures. However, specific bindings may decrease after prolonged incubation at higher temperatures. Thus, the effect of temperature varies in different cases. The effects of temperature on two-site enzyme immunoassays of human ferritin and human chorionic gonadotropin (hCG) using rabbit anti-ferritin and anti-hCG Fab′-peroxidase conjugates are shown in Figs. 4.6 and 4.7 (Imagawa et al., 1982c).

In some cases, nonspecific bindings of antigen- and antibody-enzyme conjugates are reduced at lower or higher pH values, although immunoreactions take place efficiently at neutral pH in most cases. The favorable effect of a lower pH value in immune complex transfer enzyme immunoassay V (Fig. 5.5) for antibody IgG to HIV-1 p24 antigen is shown in Fig. 4.8 (Hashida et al., 1994a).

In many but not all cases, nonspecific bindings of antigen- and antibody-enzyme conjugates continue to decrease for a few days or months after coating solid phases with antigens and antibodies.

The nonspecific bindings of antigen- and antibody-enzyme conjugates are reduced in the presence of serum from various species of animals in many cases, but enhanced in some cases (Table 4.5). The nonspecific binding of monoclonal mouse anti-HIV-1 p24 Fab′ (IgG$_1$)-β-D-galactosidase conjugate in immune complex transfer enzyme immunoassay X (Fig. 5.10) for HIV-1 p24 antigen using polystyrene beads as a solid phase was reduced considerably in the presence of human serum and markedly in the presence of rabbit serum. The nonspecific binding of monoclonal mouse (anti-hepatitis B surface antigen) Fab′ (IgG$_1$)-β-D-galactosidase conjugate in immune complex transfer enzyme immunoassay X (Fig. 5.10) for hepatitis B surface antigen using polystyrene beads as a solid phase was considerably reduced in the presence of human serum and markedly enhanced in the presence of rabbit serum. The nonspecific binding of monoclonal mouse (anti-hGH) Fab′ (IgG$_1$)-β-D-galactosidase conjugate to polystyrene beads coated with rabbit (anti-hGH) IgG was enhanced 50% by horse serum and 100% by rabbit serum.

The nonspecific bindings of antigen- and antibody-enzyme conjugates vary depending on the solid phase material used. In many cases, however, low nonspecific binding is associated with low spe-

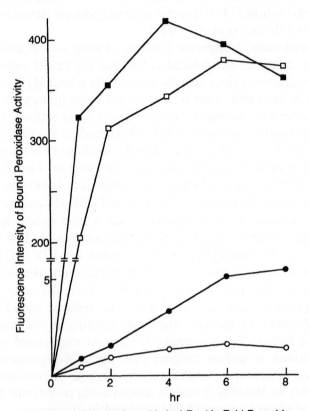

Fig. 4.6. Time courses of specific and nonspecific bindings of rabbit anti-ferritin Fab′-peroxidase conjugate to rabbit anti-ferritin IgG-coated polystyrene beads in two-site enzyme immunoassay of ferritin. The amount of human ferritin added was 0.45 ng, and the conjugate was prepared by the maleimide hinge method (Chapters 11 and 13). Open and closed symbols indicate results on incubations at 20 and 37°C, respectively. Circles and squares indicate nonspecific and specific binding, respectively.

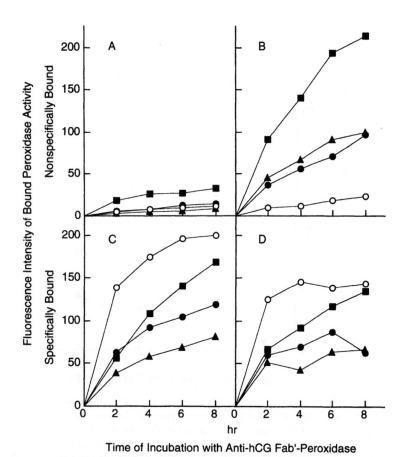

Fig. 4.7. Time courses of specific and nonspecific bindings of rabbit anti-hCG Fab′-peroxidase conjugates to rabbit anti-hCG IgG-coated polystyrene beads in two-site enzyme immunoassay of hCG. Anti-hCG IgG-coated polystyrene beads were incubated in the absence (A and B) and presence (C and D) of 1 mU hCG and, after washing, with anti-hCG Fab′-peroxidase conjugates at 20°C (A and C) and 37°C (B and D) (Imagawa et al., 1982c). Open circles and closed symbols indicate experiments with conjugates prepared by the hinge and nonhinge methods using glutaraldehyde (closed triangles) and periodate, respectively (see Chapters 11 and 13). Closed circles and closed squares indicate results obtained with monomeric and polymeric conjugates, respectively, prepared by the periodate method.

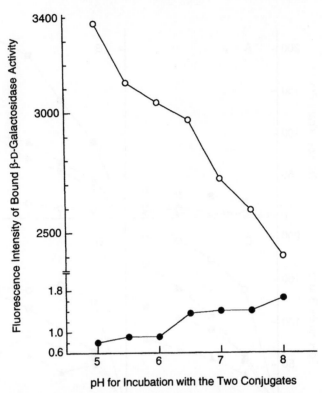

Fig. 4.8. Effect of pH on immune complex transfer enzyme immunoassay V (Fig. 5.5) of antibody IgG to HIV-1 p24 antigen. Urine samples were incubated simultaneously with 2,4-dinitrophenyl-bovine serum albumin-recombinant HIV-1 p24 conjugate and recombinant HIV-1 p24-β-D-galactosidase conjugate at pH 5–8 (Hashida et al., 1994a). Open and closed circles indicate results obtained with urine samples from an HIV-1 seropositive subject (asymptomatic carrier) and an HIV-1 seronegative subject, respectively.

cific binding, resulting in similar ratios of specific to nonspecific binding.

The nonspecific bindings of antigen- and antibody-enzyme conjugates vary depending on the enzyme used as label. The nonspecific bindings of, for example, rabbit anti-human ferritin Fab′

TABLE 4.5

Specific and nonspecific signals in the presence of serum samples from different species of animals in immune complex transfer enzyme immunoassay X for antigens (Fig. 5.10)

Serum added		Fluorescence intensity of bound β-D-galactosidase activity			
Species	Volume	HIV-1 p24 antigen amol		HBs Ag amol	
	(μL)	0	100 (2.4 pg)	0	100 (300 pg)
–	0	680	32,720	13	9,440
Rabbit	10	0.5	9,960	97	9,880
	20	–	–	149	9,180
	50	–	–	190	8,850
Human	10	–	–	1.5	3,600
	20	–	–	1.2	2,220
	50	64	6,020	1.1	1,360

HBs Ag was incubated with 2,4-dinitrophenyl-biotinyl-bovine serum albumin-monoclonal mouse anti-HBs Ag Fab′ conjugate and monoclonal mouse anti-HBs Ag Fab′-β-D-galactosidase conjugate. HIV-1 p24 antigen was incubated with 2,4-dinitrophenyl-biotinyl-bovine serum albumin-affinity-purified rabbit anti-HIV-1 p24 Fab′ conjugate and monoclonal mouse anti-HIV-1 p24 Fab′-β-D-galactosidase conjugate. The reaction mixtures were incubated with two colored polystyrene beads (3.2 mm in diameter) coated with affinity-purified (anti-2,4-dinitrophenyl group) IgG. After washing, the colored polystyrene beads were incubated with two white polystyrene beads (3.2 mm in diameter) coated successively with biotinyl-bovine serum albumin and streptavidin in the presence of 1 mmol/L ϵN-2,4-dinitrophenyl-L-lysine. β-D-Galactosidase activity bound to the white polystyrene beads was assayed for 20 h. The fluorescence intensity of 10^{-10} mol/L 4-methylumbelliferone was 1.

(Imagawa et al., 1984b) and goat anti-hCG Fab′ (Imagawa et al., 1984c) peroxidase conjugates to polystyrene beads were lower than those of the corresponding β-D-galactosidase conjugates (Fig. 4.9).

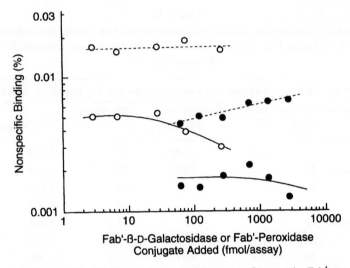

Fig. 4.9. Nonspecific bindings of goat anti-human α-fetoprotein Fab′-enzyme conjugates in two-site enzyme immunoassay of human α-fetoprotein (Imagawa et al., 1984c). The enzyme activities bound were expressed as percentages of those added. Open and closed symbols indicate the nonspecific bindings with β-D-galactosidase and peroxidase conjugates, respectively. Solid and broken lines indicate the nonspecific bindings at 20 and 37°C, respectively.

4.2. Method for efficient trapping of antigens and antibodies

In the most widely used conventional two-site enzyme immunoas-say for antigen, in which the antibody-coated solid phase is allowed to react with the antigen to be measured and, after washing, with antibody-enzyme conjugate (Fig. 3.5), the specific signal increases with the increase in the fraction of antigen trapped on the solid phase coated with antibody. When the antigen to be measured is allowed to react successively or simultaneously with antibody-enzyme conjugate and antibody-coated solid phase, the specific signal increases with the increase in the fractions of the immune complex of the two components trapped on the solid phase.

The fraction of the antigen trapped on the solid phase can be as-sessed as follows. First, the antibody-coated solid phase is incubated with antigen solution and, after washing, with antibody-enzyme conjugate (first assay). Second, another antibody-coated solid phase is incubated with the antigen solution after removal of the solid phase used in the first assay and, after washing, with antibody-enzyme conjugate (second assay). The enzyme activity bound in the second assay is much lower than that bound in the first assay, when the antigen is almost completely trapped, resulting in high sensitivity. This is the case in two-site enzyme immunoassay for ferritin (Fig. 4.10). The enzyme activities in the first and second assays are not very different when the antigen is not efficiently trapped, resulting in low sensitivity. This is the case in two-site enzyme immunoassay for α-fetoprotein (Fig. 4.11).

The trapping efficiency of antigens depends not only on the affinity but also on the concentration of specific antibodies used for coating solid phases.

Its dependence on the specific antibody concentration for coating in two-site enzyme immunoassay for human thyroid-stimulating hormone (hTSH) is shown in Table 4.6 (Ishikawa et al., 1980).

Polystyrene beads of 3.2 mm diameter were coated with four different preparations of rabbit (anti-hTSH) IgG (100 μg/mL): (1) (anti-hTSH) IgG without affinity-purification; (2) affinity-purified (anti-hTSH) IgG; (3) affinity-purified (anti-hTSH) IgG diluted 3-fold with nonspecific rabbit IgG; and (4) affinity-purified (anti-hTSH) IgG diluted 9-fold with nonspecific rabbit IgG.

A polystyrene bead coated as described above (first bead) was incubated with hTSH solution and, after washing, with anti-hTSH Fab$'$-β-D-galactosidase conjugate (first assay). Subsequently, another polystyrene bead coated in the same way was incubated with the above hTSH solution after removal of the first bead and, after washing, with anti-hTSH Fab$'$-β-D-galactosidase conjugate (second assay).

Without affinity-purification, the specific signals in the first and second assays were not very different, indicating that the fraction of hTSH trapped on the first bead was very small. By affinity-purification but without dilution with nonspecific IgG, the specific

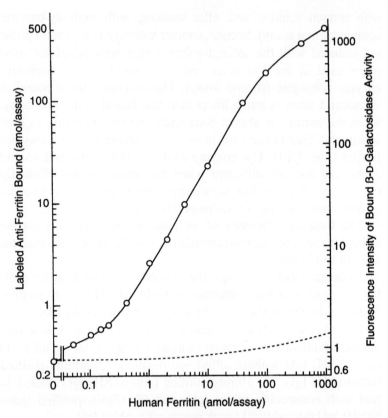

Fig. 4.10. Dose-response curves of ferritin by two-site enzyme immunoassay. The solid and dotted lines indicate the first and second assays, respectively. See text for the first and second assays.

signal in the second assay decreased to almost zero, indicating almost complete trapping of hTSH on the first bead. Namely, hTSH to be measured was almost completely trapped on the solid phase by increasing the concentration of specific anti-hTSH IgG for coating.

However, the sensitivity of the two-site enzyme immunoassay was not improved, since the specific signal in the first assay decreased in addition to increase in the nonspecific signal. This might

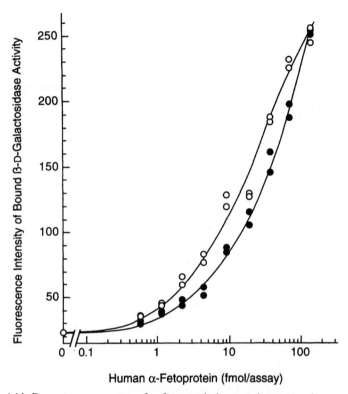

Fig. 4.11. Dose-response curves of α-fetoprotein by two-site enzyme immunoassay (Ishikawa and Kato, 1978). Solid and broken lines indicate the first and second assays, respectively. See text for the first and second assays.

have been due to the binding of more than one anti-hTSH IgG molecule per hTSH molecule on the solid phase, preventing the binding of anti-hTSH Fab'-β-D-galactosidase conjugate to hTSH trapped on the solid phase.

In contrast, when affinity-purified anti-hTSH IgG was used for coating after 3- to 9-fold dilution with nonspecific IgG, the specific signals increased 3.1- to 4.3-fold in the first assays with 2.4- to 6.4-fold decreases of the specific signals in the second assays and with

TABLE 4.6

Effect of the concentration of rabbit anti-hTSH IgG used for coating polystyrene beads on the specific and nonspecific signals in two-site enzyme immunoassay of hTSH

Rabbit anti-hTSH IgG for coating polystyrene beads		Assay	Signal (fluorescence intensity of bound β-D-galactosidase activity)	
Affinity-purification	Dilution with nonspecific IgG		hTSH added (fmol)	
			0	10
No	No	1st	4.9	25
		2nd	3.8	23
Yes	No	1st	11	28
		2nd	11	11
	3-fold	1st	7.2	69
		2nd	6.8	9.8
	9-fold	1st	4.5	90
		2nd	4.9	13

Individual polystyrene beads coated with rabbit (anti-hTSH) IgG (the first beads) were incubated with hTSH solution and, after washing, with anti-hTSH Fab'-β-D-galactosidase conjugate (1st assay). Another polystyrene bead coated with rabbit (anti-hTSH) IgG in the same way was incubated with the above hTSH solution after removal of the first bead, and, after washing, with anti-hTSH Fab'-β-D-galactosidase conjugate (2nd assay) (Ishikawa et al., 1980). β-D-galactosidase activity bound was assayed for 10 min. The fluorescence intensity of 10^{-9} mol/L 4-methylumbelliferone was 1.

only 0.9- to 1.5-fold increases in the nonspecific signals. As a result, the sensitivity was improved 2- to 4-fold.

Thus, the optimal concentration of specific antibodies for coating solid phases to obtain the highest sensitivity must be determined.

Similarly, in two-site enzyme immunoassay for antibody, in which an antigen-coated solid phase is incubated with antibody and, after washing, with antigen-enzyme conjugates, the specific signal

TABLE 4.7

Effect on the specific signal of the concentration of MBP-HIV-1 p17 antigen fusion protein (MBP-p17) used for coating polystyrene beads in two-site enzyme immunoassay of antibodies to HIV-1 p17 antigen

Antigen	Concentration for coating μg/mL	Amount for coating fmol/bead	Signal (fluorescence intensity of bound β-D-galactosidase activity)	
			Buffer	Diluted serum from an HIV-1 seropositive subject
MBP-p17	1	–	34	142
	5	–	35	652
	25	–	45	1,391
	50	–	45	1,849
	100	–	41	778
Biotinyl-	–	100	39	5,880
MBP-p17	–	300	43	10,630
	–	1000	–	7,290

MBP-p17 was immobilized on polystyrene beads by physical adsorption. Biotinyl-MBP-p17 was allowed to react with polystyrene beads that had been coated with 50 μg/mL of streptavidin by physical adsorption. A polystyrene bead coated with MBP-p17 or biotinyl-MBP-p17 was incubated with serum from an HIV-1 seropositive subject (asymptomatic carrier) diluted 1000-fold and, after washing, with recombinant HIV-1 p17-β-D-galactosidase conjugate (Ishikawa S. et al., 1999). β-D-galactosidase activity bound was assayed for 1 h. The fluorescence intensity of 10^{-9} mol/L 4-methylumbelliferone was 1.

increases as the fraction of antibody trapped increases with the increase in the concentrations of antigen coating the solid phase below a certain level. However, the specific signal decreases with higher concentrations of antigen used for coating, whereas the fraction of antibody trapped may increase. This is the case in two-site enzyme immunoassay for antibodies to HIV-1 p17 antigen using maltose-binding protein-HIV-1 p17 fusion protein-coated polystyrene beads and recombinant HIV-1 p17 antigen-β-D-galactosidase conjugate as shown in Table 4.7 (Ishikawa S. et al., 1999).

Therefore, the optimal concentration of antigens for coating the solid phase must be determined to achieve maximal sensitivity.

4.3. Methods using as full reactivities of antigens and antibodies as possible

Immunoreactions on solid phases tend to be limited to various extents, probably by steric hindrance as described in Chapter 3. This problem can be overcome in various ways in some but not all cases. One way is to immobilize antigens and antibodies indirectly on the solid phase, and another way is to form the immune complexes of antigens and antibodies in solution and then trap them on a solid phase.

4.3.1. Indirect immobilization of antigens

The first example of this method was immobilization of insulin for assay of anti-insulin IgG (Kato et al., 1978).

Insulin was immobilized in two different ways. In one method, insulin was immobilized directly on pieces of silicone rubber by physical adsorption. In the other method, bovine serum albumin was immobilized directly on pieces of silicone rubber by physical adsorption, and then treated with glutaraldehyde to introduce aldehyde groups into the immobilized bovine serum albumin molecules. Finally, it was allowed to react with insulin in the absence and presence of bovine serum albumin.

These directly and indirectly immobilized insulin preparations were allowed to react with guinea pig anti-insulin IgG and subsequently with either (anti-guinea pig IgG) Fab'-β-D-galactosidase conjugate or insulin-β-D-galactosidase conjugate (Table 4.8).

With the two conjugates, β-D-galactosidase activities bound to indirectly immobilized insulin in the presence of anti-insulin IgG (positive signals) were higher than those bound to directly immobilized insulin, indicating that indirectly immobilized insulin was

TABLE 4.8

Effects of direct and indirect immobilizations of insulin on the specific signal in enzyme immunoassay for anti-insulin IgG

Concentration for immobilization		Conjugate used	Signal (fluorescence intensity of bound β-D-galactosidase activity)					
Insulin (μg/mL)	BSA (μg/mL)		Dilution of anti-insulin serum (-fold)					
			Buffer	3×10^7	3×10^6	3×10^5	3×10^4	3×10^3
Direct immobilization		(Anti-guinea pig IgG) Fab'-β-D-galactosidase						
220			5.3	7.9	29	69	–	–
Indirect immobilization								
220	0		4.1	9.8	63	403	–	–
22	320		4.1	8.7	49	338	–	–
2.2	320		4.1	7.2	27	232	–	–
Direct immobilization		Insulin-β-D-galactosidase						
220			4.9	–	–	4.5	13	118
Indirect immobilization								
220	0		2.3	–	–	3.4	16	280
22	320		2.3	–	–	3.8	24	354
2.2	320		1.9	–	–	7.5	52	325

Direct immobilization: insulin was immobilized directly on pieces of silicone rubber by physical adsorption. Indirect immobilization: pieces of silicone rubber were coated with bovine serum albumin by physical adsorption, and treated first with glutaraldehyde and then with insulin in the absence and presence of bovine serum albumin (Kato et al., 1978). Bound β-D-galactosidase activity was assayed for 10 min. The fluorescence intensity of 10^{-9} mol/L 4-methylumbelliferone was 1. BSA: bovine serum albumin.

more reactive with anti-insulin IgG. However, the positive signals with insulin-β-D-galactosidase conjugate were much lower than those with (anti-guinea pig IgG) Fab'-β-D-galactosidase conjugate, indicating that anti-insulin IgG bound not only to the directly immobilized insulin but also to the indirectly immobilized insulin was not freely reactive with the insulin-β-D-galactosidase conjugate. This situation was only slightly improved by decreasing the amount of insulin immobilized.

The second example was immobilization of recombinant HIV-1 p17 antigen on polystyrene beads for assay of anti-HIV-1 p17 antibodies (Ishikawa S. et al., 1999).

Recombinant HIV-1 p17 (rp17) antigen and maltose binding protein-rp17 fusion protein were immobilized on polystyrene beads in seven different ways (Fig. 4.12). In the first and second procedures, rp17 antigen and maltose-binding protein-rp17 fusion protein were immobilized directly on polystyrene beads by physical adsorption. In the third and fourth procedures, biotinyl-rp17 antigen and biotinyl-maltose binding protein-rp17 fusion protein were indirectly immobilized by incubation with streptavidin-coated polystyrene beads. In the fifth and sixth procedures, biotinyl-rp17 antigen and biotinyl-maltose binding protein-rp17 fusion protein were indirectly immobilized by incubation with polystyrene beads coated successively with biotinyl-bovine serum albumin and streptavidin. In the seventh procedure, 2,4-dinitrophenyl-maltose binding protein-rp17 fusion protein was indirectly immobilized by incubation with affinity-purified (anti-2,4-dinitrophenyl group) IgG-coated polystyrene beads.

These immobilized antigens were tested by enzyme immunoassay using rp17-β-D-galactosidase conjugate. Serum from an HIV-1 seropositive subject (asymptomatic carrier), containing a high concentration of anti-HIV-1 p17 IgG and a very low concentration of anti-HIV-1 p17 IgM, was diluted with buffer 1000-fold for directly immobilized antigens and 10,000-fold for indirectly immobilized antigens, and individual polystyrene beads on which rp17 antigens had been immobilized in the various ways described above were

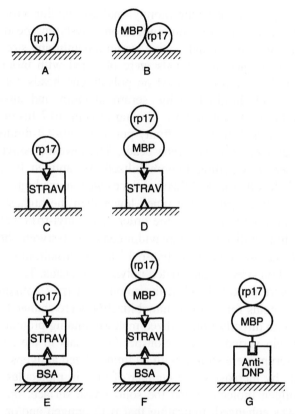

Fig. 4.12. Direct and indirect immobilizations of recombinant HIV-1 p17 (rp17) antigens on polystyrene beads. (A and B) directly immobilized rp17 antigen and maltose-binding protein (MBP)-rp17 fusion protein. (C, D, E, F and G) indirectly immobilized biotinyl-rp17 antigen, biotinyl-MBP-rp17 and 2,4-dinitrophenyl(DNP)-MBP-rp17. STRAV: streptavidin. BSA: bovine serum albumin. Possible orientations of molecules are shown. (Ishikawa S. et al., 1999).

incubated overnight with the diluted serum samples (10 μL) and, after washing, for 3.5 h with rp17-β-D-galactosidase conjugate (Table 4.9).

The highest fluorescence intensities of bound β-D-galactosidase activity in the presence of the diluted serum (the highest positive signals) were obtained with biotinyl-maltose binding protein-rp17 fusion protein indirectly immobilized on polystyrene beads coated successively with biotinyl-bovine serum albumin and streptavidin. Slightly lower positive signals were obtained with biotinyl-rp17 antigen indirectly immobilized on polystyrene beads coated successively with biotinyl-bovine serum albumin and streptavidin and 2,4-dinitrophenyl-maltose binding protein-rp17 fusion protein indirectly immobilized on affinity-purified (anti-2,4-dinitrophenyl group) IgG-coated polystyrene beads. The lowest positive signals were observed with directly immobilized rp17 antigen. Positive signals with the other immobilized antigens were much higher than the lowest positive signals, but much lower than the highest positive signals, and were higher in the order of biotinyl-rp17 antigen indirectly immobilized on streptavidin-coated polystyrene beads and biotinyl-maltose binding protein-rp17 fusion protein indirectly immobilized on streptavidin-coated polystyrene beads. These positive signals were maximal, when the amounts of rp17 antigen and its related proteins for indirect immobilization were changed. Positive signals with directly immobilized maltose binding protein-rp17 fusion protein varied greatly. Nonspecific signals in the absence of diluted serum were similar with all immobilized antigens.

Thus, by increasing the number of protein molecules between rp17 antigen molecules and the solid phase surface, the positive signal was enhanced, indicating that rp17 antigen and/or anti-p17 IgG bound to rp17 antigen on the solid phase became more reactive with anti-p17 IgG and/or rp17-β-D-galactosidase conjugate, as summarized in Table 4.9.

In order to understand the reason for the above results, the amounts of antibody IgG to p17 antigen bound to directly immobilized rp17 antigen and indirectly immobilized 2,4-dinitrophenyl-maltose binding protein-rp17 fusion protein were estimated using (anti-human IgG γ-chain) Fab'-β-D-galactosidase conjugate (Table 4.10) (Ishikawa S. et al., 1998d). These immobilized antigens were incubated with urine from an HIV-1 seropositive subject (asymptomatic carrier) in the presence and absence of excess rp17

TABLE 4.9

Effects of direct and indirect immobilizations of recombinant HIV-1 p17 antigen (rp17) on the specific signal and serum interference in two-site enzyme immunoassay for antibodies to HIV-1 p17 antigen

Antigen immobilized	Amount or concentration of antigen for immobil- ization		Serum from an HIV-1 seronegative subject diluted with buffer	Signal (fluorescence intensity of bound β-D-galactosidase activity) with		
				Buffer	Serum from an HIV-1 seropositive subject	
	(fmol/bead)	(μg/mL)	(μL)			(%)
Biotinyl-	50	–	0	22	2667	(100)
MBP-rp17[a]	50	–	10	23	2250 ± 141	(84)
Fig. 4.12(F)						
Biotinyl-rp17[a]	300	–	0	19	1772	(100)
Fig. 4.12(E)	300	–	10	15	1361 ± 99	(77)
DNP-MBP-	50	–	0	31	1610	(100)
rp17[b]	50	–	10	19	704 ± 118	(44)
Fig. 4.12(G)						
Biotinyl-	300	–	0	43	1063	(100)
MBP-rp17[c]	300	–	10	16	528	(50)
Fig. 4.12(D)						
Biotinyl-rp17[c]	10,000	–	0	42	311	(100)
Fig. 4.12(C)	10,000	–	10	14	32 ± 6.5	(6.7)
MBP-rp17[d]	–	1	0	34	142 ± 31	(100)
Fig. 4.12(B)	–	1	10	14	168 ± 72	(143)
	–	5	0	35	652 ± 566	(100)
	–	5	10	14	169 ± 75	(25)
	–	25	0	45	1391 ± 274	(100)
	–	25	10	18	54 ± 6.0	(2.7)

TABLE 4.9

(continued)

Antigen immobilized	Amount or concentration of antigen for immobilization		Serum from an HIV-1 seronegative subject diluted with buffer	Signal (fluorescence intensity of bound β-D-galactosidase activity) with		
				Buffer	Serum from an HIV-1 seropositive subject	
	(fmol/bead)	(μg/mL)	(μL)			(%)
rp17[d]	–	1	0	38	50	(100)
Fig. 4.12.A	–	1	10	16	28 ± 6.0	(100)
	–	5	0	36	49	(100)
	–	5	10	15	23	(62)
	–	25	0	42	51	(100)
	–	25	10	17	18	(11)

[a] Indirectly immobilized onto polystyrene beads coated successively with biotinyl-bovine serum albumin and streptavidin.

[b] Indirectly immobilized onto affinity-purified (2,4-dinitrophenyl group) IgG-coated polystyrene beads.

[c] Indirectly immobilized onto streptavidin-coated polystyrene beads.

[d] Directly immobilized.

Directly immobilized MBP-rp17 and rp17 were tested with 1000-fold diluted serum from an HIV-1 seropositive subject (asymptomatic carrier), but other antigens were tested with 10,000-fold diluted serum. A polystyrene bead coated with each antigen was incubated with 10 μL of the diluted serum and, after washing, with rp17-β-D-galactosidase conjugate. β-D-galactosidase activity bound to the polystyrene bead was assayed for 1 h. The fluorescence intensity of 10^{-10} mol/L 4-methylumbelliferone was 1.

MBP: maltose binding protein; rp17: recombinant HIV-1 p17 antigen; DNP: 2,4-dinitrophenyl group (Ishikawa S. et al., 1999).

antigen and, after washing, with (anti-human IgG γ-chain) Fab'-β-D-galactosidase conjugate. The urine sample must have contained antibody IgG to p17 antigen, not antibody IgM to p17 antigen, since the concentration of antibody IgM to p17 antigen is extremely lower than that of antibody IgG to p17 antigen in serum of HIV-1 asymptomatic carriers (Hashida et al., 1998c).

The reason for use of urine from the seropositive subject in the presence of excess p17 antigen instead of urine from an HIV-1 seronegative subject to obtain the signal in the absence of antibody IgG to p17 antigen, that is, the nonspecific signal, was that the nonspecific signal is proportional to the nonspecific binding of nonspecific IgG, which varies widely in different urine samples depending on the concentration of IgG.

The amount (2 μg/assay) of rp17 antigen added was sufficient, since signals with rp17-β-D-galactosidase conjugate for urine from the seropositive subject were lowered in the presence of 2 μg of rp17 antigen to similar levels to those for urine samples from HIV-1 seronegative subjects.

The specific signal (the difference between signals in the presence and absence of excess rp17 antigen) obtained using (anti-human IgG γ-chain) Fab'-β-D-galactosidase conjugate was 37% less with the indirectly immobilized antigen than that with the directly immobilized antigen, indicating that the amount of antibody IgG to p17 antigen specifically bound to the indirectly immobilized antigen was smaller than that specifically bound to the directly immobilized antigen. In contrast, the specific signal obtained using rp17-β-D-galactosidase conjugate was 26-fold higher with the indirectly immobilized antigen than that with the directly immobilized antigen.

Thus, the reactivity with rp17-β-D-galactosidase conjugate of antibody IgG to p17 antigen specifically bound to rp17 antigen on the solid phase was markedly enhanced by indirect immobilization of the antigen, probably due to alleviation of steric hindrance.

The sensitivity of enzyme immunoassay using rp17-β-D-galactosidase conjugate and biotinyl-maltose binding protein-rp17 fusion protein (50 fmol/bead) indirectly immobilized on polystyrene beads coated successively with biotinyl-bovine serum albumin and streptavidin is approximately 1000-fold higher than that of enzyme immunoassay using rp17-β-D-galactosidase conjugate and directly immobilized rp17 antigen (25 μg/mL) and Western blotting for the HIV-1 p17 band. In HIV-1 seroconversion

TABLE 4.10

Effects of direct and indirect immobilizations of recombinant HIV-1 p17 antigen (rp17) on the specific and nonspecific signals and serum interference in two-site enzyme immunoassays for antibodies to p17 antigen in urine using rp17-β-D-galactosidase conjugate and (anti-human IgG γ-chain) Fab'-β-D-galactosidase conjugate

Immobilized antigen (concentration or amount for immobilization)	Serum from seronegative subjects added (μL)	Signal with rp17-Gal Excess of rp17 (2 μg) (+)	(−)	Specific signal with rp17-Gal	Signal with anti-hIgG-Gal Excess of rp17 (2 μg) (+)	(−)	Specific signal with anti-hIgG-Gal
Directly immobilized rp17 (25 μg/mL)	0	39	149	110	3,862	11,190	7,328
	10	19	23	4	5,310	8,398	3,088
Indirectly immobilized DNP-MBP-rp17 (200 fmol/bead)	0	27	2,833 ± 80 (SD) (2,754–2,914, n = 3)	2,806	2,132	6,724	4,592
	10	17 ± 2.6 (SD) (13–19, n = 5)	2,122 ± 349 (SD) (1,710–2,558, n = 5)	2,105	11,018 ± 458 (SD) (10,542–11,628, n = 5)	12,535 ± 965 (SD) (11,508–14,088, n = 5)	1,517

Immobilized antigens were incubated successively with 30 μL of urine from an HIV-1 seropositive subject (asymptomatic carrier) in the presence and absence of rp17 antigen (2 μg/assay) and serum from HIV-1 seronegative subjects and, after washing, with rp17-β-D-galactosidase conjugate or (anti-human IgG γ-chain) Fab'-β-D-galactosidase conjugate (Ishikawa S. et al., 1998d). β-D-galactosidase activity bound to the polystyrene bead was assayed for 1 h and the fluorescence intensity of 10^{-10} mol/L 4-methylumbelliferone was 1. DNP: 2,4-dinitrophenyl group; MBP: maltose-binding protein; Gal: β-D-galactosidase from $E. coli$. Values in parentheses indicate their ranges.

serum panels, this sensitive enzyme immunoassay using 10 μL of serum gave positive results at least as early as the conventional enzyme immunoassay using two recombinant proteins of HIV-1 (gp41 and p24) as antigens (Recombinant HIV-1/HIV-2 third generation, EIA, Abbott), a gelatin particle agglutination test (SERODIA-HIV, Fujirebio) and Western blotting for HIV-1 p24, p51, p55, p66 and gp160 bands and at least nine days earlier than Western blotting for the HIV-1 p17 band.

The third example is immobilization of recombinant HIV-1 p24 antigen on polystyrene beads for assay of anti-HIV-1 p24 antibodies (to be published).

Recombinant p24 (rp24) antigen of HIV-1 and maltose binding protein-rp24 fusion protein were immobilized on polystyrene beads in various ways (Fig. 4.13). In the first and second procedures, rp24 antigen and maltose binding protein-rp24 fusion protein were immobilized directly on polystyrene beads by physical adsorption. In the third and fourth procedures, biotinyl-rp24 antigen and biotinyl-maltose binding protein-rp24 fusion protein were indirectly immobilized by incubation with streptavidin-coated polystyrene beads. In the fifth and sixth procedures, biotinyl-rp24 antigen and biotinyl-maltose binding protein-rp24 fusion protein were indirectly immobilized by incubation with polystyrene beads coated successively with biotinyl-bovine serum albumin and streptavidin. In the seventh and eighth procedures, 2,4-dinitrophenyl-rp24 and 2,4-dinitrophenyl-maltose binding protein-rp24 fusion protein were indirectly immobilized by incubation with affinity-purified (anti-2,4-dinitrophenyl group) IgG-coated polystyrene beads.

These immobilized antigens were tested by enzyme immunoassay using rp24-β-D-galactosidase conjugate. Serum from an HIV-1 seropositive subject (asymptomatic carrier) was diluted 10,000-fold with buffer, and individual polystyrene beads on which rp24 antigens had been immobilized in various ways were incubated with the diluted serum (10 μL) for 1 h and, after washing, with rp24-β-D-galactosidase conjugate for 1 h (Table 4.11).

TABLE 4.11

Effects of direct and indirect immobilizations of recombinant HIV-1 p24 antigen (rp24) on the specific signal and serum interference in two-site enzyme immunoassay for antibodies to HIV-1 p24 antigen

Antigen immobilized	Amount or concentration of antigen for immobilization		Serum from an HIV-1 seronegative subject diluted with buffer	Signal (fluorescence intensity of bound β-D-galactosidase activity) with	
	(fmol/bead)	(μg/mL)	(μL)	Buffer	Serum from an HIV-1 seropositive subject (%)
Biotinyl-MBP-rp24[a]	30	—	0	3.5	846 (100)
Fig. 4.13(F)	30	—	10	3.2	762 (90)
Biotinyl-rp24[a]	30	—	0	3.5	809 (100)
Fig. 4.13(E)	30	—	10	2.8	781 (97)
DNP-MBP-rp24[b]	30	—	0	7.0	689 (100)
Fig. 4.13(H)	30	—	10	9.2	628 (91)
DNP-rp24[b]	300	—	0	6.0	383 (100)
Fig. 4.13(G)	300	—	10	9.4	349 (90)
Biotinyl-MBP-rp24[c]	100	—	0	16	387 (100)
Fig. 4.13(D)	100	—	10	7.0	183 (47)

Biotinyl-rp24[c]	100	—	0	15	492	(100)
Fig. 4.13(C)	100	—	10	6.7	153	(31)
MBP-rp24[d]		1	0	12	62	(100)
Fig. 4.13(B)		1	10	2.8	57	(108)
		5	0	20	233	(100)
		5	10	4.0	51	(22)
rp24[d]		5	0	42	73	(100)
Fig. 4.13(A)		5	10	3.1	6.7	(12)
		25	0	57	125	(100)
		25	10	4.0	5.8	(2.6)

[a] Indirectly immobilized on polystyrene beads coated successively with biotinyl-bovine serum albumin and streptavidin.
[b] Indirectly immobilized on polystyrene beads coated with affinity-purified (anti-2,4-dinitrophenyl group) IgG.
[c] Indirectly immobilized onto streptavidin-coated polystyrene beads.
[d] Directly immobilized.

A polystyrene bead coated with each antigen was incubated with serum (10 μL) from an HIV-1 seropositive subject (asymptomatic carrier), diluted 10,000-fold with buffer, and, after washing, with rp24-β-D-galactosidase conjugate. β-D-galactosidase activity bound was assayed for 1 h. The fluorescence intensity of 10^{-10} mol/L 4- methylumbelliferone was 1. MBP: maltose binding protein; rp24: recombinant HIV-1 p24 antigen; DNP: 2,4-dinitrophenyl group.

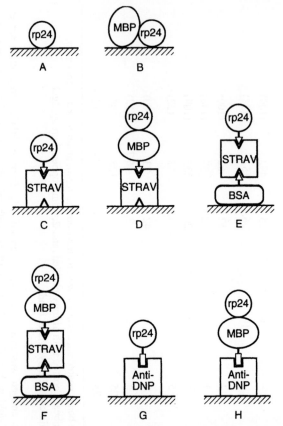

Fig. 4.13. Direct and indirect immobilizations of recombinant HIV-1 p24 (rp24) antigens on polystyrene beads. (A and B) directly immobilized rp24 antigen and maltose-binding protein (MBP)-rp24 fusion protein. (C, D, E, F, G and H) indirectly immobilized biotinyl-rp24 antigen, biotinyl-MBP-rp24 and 2,4-dinitrophenyl(DNP)-MBP-rp24. STRAV: streptavidin. BSA: bovine serum albumin. Possible orientations of molecules are shown.

The highest fluorescence intensities of bound β-D-galactosidase activity in the presence of the diluted serum (the highest positive signals) were obtained with biotinyl-rp24 antigen and biotinyl-maltose binding protein-rp24 fusion protein indirectly immobilized on polystyrene beads coated successively with biotinyl-bovine serum albumin and streptavidin. The second highest positive signals were obtained with 2,4-dinitrophenyl-maltose binding protein-rp24 fusion protein indirectly immobilized on affinity-purified (anti-2,4-dinitrophenyl group) IgG-coated polystyrene beads. The lowest and the second lowest positive signals were observed with directly immobilized rp24 antigen and maltose binding protein-rp24 fusion protein, respectively. Positive signals with other immobilized antigens were higher than the second lowest positive signals but lower than the second highest positive signals. Nonspecific signals in the absence of the diluted serum were similar with all the immobilized antigens.

Thus, the positive signal was enhanced by increasing the number of protein molecules between rp24 antigen molecules and the solid phase surface, indicating that rp24 antigen and/or anti-p24 IgG bound to rp24 antigen on the solid phase became more reactive with anti-p24 IgG and/or rp24-β-D-galactosidase conjugate, as summarized in Table 4.11.

4.3.2. Indirect immobilization of antibodies

An example of this method is immobilization of anti-hGH Fab′ on polystyrene beads for two-site immunoassay of hGH.

Rabbit anti-hGH IgG and biotinyl-rabbit anti-hGH Fab′ were immobilized on polystyrene beads in five different ways (Fig. 4.14). First, rabbit anti-hGH IgG was immobilized directly on polystyrene beads by physical adsorption (Fig. 4.14A). Second, biotinyl-rabbit anti-hGH Fab′ was indirectly immobilized on polystyrene beads that had been coated with streptavidin by physical adsorption (Fig. 4.14B). Third, biotinyl-rabbit anti-hGH Fab′ was indirectly immobilized on polystyrene beads that had been coated with biotinyl-bovine serum albumin by physical adsorption and subsequently with streptavidin (Fig. 4.14C). Fourth, biotinyl-anti-hGH Fab′ was immobilized on polystyrene beads that had been coated with streptavidin by physical adsorption and subsequently with biotinyl-bovine serum albumin and streptavidin (Fig. 4.14D). Fifth, biotinyl-anti-hGH Fab' was immobilized on polystyrene beads that had been coated with biotinyl-bovine serum albumin by physical adsorption and subsequently with streptavidin, biotinyl-bovine serum albumin and streptavidin (Fig. 4.14E).

These polystyrene beads (one bead/assay) were incubated for 2 h with 2 μL of human serum in the presence of monoclonal mouse anti-hGH Fab'-β-D-galactosidase conjugate, and β-D-galactosidase activity bound to the polystyrene beads was assayed by fluorometry (Table 4.12).

The specific signal (difference between the fluorescence intensities of bound β-D-galactosidase activity in the presence and absence of human serum) with biotinyl-anti-hGH Fab' indirectly immobilized on polystyrene beads coated successively with biotinyl-bovine serum albumin and streptavidin was 5.8-fold higher than those with anti-hGH IgG immobilized directly on polystyrene beads and slightly higher than those with biotinyl-anti-hGH Fab' indirectly immobilized in the other ways. Signals with biotinyl-anti-hGH Fab' indirectly immobilized on polystyrene beads coated with streptavidin varied greatly. Signals in the absence of hGH were similar with different polystyrene beads.

Thus, the specific signal increased by indirect immobilization of anti-hGH IgG, indicating that anti-hGH IgG and/or hGH bound to anti-hGH IgG on the solid phase became more reactive with hGH and/or anti-hGH Fab'-β-D-galactosidase conjugate, probably due to alleviation of steric hindrance.

4.3.3. Immunoreaction in solution and subsequent trapping on a solid phase of the immune complex formed

Immunoreactions on solid phases are limited to various extents as described in Chapter 3. This limitation may be overcome by reaction of antigens and antibodies in solution and subsequent trapping

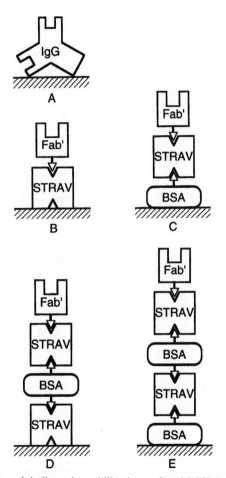

Fig. 4.14. Direct and indirect immobilizations of anti-hGH IgG and biotinyl-anti-hGH Fab′ on polystyrene beads. (A) directly immobilized anti-hGH IgG. (B, C, D and E) indirectly immobilized biotinyl-anti-hGH Fab′. STRAV: streptavidin. BSA: bovine serum albumin. Possible orientations of molecules are shown.

TABLE 4.12

Effects of direct and indirect immobilizations of anti-human growth hormone (hGH) IgG and Fab′ on the specific signal and serum interference in two-site enzyme immunoassay for hGH

Protein used for coating polystyrene beads	Amount or concentration of anti-hGH IgG or bio-tinyl-anti-hGH Fab′ used for coating polystyrene beads (pmol/bead) (μg/mL)		Signal (fluorescence intensity of bound β-D-galactosidase activity) Serum (μL)			Ratio of the specific signal with 20 μL of serum to that with 2 μL $\dfrac{(C)-(A)}{(B)-(A)}$
	(pmol/bead)	(μg/mL)	0 (A)	2 (B)	20 (C)	
Anti-hGH IgG Fig. 4.14(A)	–	100	20	164	276	1.8
Biotinyl-anti-hGH Fab′ Streptavidin Fig. 4.14(B)	4.0	–	26 ± 5.7	629 ± 70	2309 ± 454	3.8 ± 0.4
	8.0	–	31 ± 9.1	691 ± 50	3353 ± 356	5.0 ± 0.4
Biotinyl-anti-hGH Fab′ Streptavidin Biotinyl-BSA Fig. 4.14(C)	1.0	–	11	–	5752	–
	2.0	–	20	854	6744	8.1
Biotinyl-anti-hGH Fab′ Streptavidin Biotinyl-BSA Streptavidin Fig. 4.14(D)	1.0	–	13	584	4254	7.4
	2.0	–	17	750	5354	7.3
Biotinyl-anti-hGH Fab′ Streptavidin Biotinyl-BSA Streptavidin Biotinyl-BSA Fig. 4.14(E)	2.0	–	10	720	5524	7.8

Individual polystyrene beads were incubated with buffer or human serum in the presence of monoclonal mouse anti-hGH Fab′-β-D-galactosidase conjugate. Bound β-D-galactosidase activity was assayed for 1 h. The fluorescence intensity of 10^{-10} mol/L 4-methylumbelliferone was 1. Signals with biotinyl-anti-hGH Fab′ immobilized on streptavidin-coated polystyrene beads were expressed as means ±SD, since they varied considerably.
BSA: bovine serum albumin.

of the immune complexes formed on solid phases, although this is not satisfactory in all cases. Some examples are described below.

The first examples are reactions of human thyroid stimulating hormone (hTSH) and hGH with anti-hTSH and anti-hGH antibodies (Hashida et al., 1988c).

hTSH and hGH were allowed to react simultaneously with 2,4-dinitrophenyl monoclonal mouse antibody IgG and rabbit antibody Fab'-β-D-galactosidase conjugates, and the immune complexes formed, comprising the three components, were trapped on polystyrene beads coated with affinity-purified (anti-2,4-dinitrophenyl group) IgG. In conventional two-site enzyme immunoassays, monoclonal mouse antibody IgG-coated polystyrene beads were allowed to react with the antigens and subsequently with rabbit antibody Fab'-β-D-galactosidase conjugates.

β-D-galactosidase activity bound in the presence of the antigens by simultaneous reactions was 2.7-fold higher for hTSH and 7.1-fold higher for hGH than that bound by sequential reactions, indicating that the immune complexes were more efficiently formed in solution than on the polystyrene beads, although β-D-galactosidase activity nonspecifically bound by the simultaneous reaction in the absence of the antigens was 2.4-fold higher for hTSH and 8.6-fold higher for hGH than those bound by the sequential reactions (Table 4.13).

The second example is the reaction of HIV-1 p24 antigen and anti-p24 antibodies for the assay of HIV-1 p24 antigen (Ishikawa S. et al., 1998c). HIV-1 p24 antigen and anti-HIV-1 p24 antibodies were treated in three different ways (Fig. 4.15).

First, HIV-1 p24 antigen was allowed to react simultaneously for 15 min with 2,4-dinitrophenyl-biotinyl-bovine serum albumin-affinity purified anti-p24 Fab' conjugate and monoclonal anti-p24 Fab'-β-D-galactosidase conjugate. The immune complex formed, consisting of the three components, was trapped for 5 min on a polystyrene bead coated with affinity-purified (anti-2,4-dinitrophenyl group) IgG. Second, a polystyrene bead coated with affinity-purified (anti-2,4-dinitrophenyl group) IgG was incubated

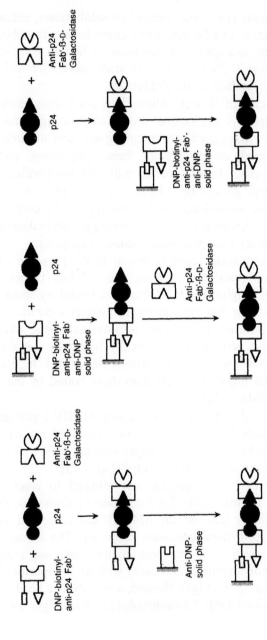

Fig. 4.15. Three different sequences of immunoreactions for the formation of the immune complex comprising 2,4-dinitrophenyl(DNP)-biotinyl-bovine serum albumin-affinity-purified anti-HIV-1 p24 Fab′ conjugate, HIV-1 p24 antigen and monoclonal mouse anti-HIV-1 p24 Fab′-β-D-galactosidase conjugate. Left: simultaneous. Middle: sequential. Right: semi-sequential.

TABLE 4.13

Comparison of immunoreactions in solution and on a solid phase in two-site enzyme immunoassays for antigens

Immunoreaction (Fig. 4.15)	Antigen	Signal (%)		
		hTSH	hGH	HIV-1 p24 antigen
Sequential,	–	100	100	100
on solid phase	+	100	100	100
Semi-sequential	–	–	–	152
	+	–	–	337
Simultaneous,	–	240	860	–
in solution	+	270	710	280

For sequential immunoreactions on a solid phase, polystyrene beads that had been coated successively with affinity-purified (anti-2,4-dinitrophenyl group) IgG and 2,4-dinitrophenyl-antibodies were allowed to react sequentially with antigens and antibody-β-D-galactosidase conjugates. For semi-sequential immunoreaction, HIV-1 p24 antigen was allowed to react sequentially with antibody-β-D-galactosidase conjugate and with polystyrene beads that had been coated successively with affinity-purified (anti-2,4-dinitrophenyl group) IgG and 2,4-dinitrophenyl antibody. For simultaneous immunoreactions in solution, antigens were allowed to react simultaneously with 2,4-dinitrophenyl-antibodies and antibody-β-D-galactosidase conjugates and subsequently with affinity-purified (anti-2,4-dinitrophenyl group) IgG-coated polystyrene beads.

hTSH: human thyroid-stimulating hormone; hGH: human growth hormone.

sequentially with 2,4-dinitrophenyl-biotinyl-bovine serum albumin-affinity-purified anti-p24 Fab′ conjugate for 5 min, with HIV-1 p24 antigen for 5 min and with monoclonal anti-p24 Fab′-β-D-galactosidase conjugate for 20 min. Third, a polystyrene bead coated successively with affinity-purified (anti-2,4-dinitrophenyl group) IgG and 2,4-dinitrophenyl-biotinyl-bovine serum albumin-affinity-purified anti-p24 Fab′ conjugate was incubated for 20 min with a reaction mixture, in which HIV-1 p24 antigen had been incubated for 10 min with monoclonal anti-p24 Fab'-β-D-galactosidase conjugate to form an immune complex of the two components (semi-sequential reaction).

β-D-galactosidase activity bound in the presence of the antigen by the semi-sequential reaction was approximately 20% higher than that bound by the simultaneous reaction and more than 3-fold higher than that bound by the sequential reactions, although β-D-galactosidase activity nonspecifically bound in the absence of the antigen by the semi-sequential reaction was 1.5-fold higher than that formed by the sequential reaction (Table 4.13).

Similar results were obtained on assay of atrial natriuretic peptides (Hashida et al., 1991a).

Thus, the immune complex consisting of the three components was formed on the solid phase in larger amounts by reaction of the two or three components in solution than by sequential reaction of the three components on the solid phase.

As in the two-site enzyme immunoassay for antigens described above, immunoreactions can be allowed to take place in solution for assays of antibodies. For example, anti-thyroglobulin IgG was allowed to react simultaneously with 2,4-dinitrophenyl-thyroglobulin and thyroglobulin-peroxidase conjugate. The immune complex formed, consisting of the three components, was trapped on affinity-purified (anti-2,4-dinitrophenyl group) IgG-coated polystyrene beads. The resulting sensitivity to anti-thyroglobulin IgG was improved 3-fold as compared with that of the conventional enzyme immunoassay, in which thyroglobulin-coated polystyrene beads were incubated with anti-thyroglobulin IgG and, after washing, with thyroglobulin-peroxidase conjugate (Kohno et al., 1988b).

Theoretically, however, twice as much of the immune complex consisting of the three components must be formed by sequential reactions of immobilized 2,4-dinitrophenyl-thyroglobulin, anti-thyroglobulin IgG and thyroglobulin-peroxidase conjugate as by simultaneous reactions of the three components, provided that there is no steric hindrance. When antibody IgG to be measured is allowed to react simultaneously with 2,4-dinitrophenyl-antigen

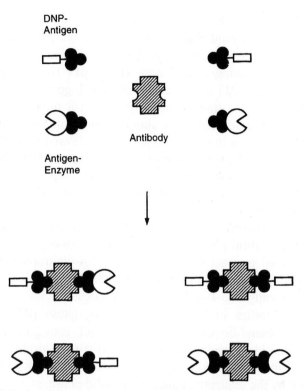

Fig. 4.16. Ratio of the amounts of three different immune complexes formed following simultaneous incubation of 2,4-dinitrophenyl(DNP)-antigen, antibody and antigen-enzyme conjugate.

and antigen-enzyme conjugate, the amount of the immune complex formed consisting of the three components must be equal to the combined amount of the immune complex comprising one antibody IgG molecule and two 2,4-dinitrophenyl-antigen molecules and the immune complex comprising one antibody IgG molecule and two antigen-enzyme conjugate molecules (Fig. 4.16). In contrast, sequential reaction of 2,4-dinitrophenyl-antigen, antibody IgG and antigen-enzyme conjugate must form only the immune complex consisting of the three components.

On the basis of the above considerations, immunoreactions in solution and on a solid phase were compared under the same conditions in enzyme immunoassays for antibodies to three different HIV-1 antigens using recombinant HIV-1 p17 (rp17) antigen, a synthetic peptide (23 amino acids) of HIV-1 gp41 and recombinant HIV-1 reverse transcriptase (rRT) with a molecular weight of 117 kDa (Table 4.14). For simultaneous immunoreactions in solution, antibodies to HIV-1 antigens were allowed to react simultaneously with 2,4-dinitrophenyl-HIV-1 antigen and HIV-1 antigen-β-D-galactosidase conjugates. The immune complexes consisting of the three components were trapped on polystyrene beads coated with affinity-purified (anti-2,4-dinitrophenyl group) IgG. For sequential immunoreactions on a solid phase, polystyrene beads coated with affinity-purified (anti-2,4-dinitrophenyl group) IgG were allowed to react successively with 2,4-dinitrophenyl-HIV-1 antigen conjugates, serum containing antibodies to HIV-1 antigens and HIV-1 antigen-β-D-galactosidase conjugates.

For antibodies to HIV-1 reverse transcriptase (RT) antigen, 2,4-dinitrophenyl-bovine serum albumin-rRT conjugate and rRT-β-D-galactosidase conjugate were used. β-D-galactosidase activity bound by the simultaneous reaction in solution was 1.8-fold higher than that by the sequential reactions on solid phase.

For antibodies to HIV-1 p17 antigen, 2,4-dinitrophenyl-maltose binding protein-rp17 fusion protein and rp17-β-D-galactosidase conjugate were used. β-D-galactosidase activity bound by the sequential reactions on solid phase was 2.7-fold higher than that bound by the simultaneous reaction in solution.

For antibodies to HIV-1 gp41 antigen, 2,4-dinitrophenyl-bovine serum albumin-synthetic HIV-1 gp41 peptide conjugate and synthetic HIV-1 gp41 peptide-β-D-galactosidase conjugate were used. β-D-galactosidase activity bound by the sequential reactions on solid phase was 3.9-fold higher than that bound by the simultaneous reaction in solution.

From the above results for antibodies to the three different HIV-1 antigens, the following possibility is suggested. The im-

TABLE 4.14

Comparison of signals by immunoreactions in solution and on a solid phase in two-site enzyme immunoassays for antibodies

Immunoreaction	Serum from HIV-1	Signal (fluorescence intensity of bound β-D-galactosidase activity)		
		Anti-reverse transcriptase	Anti-p17	Anti-gp41
Simultaneous, in solution	Seronegative	31	10	24
	Seropositive	1404	519	777
Sequential, on a solid phase	Seronegative	66	46	150
	Seropositive	767	1422	3063

For simultaneous immunoreactions in solution, serum samples were incubated simultaneously with 2,4-dinitrophenyl-bovine serum albumin-HIV-1 antigen conjugate and HIV-1 antigen-β-D-galactosidase conjugate and subsequently with polystyrene beads coated with affinity-purified (anti-2,4-dinitrophenyl group) IgG. For sequential immunoreactions on solid phase, polystyrene beads coated with affinity-purified (anti-2,4-dinitrophenyl group) IgG were incubated sequentially with 2,4-dinitrophenyl-bovine serum albumin-HIV-1 antigen conjugate, serum samples and HIV-1 antigen-β-D-galactosidase conjugate. The HIV-1 antigens used were recombinant HIV-1 reverse transcriptase, recombinant HIV-1 p17 antigen and synthetic HIV-1 gp41 peptide consisting of 23 amino acids. β-D-galactosidase activity bound was assayed for 1 h. The fluorescence intensity of 1×10^{-10} mol/L 4-methylumbelliferone was 1.

mune complex comprising 2,4-dinitrophenyl-antigen, the antibodies to be measured and the antigen-enzyme conjugate can be efficiently formed in larger amounts by sequential reactions of the three components on a solid phase coated with affinity-purified (2,4-dinitrophenyl group) IgG than by trapping after simultaneous reaction of the three components in solution, provided that the antigen molecules used in the enzyme immunoassay for antibodies are sufficiently small, causing less steric hindrance in sequential immunoreactions on the solid phase.

This possibility is consistent with the following facts observed with antibodies to insulin with a molecular weight of 5.8 kDa and thyroglobulin with a molecular weight of 670 kDa. The immune complex formed by sequential reaction of insulin-bovine serum albumin-coated polystyrene beads, anti-insulin antibodies and insulin-peroxidase conjugate was 4-fold larger in amount than that formed by simultaneous reaction of 2,4-dinitrophenyl-nonspecific rabbit IgG-insulin conjugate, anti-insulin antibodies and insulin-peroxidase conjugate and subsequent trapping on polystyrene beads coated with affinity-purified (anti-2,4-dinitrophenyl group) IgG (Kohno and Ishikawa, 1988a). The immune complex formed by simultaneous reaction of 2,4-dinitrophenyl-thyroglobulin, anti-thyroglobulin antibodies and thyroglobulin-peroxidase conjugate and subsequent trapping on polystyrene beads coated with affinity-purified (anti-2,4-dinitrophenyl group) IgG was twice as much in amount as that formed by sequential reactions of thyroglobulin-coated polystyrene beads, anti-thyroglobulin antibodies and thyroglobulin-peroxidase conjugate (Kohno et al., 1988b).

However, immunoreactions in solution and on a solid phase may depend on the properties of the antigens used besides their molecular weights.

4.4. Methods to reduce serum interference

Serum interference can be reduced in various ways, although not satisfactorily in all cases.

4.4.1. Choice of enzyme labels

The degree of serum interference varies depending on the enzyme used as a label. In two-site enzyme immunoassay for hGH using polystyrene beads, for example, serum interference is more se-

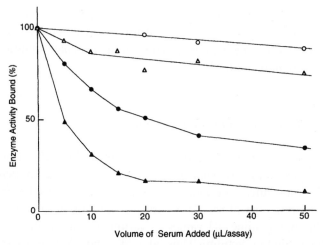

Fig. 4.17. Serum interference in two-site enzyme immunoassay of human growth hormone (hGH) using anti-hGH IgG-coated polystyrene beads, anti-hGH Fab′-peroxidase conjugate and anti-hGH Fab′-β-D-galactosidase conjugate (Ishikawa et al., 1986). Circles and triangles indicate results obtained with peroxidase and β-D-galactosidase conjugates, respectively. Open and closed symbols indicate experiments using 0.4 and 0.1 mol/L NaCl, respectively.

rious with β-D-galactosidase from *E. coli* than with horseradish peroxidase (Fig. 4.17) (Ishikawa et al., 1986).

4.4.2. Use of high ionic concentrations

Serum interference may be caused by serum proteins physically adsorbed on the solid phase, and this can be significantly reduced by high ionic concentrations. In fact, certain concentrations of inorganic salts considerably reduce serum interference without causing marked inhibition of immunoreactions. This is the case in two-site enzyme immunoassays for hGH (Table 4.15 and Figs. 4.18 and 4.19) (Hashida et al., 1983) and insulin (Figs. 4.20 and 4.21) (Imagawa et al., 1983) using horseradish peroxidase as a label. In these immunoassays, appropriate concentrations (0.4–0.5 mol/L) of

NaCl, KCl and LiCl cause considerable reduction of serum inter-ference with only slight inhibition of immunoreactions, while high concentrations of $MgCl_2$, $CaCl_2$ and sodium phosphate significantly inhibit immunoreactions.

4.4.3. Indirect immobilization of antigens

The extents of serum interference by proteins physically adsorbed on solid phases may depend on the orientations of the antigen and antibody molecules immobilized on the surface of the solid phases. The conformations of the Fc portions of IgG molecules may vary at acidic and alkaline pH values to various extents with little loss of antigen-binding activity. Thus, at acidic and alkaline pH values, IgG molecules may be oriented in different manners on the sur-face of solid phases. Consistent with this idea, serum interference is significantly alleviated on enzyme immunoassay of insulin us-ing anti-insulin Fab′-peroxidase conjugate and polystyrene beads coated with acid-treated anti-insulin IgG (Table 4.16) (Ruan et al., 1986).

However, simply physical or direct adsorption of conformation-ally altered antigen and antibody molecules on solid phases may results in limited changes of their orientations on the surface of the solid phases and, therefore, limited reduction of serum inter-ference. More effective methods for immobilization of antigen and antibody molecules on solid phases are available to reduce serum interference. Some examples are described below.

The first example of this method is recombinant HIV-1 p17 (rp17) antigen and its related antigens directly and indirectly immo-bilized in seven different ways for the assay of antibodies to HIV-1 p17 antigen, shown in Fig. 4.12 (Ishikawa S. et al., 1999).

These immobilized antigens were tested by enzyme immunoas-say using rp17-β-D-galactosidase conjugate. Serum from an HIV-1 seropositive subject (asymptomatic carrier) was diluted with buffer 1000-fold for the directly immobilized antigens and 10,000-fold

TABLE 4.15

Effects of various inorganic salts on the specific signal and serum interference in two-site enzyme immunoassay of hGH

Concentrations of inorganic salt (mol/L)		Serum added	Signal (fluorescence intensity of bound peroxidase activity)	
NaCl	Other salts	(μL)		(%)
0.1	–	0	250	(100)
		20	125	(50)
0.4	–	0	224	(100)
		20	218	(97)
0.1	0.3, KCl	0	222	(100)
		20	219	(99)
0.1	0.3, LiCl	0	204	(100)
		20	190	(93)
0.1	0.15, $MgCl_2$	0	169	(100)
		20	109	(64)
0.1	0.15, $CaCl_2$	0	165	(100)
		20	135	(82)
0.1	0.3, sodium phosphate, pH 7.0	0	194	(100)
		20	174	(90)

A polystyrene bead coated with rabbit anti-hGH IgG was incubated with 100 pg of hGH at the indicated final concentrations of inorganic salts in the absence and presence of serum (20 μL) containing 1 pg (50 pg/mL) of hGH and, after washing, with anti-hGH Fab'-peroxidase conjugate (Hashida et al., 1983). Anti-hGH Fab' conjugated with peroxidase was not affinity-purified. Peroxidase activity was assayed for 1.5 h.

TABLE 4.16

Recovery of insulin added to human serum in two-site enzyme immunoassay of insulin

Acid-treatment of anti-insulin IgG for coating polystyrene beads	Conditions for incubation with				Addition of normal guinea pig $F(ab')_2$	Detection limit of insulin		Volume of serum used	Recovery of insulin
	Serum samples		Anti-insulin Fab'-peroxidase			nU	mU/L	µL	(%)
	°C	h	°C	h					
No	37	4	20	4	No	1.0	0.1	10	105(a)
No	37	4	20	4	Yes	0.6	–	50	67(a)
No	20	4	20	4	Yes	0.8	–	50	73(a)
No	20	1	20	3	Yes	1.0	–	50	83(a)
Yes	20	1	20	3	Yes	1.0	0.02	50	97–106(b)

The recovery test was performed (a) by adding 20 mU/L of insulin standard to pooled serum containing 28.9 mU/L of insulin, or (b) by addition of 6.0–20 mU/L of insulin standard to five serum samples containing 3.4–37 mU/L of insulin. Peroxidase activity bound was determined by a 60 min assay (Ruan et al., 1986).

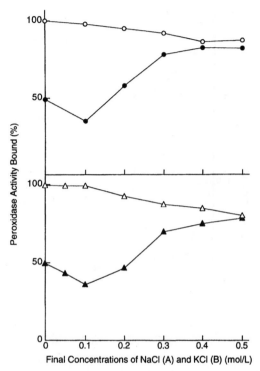

Fig. 4.18. Effects of NaCl and KCl concentrations on serum interference in two-site enzyme immunoassay of hGH. Individual polystyrene beads coated with rabbit anti-hGH IgG were incubated with 100 pg of hGH in the absence (open symbols) and presence (closed symbols) of serum (20 μL) containing 1 pg of hGH in a total volume of 150 μL containing NaCl (circles) or KCl (triangles) and, after washing, with anti-hGH Fab'-peroxidase conjugate (Hashida et al., 1983). The anti-hGH Fab' conjugated to peroxidase was not affinity-purified.

for the indirectly immobilized antigens, and individual polystyrene beads on which rp17 antigens had been immobilized in various ways as described above were incubated overnight with the diluted serum samples (10 μL) in the absence and presence of serum (10 μL) from HIV-1 seronegative subjects. Then, after washing,

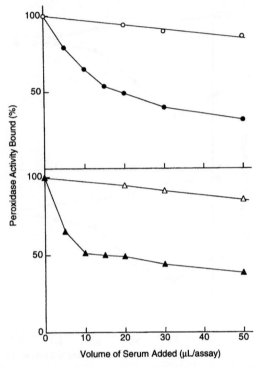

Fig. 4.19. Effect of serum volume on serum interference in two-site enzyme immunoassay of hGH. Individual polystyrene beads coated with rabbit anti-hGH
IgG were incubated with 100 pg of hGH and various volumes of serum containing 50 pg/mL hGH at a final concentration of 0.1 mol/L (closed symbols), 0.4
mol/L (open symbols) NaCl (circles) or KCl (triangles) in a total volume of 150
μL (Hashida et al., 1983). The anti-hGH Fab′ conjugated to peroxidase was not
affinity-purified.

the beads were incubated for 3.5 h with rp17-β-D-galactosidase
conjugate (Table 4.9) (Ishikawa S. et al., 1999).

The extent of serum interference tends to increase with increase in the amounts or concentrations of the antigens used for
immobilization. The amounts of indirectly immobilized antigens
shown in Table 4.9 were optimal for providing the highest signal

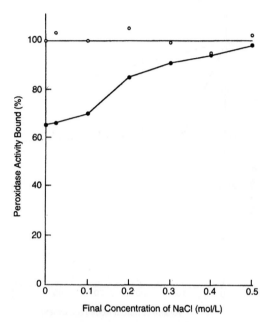

Fig. 4.20. Effect of NaCl concentration on serum interference in two-site en-zyme immunoassay of insulin. Individual polystyrene beads coated with guinea pig anti-insulin IgG were incubated with insulin in the absence (open symbols) and presence (closed symbols) of nonspecific serum (20 μL) in a total volume of 150 μL and, after washing, with anti-insulin Fab′-peroxidase conjugate. The anti-insulin Fab′ conjugated to peroxidase was not affinity-purified.

and the least serum interference. With biotinyl-rp17 antigen and biotinyl-maltose binding protein-rp17 fusion protein indirectly im-mobilized on polystyrene beads coated successively with biotinyl-bovine serum albumin and streptavidin, only slight serum inter-ference was observed. In contrast, serum interference was serious with rp17 antigen and maltose binding protein-rp17 fusion pro-tein directly immobilized at higher concentrations (25–100 μg/mL) and biotinyl-rp17 indirectly immobilized on streptavidin-coated polystyrene beads, although there was little or no serum interfer-ence using lower concentrations (1–5 μg/mL) of rp17 antigen and

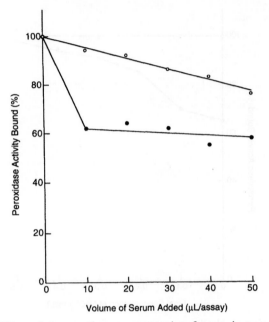

Fig. 4.21. Effect of serum volume on serum interference in two-site enzyme immunoassay of insulin. Individual polystyrene beads coated with guinea pig anti-insulin IgG were incubated with insulin and various volumes of nonspecific serum at a final concentration of 0.1 mol/L (closed symbols) or 0.4 mol/L (open symbols) NaCl in a total volume of 150 μL. The anti-insulin Fab' conjugated to peroxidase was not affinity-purified.

maltose binding protein-rp17 fusion protein for direct immobilization. Less serious but considerable serum interference was observed with 2,4-dinitrophenyl- and biotinyl-maltose binding protein-rp17 fusion proteins indirectly immobilized on affinity-purified (anti-2,4-dinitrophenyl group) IgG- and streptavidin-coated polystyrene beads.

Thus, serum interference in the above enzyme immunoassay tends to be alleviated to greater extents with increasing numbers of protein molecules between rp17 antigen molecules and solid phase surface, as summarized in Table 4.9.

The second example is immobilization of recombinant HIV-1 p24 antigen on polystyrene beads for assay of anti-HIV-1 p24 antibodies (to be published). Recombinant p24 (rp24) antigen of HIV-1 and maltose binding protein-rp24 fusion protein were immobilized on polystyrene beads in various ways (Fig. 4.13), and the immobilized antigens were tested by enzyme immunoassay. Serum from an HIV-1 seropositive subject (asymptomatic carrier) was diluted 10,000-fold with buffer, and individual polystyrene beads on which rp24 antigens had been immobilized in various ways were first incubated with the diluted serum (10 μL) in the absence and presence of serum (10 μL) from HIV-1 seronegative subjects for 1 h and, then after washing, with rp24-β-D-galactosidase conjugate for 1 h (Table 4.11).

With biotinyl-rp24 antigen and biotinyl-maltose binding protein-rp24 fusion protein indirectly immobilized on polystyrene beads coated successively with biotinyl-bovine serum albumin and streptavidin and 2,4-dinitrophenyl-rp24 antigen and 2,4-dinitrophenyl-maltose binding protein-rp24 fusion protein indirectly immobilized on (anti-2,4-dinitrophenyl group) IgG-coated polystyrene beads, only slight serum interference was observed. The most serious serum interference was observed with directly immobilized rp24 antigen and maltose binding protein-rp24 fusion protein. Less serious, but considerable serum interference was observed with biotinyl-rp24 antigen and biotinyl-maltose binding protein-rp24 fusion proteins indirectly immobilized on streptavidin-coated polystyrene beads, and serum interference increased with increase in the amounts of the antigens used for immobilization.

Thus, serum interference tended to be alleviated to greater extents by increasing the number of protein molecules between rp24 antigen molecules and the solid phase surface.

TABLE 4.17

Effect of the concentration of affinity-purified (anti-2,4-dinitrophenyl group) IgG for coating polystyrene beads on the specific signal and serum interference in two-site enzyme immunoassay of HIV-1 p24 antigen using 2,4-dinitrophenyl-biotinyl-bovine serum albumin-affinity-purified rabbit anti-HIV-1 p24 Fab′ conjugate and monoclonal mouse anti-HIV-1 p24 Fab′-β-D-galactosidase conjugates

Concentration of (anti-2,4-dinitrophenyl group) IgG for coating polystyrene beads (μg/mL)	Serum added (μL)	Fluorescence intensity for bound β-D-galactosidase activity	(%)
5	0	339	(100)
	50	303	(89)
10	0	832	(100)
	50	495	(59)
20	0	871	(100)
	50	441	(51)
50	0	963	(100)
	50	370	(38)
100	0	1096	(100)
	50	307	(28)

HIV-1 p24 antigen (100 amol) was incubated simultaneously with 100 fmol of 2,4-dinitrophenyl-biotinyl-bovine serum albumin-affinity-purified rabbit anti-HIV-1 p24 Fab′ conjugate and 10 fmol of monoclonal mouse anti-HIV-1 p24 Fab′-ß-D-galactosidase conjugate in the presence and absence of 50 μL of serum in a total volume of 150 μL and subsequently with two polystyrene beads (3.2 mm diameter) coated with affinity-purified (anti-2,4-dinitrophenyl group) IgG. β-D-galactosidase activity bound was assayed for 1 h. The fluorescence intensity of 1×10^{-10} mol/L 4-methylumbelliferone was 1.

TABLE 4.18

Effects of concentrations of antigens for coating polystyrene beads on the specific signal and serum interference in two-site enzyme immunoassays of antibodies to HIV-1 p17 and p24 antigens

| Antigen | Amount of antigen for immobilization fmol/assay | Signal (fluorescence intensity of β-D-galactosidase activity bound) | |
| | | Serum added (μL) | |
		0	10
DNP-MBP-rp17	50	1161 (100)	704 (44)
	100	1990 (100)	622 (31)
	300	1682 (100)	232 (14)
Biotinyl-MBP-rp24	100	316 (100)	162 (51)
	300	258 (100)	94 (36)

2,4-dinitrophenyl-maltose-binding protein-recombinant HIV-1 p17 (rp17) fusion protein (DNP-MBP-rp17) and biotinyl-MBP-recombinant p24 (rp24) fusion protein were immobilized on polystyrene beads coated with affinity-purified (anti-2,4-dinitrophenyl group) IgG and streptavidin, respectively. A coated polystyrene bead was incubated with serum from an HIV-1 seropositive subject (asymptomatic carrier) and, after washing, with rp17- and rp24-β-D-galactosidase conjugates. β-D-galactosidase activity bound was assayed for 1 h. The fluorescence intensity of 1×10^{-10} fmol/L 4-methylumbelliferone was 1.
Values in parentheses are percentages of signals.

4.4.4. Indirect immobilization of antibodies

Examples of this method are anti-hGH Fab′ immobilized on polystyrene beads in five different ways as described above for the assay of hGH (Fig. 4.14). These five different polystyrene beads (one bead/assay) were incubated with 2 and 20 μL of serum from a healthy subject in the presence of monoclonal mouse anti-hGH Fab′-β-D-galactosidase conjugate (Table 4.12).

Serum interference was examined by calculating the ratio of the signal with 20 μL of serum to that with 2 μL of serum, which should be 10 without serum interference. The highest ratios

(7.3–8.1) were obtained with biotinyl-anti-hGH Fab' indirectly immobilized on two to four layers of streptavidin and biotinyl-bovine serum albumin, and the lowest ratio (1.8) was observed with anti-hGH IgG immobilized directly on polystyrene beads by physical adsorption.

Thus, the lowest serum interference was obtained with biotinyl-anti-hGH Fab' indirectly immobilized on two to four layers of streptavidin and biotinyl-bovine serum albumin, and the highest serum interference with anti-hGH IgG immobilized directly on polystyrene beads by physical adsorption.

4.4.5. Low concentrations of antigens and antibodies for coating solid phases

Serum interference is significantly reduced by changing the concentrations of antigens and antibodies used for coating solid phases. In two-site enzyme immunoassay for HIV-1 p24 antigen using affinity-purified (anti-2,4-dinitrophenyl group) IgG-coated polystyrene solid phases, 2,4-dinitrophenyl-biotinyl-bovine serum albumin-affinity-purified rabbit anti-p24 Fab' conjugate and monoclonal mouse anti-p24 Fab'-β-D-galactosidase conjugate, serum interference decreased with decrease in the concentration of affinity-purified (anti-2,4-dinitrophenyl group) IgG used for coating the polystyrene solid phase (Table 4.17). Similarly, coating polystyrene beads with decreasing concentrations of maltose-binding protein-HIV-1 p17 and p24 fusion proteins results in less serious serum interference in two-site enzyme immunoassays for antibodies to HIV-1 (Table 4.18). However, the specific binding also decreases with decrease in the concentrations of antigens and antibodies used for coating solid phases. Therefore, the optimal concentrations of antigens and antibodies for coating solid phases must be determined to obtain maximal ratio of specific binding to nonspecific binding.

4.4.6. Miscellaneous conditions

Serum interference is significantly reduced in many but not all cases by changing conditions such as the temperature, incubation time and age of solid phases after coating with antigens and antibodies.

Physical adsorption of proteins on the surface of solid phases increases on longer incubations at higher temperatures. Therefore, serum interference is significantly alleviated by shorter incubations at lower temperatures. This is the case in two-site enzyme immunoassay for insulin using horseradish peroxidase as a label (Table 4.16) (Ruan et al., 1986).

Serum interference becomes less serious with time after coating solid phases with antigens and antibodies. This is the case in two-site enzyme immunoassay for HIV-1 p24 antigen using affinity-purified (anti-2,4-dinitrophenyl group) IgG-coated polystyrene beads, 2,4-dinitrophenyl-biotinyl-bovine serum albumin-affinity-purified rabbit anti-p24 Fab′ conjugate and monoclonal mouse anti-p24 Fab′-β-D-galactosidase conjugate. Serum interference was considerably reduced a few months after coating the polystyrene solid phases with affinity-purified (anti-2,4-dinitrophenyl group) IgG.

CHAPTER 5

Principle of the immune complex transfer enzyme immunoassay

Immune complex transfer methods are the most practically effective for reducing the nonspecific signal in noncompetitive heterogeneous solid phase enzyme immunoassays, as described in Chapter 4. The immune complexes consisting of analytes and the corresponding labeled reactants are trapped on the first solid phase. After washing, the immune complexes are specifically eluted from the first solid phase and are transferred to a second clean solid phase. This dramatically reduces the nonspecific binding of the labeled reactants, greatly improving the sensitivity. The principles of eight methods proposed for antibodies (Ishikawa et al., 1993) and two for antigens (Ishikawa et al., 1991) are described below.

5.1. Immune complex transfer enzyme immunoassay of antibodies

In the immune complex transfer enzyme immunoassay I (Fig. 5.1) developed first (Kohno and Ishikawa, 1987), the specific antibody to be measured is allowed to react with 2,4-dinitrophenyl-biotinyl-antigen, and the immune complex formed, consisting of the two components, is trapped on a solid phase coated with affinity-purified (anti-2,4-dinitrophenyl group) IgG (first solid phase). After washing to remove most of the interfering substances, including nonspecific immunoglobulins, the immune complex is eluted from the first

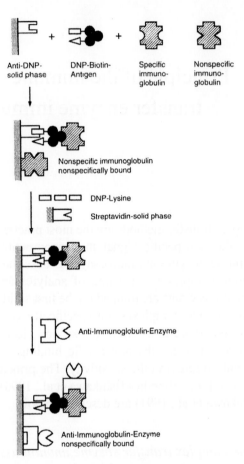

Fig. 5.1. Immune complex transfer enzyme immunoassay I for antibodies.
DNP: 2,4-dinitrophenyl group.

solid phase with excess ϵN-2,4-dinitrophenyl-L-lysine and is transferred to a solid phase coated with avidin (second solid phase). The
second solid phase is allowed to react with anti-immunoglobulin
Fab′-enzyme conjugate to measure the specific antibody in the
immune complex, and the enzyme activity bound to the second
solid phase is correlated with the amount or concentration of the

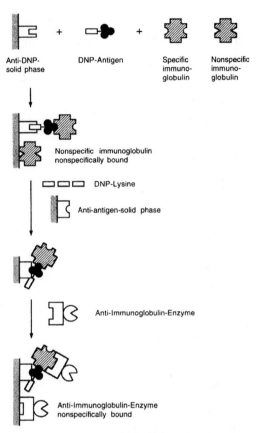

Fig. 5.2. Immune complex transfer enzyme immunoassay II for antibodies. DNP: 2,4-dinitrophenyl group.

specific antibody to be measured. By transfer of the immune complex from the first solid phase to the second one, nonspecific immunoglobulins and other interfering substance(s) are removed well, reducing the nonspecific signal in the absence of the specific antibodies to be measured. However, the nonspecific binding of anti-immunoglobulin Fab'-enzyme conjugate to the second solid

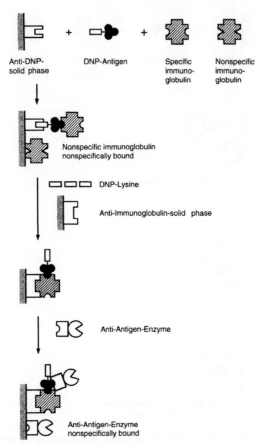

Fig. 5.3. Immune complex transfer enzyme immunoassay III for antibodies.
DNP: 2,4-dinitrophenyl group.

phase limits the sensitivity. This original method has been modified
in various ways as described below.

In immune complex transfer enzyme immunoassay II (Fig. 5.2)
(Kohno et al., 1988c), the specific antibody to be measured is
allowed to react with 2,4-dinitrophenyl-antigen, and the immune
complex formed of the two components is trapped on a solid
phase coated with affinity-purified (anti-2,4-dinitrophenyl group)

IgG (first solid phase). After washing, the immune complex is eluted from the first solid phase with excess ϵN-2,4-dinitrophenyl-L-lysine and is transferred to a solid phase coated with antibody IgG to the antigen (second solid phase). The second solid phase is allowed to react with anti-immunoglobulin Fab'-enzyme conjugate to measure the specific antibody in the immune complex. As in immune complex transfer enzyme immunoassay I, nonspecific immunoglobulins and other interfering substance(s) are efficiently removed by transfer of the immune complex, resulting in a low nonspecific signal and high sensitivity. However, the nonspecific binding of the anti-immunoglobulin Fab'-enzyme conjugate to the second solid phase limits the sensitivity.

In immune complex transfer enzyme immunoassay III (Fig. 5.3) (Kohno et al., 1988d), the specific antibody to be measured is allowed to react with 2,4-dinitrophenyl-antigen, and the immune complex formed of the two components is trapped on a solid phase coated with affinity-purified (anti-2,4-dinitrophenyl group) IgG (first solid phase). After washing, the immune complex is eluted from the first solid phase with excess ϵN-2,4-dinitrophenyl-L-lysine and is transferred to a solid phase coated with anti-immunoglobulin IgG (second solid phase). The second solid phase is allowed to react with anti-antigen Fab'-enzyme conjugate to measure 2,4-dinitrophenyl-antigen in the immune complex. Interference by nonspecific immunoglobulins is eliminated. However, the non-specific binding of the anti-antigen Fab'-enzyme conjugate to the second solid phase limits the sensitivity.

In immune complex transfer enzyme immunoassay IV (Fig. 5.4) (Kohno and Ishikawa, 1988b), the specific antibody to be measured is allowed to react with 2,4-dinitrophenyl-antigen-enzyme conjugate, and the immune complex of the two components formed is trapped on a solid phase coated with affinity-purified (anti-2,4-dinitrophenyl group) IgG (first solid phase). After washing, the immune complex is eluted from the first solid phase with excess ϵN-2,4-dinitrophenyl-L-lysine and is transferred to solid phase coated with anti-immunoglobulin IgG (second solid phase). There

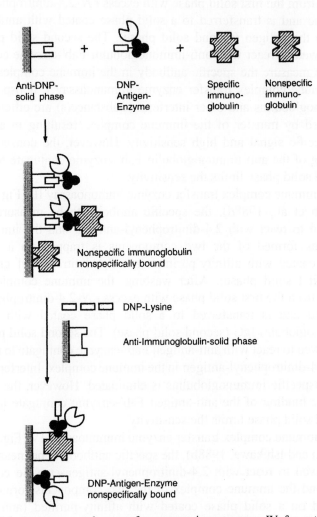

Fig. 5.4. Immune complex transfer enzyme immunoassay IV for antibodies. DNP: 2,4-dinitrophenyl group.

is no interference by nonspecific immunoglobulins. However, the nonspecific binding of 2,4-dinitrophenyl-antigen-enzyme conjugate to the second solid phase limits the sensitivity.

In immune complex transfer enzyme immunoassay V (Fig. 5.5) (Kohno et al., 1989b), the specific antibody to be measured is allowed to react simultaneously with 2,4-dinitrophenyl-antigen and antigen-enzyme conjugate. The immune complex consisting of the three components formed is trapped on a solid phase coated with affinity-purified (anti-2,4-dinitrophenyl group) IgG (first solid phase). Alternatively, the first solid phase is allowed to react sequentially with 2,4-dinitrophenyl-antigen, the specific antibody to be measured and antigen-enzyme conjugate. After washing, the immune complex is eluted from the first solid phase with excess ϵN-2,4-dinitrophenyl-L-lysine and is transferred to a solid phase coated with affinity-purified anti-immunoglobulin IgG (second solid phase). The nonspecific binding of antigen-enzyme conjugate is reduced by transfer of the immune complex. Therefore, this method is more sensitive than immune complex transfer enzyme immunoassays I, II, III and IV described above.

In immune complex transfer enzyme immunoassay VI (Fig. 5.6) (Ishikawa et al., 1991), 2,4-dinitrophenyl-biotinyl-antigen and streptavidin-coated solid phases are substituted for the 2,4-dinitrophenyl-antigen and affinity-purified anti-immunoglobulin IgG-coated solid phases, respectively, in immune complex transfer enzyme immunoassay V. This method detects antibodies of all classes and must be as sensitive as immune complex transfer enzyme immunoassay V.

In immune complex transfer enzyme immunoassay VII (Fig. 5.7) (Ishikawa et al., 1993), the specific antibody to be measured is allowed to react with 2,4-dinitrophenyl-antigen-enzyme conjugate, and the immune complex of the two components formed is trapped on a solid phase coated with affinity-purified (anti-2,4-dinitrophenyl group) IgG (first solid phase). After washing, the immune complex is eluted from the first solid phase with excess ϵN-2,4-dinitrophenyl-L-lysine and, after reaction with biocytin-

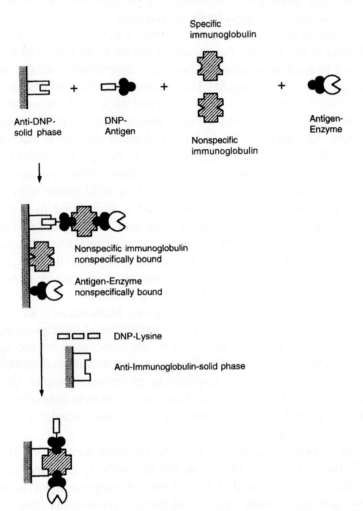

Fig. 5.5. Immune complex transfer enzyme immunoassay V for antibodies. DNP: 2,4-dinitrophenyl group.

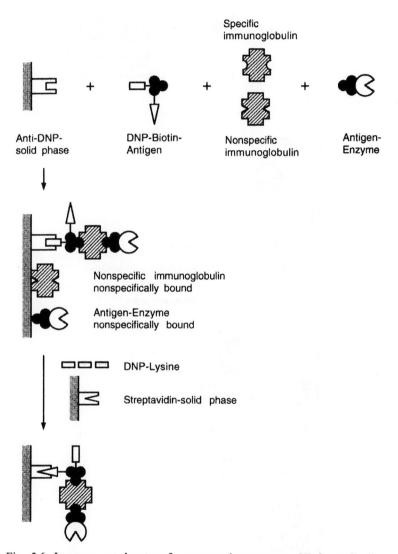

Fig. 5.6. Immune complex transfer enzyme immunoassay VI for antibodies. DNP: 2,4-dinitrophenyl group.

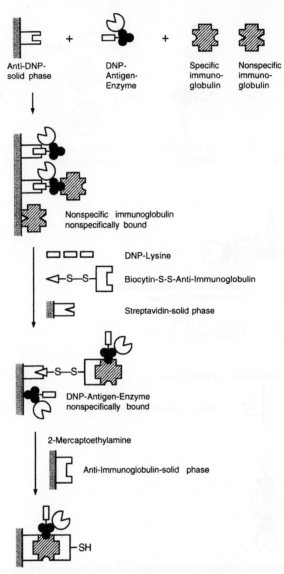

Fig. 5.7. Immune complex transfer enzyme immunoassay VII for antibodies. DNP: 2,4-dinitrophenyl group. S—S: disulfide bond.

S—S-anti-immunoglobulin IgG, is transferred to a streptavidin-coated solid phase (second solid phase). The immune complex is eluted from the second solid phase by reduction with 2-mercaptoethylamine and is transferred to a solid phase coated with anti-immunoglobulin IgG (the third solid phase). The nonspecific binding of 2,4-dinitrophenyl-antigen-enzyme conjugate is reduced by the second transfer of the immune complex. Therefore, this assay is more sensitive than immune complex transfer enzyme immunoassay IV (Fig. 5.4).

In immune complex transfer enzyme immunoassay VIII (Fig. 5.8) (Ishikawa et al., 1993), the specific antibody to be measured is allowed to react simultaneously with 2,4-dinitrophenyl-antigen and antigen-enzyme conjugate. The immune complex consisting of the three components formed is trapped on a solid phase coated with affinity-purified (anti-2,4-dinitrophenyl group) IgG (first solid phase). After washing, the immune complex is eluted from the first solid phase with excess ϵN-2,4-dinitrophenyl-L-lysine and, after reaction with biocytin-S—S-anti-immunoglobulin IgG, is transferred to a streptavidin-coated solid phase (second solid phase). The immune complex is eluted from the second solid phase by reduction with 2-mercaptoethylamine and is transferred to an affinity-purified anti-immunoglobulin IgG-coated solid phase (the third solid phase). This must improve the sensitivity over that of immune complex transfer enzyme immunoassay V (Fig. 5.5).

Obviously from the principles described above, all these methods can distinguish the immunoglobulin classes of antibodies to be measured except immune complex transfer enzyme immunoassay VI, which measures all antibodies regardless of their immunoglobulin class.

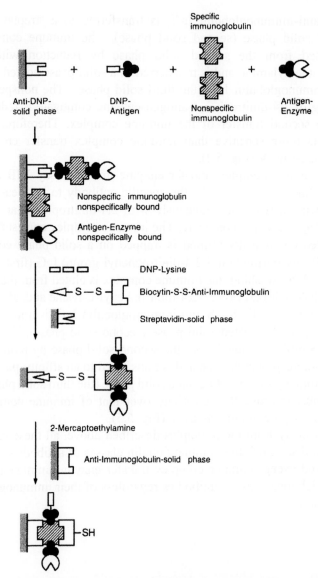

Fig. 5.8. Immune complex transfer enzyme immunoassay VIII for antibodies.
DNP: 2,4-dinitrophenyl group. S—S: disulfide bond.

5.2. Immune complex transfer enzyme immunoassays of antigens

The sensitivities of noncompetitive heterogeneous two-site (sandwich) enzyme immunoassays of antigens can also be improved in the same way by immune complex transfer as in the immunoassays for antibodies described above.

In immune complex transfer enzyme immunoassay IX developed first (Fig. 5.9) (Hashida et al., 1988c), the antigen to be measured is allowed to react simultaneously with 2,4-dinitrophenyl-antibody IgG and antibody Fab'-enzyme conjugate. The immune complex consisting of the three components formed is trapped on a solid phase coated with affinity-purified (anti-2,4-dinitrophenyl group) IgG (first solid phase). Alternatively, the first solid phase is allowed to react sequentially with 2,4-dinitrophenyl-antibody IgG, the antigen to be measured and antibody Fab'-enzyme conjugate. The first solid phase is washed to eliminate excess Fab'-enzyme conjugate. The immune complex is then eluted from the first solid phase with excess ϵN-2,4-dinitrophenyl-L-lysine and is transferred to a solid phase coated with (anti-IgG Fc portion) IgG (second solid phase). By this transfer, the Fab'-β-D-galactosidase conjugate nonspecifically bound to the first solid phase is eliminated more completely, markedly reducing the background noise with much less decrease in the specific binding and, therefore, considerably improving the sensitivities to antigens.

In immune complex transfer enzyme immunoassay X (Fig. 5.10) (Hashida and Ishikawa, 1990), 2,4-dinitrophenyl-biotinyl-antibody and streptavidin-coated solid phases are substituted for the 2,4-dinitrophenyl-antibody IgG and (anti-IgG Fc portion) IgG-coated solid phases, respectively, used in immune complex transfer enzyme immunoassay IX (Fig. 5.9). The antigen to be measured is allowed to react simultaneously with 2,4-dinitrophenyl-biotinyl-antibody and antibody Fab'-enzyme conjugate. The immune complex consisting of the three components formed is trapped on a solid phase coated with affinity-purified (anti-2,4-dinitrophenyl group)

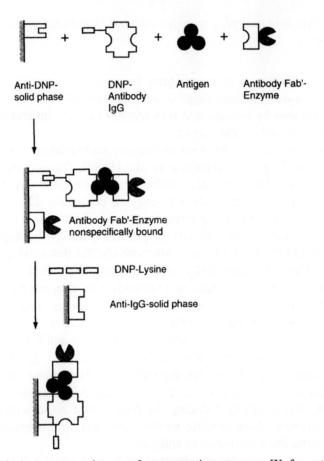

Fig. 5.9. Immune complex transfer enzyme immunoassay IX for antigens.
DNP: 2,4-dinitrophenyl group.

IgG (first solid phase). Alternatively, the first solid phase is allowed
to react sequentially with 2,4-dinitrophenyl-biotinyl-antibody, the
antigen to be measured and antibody-enzyme conjugate. The immune complex is eluted from the first solid phase with excess ϵN-
2,4-dinitrophenyl-L-lysine and transferred to streptavidin-coated
solid phase (second solid phase).

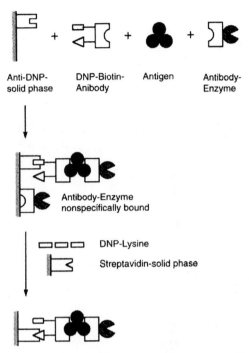

Fig. 5.10. Immune complex transfer enzyme immunoassay X for antigens. DNP: 2,4-dinitrophenyl group.

5.3. Immune complex transfer enzyme immunoassay for simultaneous detections of antigens and antibodies

An immune complex transfer enzyme immunoassay for both antigens and antibodies was developed (Fig. 5.11) (Hashida et al., 1996b). In this procedure, the antigen and specific antibody are allowed to react simultaneously with 2,4-dinitrophenyl-biotinyl-antibody IgG (or Fab′), antibody Fab′-enzyme conjugate, 2,4-dinitrophenyl-antigen and antigen-enzyme conjugate. The immune complexes consisting of the three components formed are trapped on a solid phase coated with affinity-purified (anti-2,4-dinitrophenyl group) IgG (first solid phase). After washing to eliminate excess

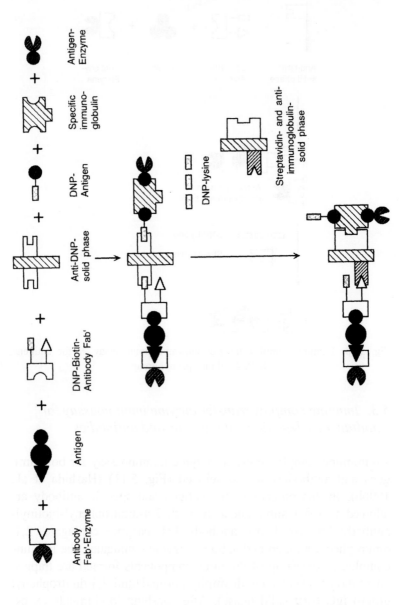

amounts of the reagents, the immune complexes are eluted from the first solid phase with excess ϵN-2,4-dinitrophenyl-L-lysine and are transferred to a solid phase coated with both streptavidin and affinity-purified anti-immunoglobulin IgG (second solid phase). The sensitivities to antigens and specific antibodies achieved by this method must be as high as those in immune complex transfer enzyme immunoassays V and X, respectively.

CHAPTER 6

Potential of the immune complex transfer enzyme immunoassay to improve the sensitivity and its limitations

In the immune complex transfer enzyme immunoassays described in Chapter 5, the signal in the absence of the antigens and antibodies to be measured (analytes), that is the nonspecific signal, is reduced much more than the specific signal, that is, the difference between the signals in the presence and absence of analytes. As a result, the detection limit of analytes is lowered to various extents depending on the case (Ishikawa et al., 1991). Evaluations of the various immune complex transfer methods described in Chapter 5 are described below, although these evaluations are not yet complete. The polystyrene beads used were 3.2 mm in diameter, and the incubations were performed in a total volume of 150 μL throughout.

6.1. Improvement of sensitivity to antibodies

The immune complex transfer enzyme immunoassays I to VIII described in Chapter 5 (Figs. 5.1–5.8) have been evaluated using antibodies to various antigens including insulin (Ishikawa et al., 1989b), thyroglobulin (Ishikawa and Kohno, 1989), β-D-galactosidase (Kohno et al., 1991b), HTLV-I antigens (Ishikawa et al., 1990a) and HIV-1 antigens (Hashida et al., 1997). The detection limit of antibodies was tentatively determined using antibody IgGs to insulin and thyroglobulin affinity-purified from guinea pig anti-insulin sera and human sera of patients with Graves' diseases.

6.1.1. Immune complex transfer enzyme immunoassay I

The first trial of immune complex transfer enzyme immunoassay I (Fig. 5.1) was on anti-insulin IgG in guinea pig serum (Kohno and Ishikawa, 1987).

A polystyrene bead coated with rabbit (anti-2,4-dinitrophenyl group) IgG (first solid phase) was incubated for 4 h simultaneously with guinea pig anti-insulin serum (10 μL) and 30 fmol of 2,4-dinitrophenyl-biotinyl-nonspecific rabbit IgG-insulin conjugate in the presence of excess nonspecific rabbit IgG. Then, after washing, it was incubated overnight with excess ϵN-2,4-dinitrophenyl-L-lysine in the presence of excess nonspecific rabbit IgG to elute the immune complex of the two components. The eluate was incubated with a polystyrene bead coated with avidin (second solid phase) for 3 h. Finally, the second solid phase was incubated for 3 h with 600 fmol (50 ng) of rabbit (anti-guinea pig IgG) Fab'-peroxidase conjugate to measure guinea pig anti-insulin IgG in the immune complex trapped. Peroxidase activity bound to the second solid phase was assayed for 10 min by fluorometry using p-hydroxyphenylpropionic acid as a hydrogen donor.

The detection limit of anti-insulin IgG was 15 pg/assay. This value was similar to that (20 pg/assay) by the conventional enzyme immunoassay, in which a polystyrene bead coated with insulin-bovine serum albumin was incubated for 3 h with guinea pig anti-insulin serum and, after washing, was incubated for 3 h with 600 fmol of rabbit (anti-guinea pig IgG) Fab'-peroxidase conjugate.

However, the detection limit of anti-insulin IgG in guinea pig serum by immune complex transfer enzyme immunoassay I was 1.5 ng/mL, which was 10,000-fold lower than that by the conventional enzyme immunoassay (Table 6.1), and 300-fold lower than that by an improved conventional enzyme immunoassay, in which a polystyrene bead coated with insulin-nonspecific rabbit IgG was incubated for 3 h with guinea pig anti-insulin serum in the presence of excess nonspecific rabbit IgG and, after washing, was incubated for 3 h with 600 fmol of rabbit (anti-guinea pig IgG) Fab′-peroxidase conjugate.

Immune complex transfer enzyme immunoassay I (Fig. 5.5) for anti-insulin IgG in human serum (50 μL) was also 1000-fold more sensitive than the conventional enzyme immunoassay and 100-fold more sensitive than the improved conventional enzyme immunoassay (Table 6.1) (Kohno et al., 1988a).

6.1.2. Immune complex transfer enzyme immunoassay II

Immune complex transfer enzyme immunoassay II (Fig. 5.2) was evaluated using anti-thyroglobulin IgG in human serum (Kohno et al., 1989a).

A polystyrene bead coated with affinity-purified rabbit (anti-2,4-dinitrophenyl group) IgG (first solid phase) was incubated overnight simultaneously with anti-thyroglobulin IgG in human serum (20 μL) and 50 fmol of 2,4-dinitrophenyl-thyroglobulin in the presence of excess nonspecific rabbit IgG and, after washing, was incubated for 3 h with excess ϵN-2,4-dinitrophenyl-L-lysine for 3 h to elute the immune complex of the two components. The eluate was incubated with a polystyrene bead coated with rabbit anti-thyroglobulin IgG (second solid phase) for 3 h. The second solid phase was incubated with 600 fmol (50 ng) of rabbit (anti-human IgG γ-chain) Fab′-horseradish peroxidase conjugate for 3 h to measure the amount of anti-thyroglobulin IgG in the immune complex trapped.

The detection limit of anti-thyroglobulin IgG in serum by immune complex transfer enzyme immunoassay II was 5.5 ng/mL. This was 1000- to 3000-fold lower than those by the hemagglutination method and the conventional enzyme immunoassay, in which a thyroglobulin-coated polystyrene bead was incubated with

TABLE 6.1

Sensitivities of various immunoassays for anti-insulin antibodies and anti-thyroglobulin antibodies in serum

Enzyme immunoassay (EIA)	Protein for coating solid phase	Conjugate	Improvement of sensitivity (-fold)			Reference
			Anti-insulin	Anti-thyroglobulin	Anti-HIV-1 p17	
Conventional EIA	Ag	Anti-Ig-Enz	1	1	—	
Western blotting	Ag	Anti-Ig-Enz	—	—	1	
Immune complex transfer EIA						
I	Anti-DNP Avidin	DNP-Biotin-Ag Anti-Ig-Enz	1,000–10,000	—	—	Kohno and Ishikawa (1987) Kohno et al. (1988a)
II	Anti-DNP Anti-Ag	DNP-Ag Anti-Ig-Enz	—	1,000–3,000	—	Kohno et al. (1988c; 1989a)
III	Anti-DNP Anti-Ig	DNP-Ag Anti-Ag-Enz	—	3,000–10,000	—	Kohno et al. (1988d, e)
IV	Anti-DNP Anti-Ig	DNP-BSA-Ag — Enz	1,000–10,000	—	—	Kohno and Ishikawa (1988b)
V	Anti-DNP Anti-Ig	DNP-Ag Ag-Enz	30,000–300,000	50,000–150,000	30,000–300,000	Kohno et al. (1989b, c; 1991b), Hirota et al. (1991), Ishikawa et al. (1998)

The sensitivities compared were in terms of ng/mL of serum, not in terms of pg/assay. The sensitivity of the conventional enzyme immunoassay for anti-insulin IgG can be improved 10- to 30-fold by incubation of insulin-nonspecific rabbit IgG-coated polystyrene beads (in place of insulin-bovine serum albumin-coated polystyrene beads) with serum samples in the presence of excess nonspecific rabbit IgG. Ag: antigen; Ig: immunoglobulin; Enz: enzyme; DNP: 2,4-dinitrophenyl group.

serum samples for 3 h and subsequently with 600 fmol of rabbit (anti-human IgG γ-chain) Fab'-peroxidase conjugate for 3 h (Table 6.1).

Anti-thyroglobulin IgG was demonstrated in 9.4% of the healthy subjects and all patients with Graves' disease and chronic thyroiditis by immune complex transfer enzyme immunoassay II, but only in 0.8–1.2% of the healthy subjects, 40–44% of the patients with Graves' disease and 33–67% of the patients with chronic thyroiditis by the hemagglutination method and the conventional enzyme immunoassay (Table 6.2 and Fig. 6.1).

TABLE 6.2

Detection rates of anti-thyroglobulin IgG in serum samples from healthy subjects and patients with thyroid diseases by conventional methods and immune complex transfer enzyme immunoassays II, III and V

Method	Detection rate of anti-thyroglobulin IgG (%)		
	Healthy subjects	Patients with	
		Graves' disease	Chronic thyroiditis
Hemagglutination	1.3	38–40	67–75
Conventional ELISA	0.8–1.3	38–44	33–50
Immune complex transfer enzyme immunoassay			
II	9.4	100	100
III	38	100	100
V	almost 100	100	100

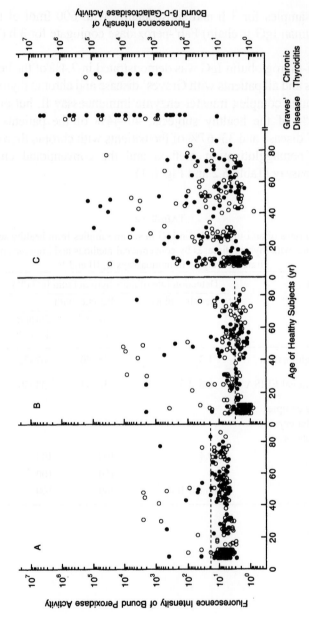

Fig. 6.1. Detection of anti-thyroglobulin IgG in healthy subjects by immune complex transfer enzyme immunoassays II, III and V (Figs. 5.2, 5.3 and 5.5). The enzyme labels used were horseradish peroxidase in immunoassays II (A) and III (B), and β-D-galactosidase from *E. coli* in immunoassay V (C). Dotted lines indicate fluorescence intensities of bound enzyme activities obtained by preincubation with excess thyroglobulin.

6.1.3. Immune complex transfer enzyme immunoassay III

Immune complex transfer enzyme immunoassay III (Fig. 5.3) was also evaluated using anti-thyroglobulin IgG in human serum (Kohno et al., 1988e).

Two polystyrene beads coated with affinity-purified rabbit (anti-2,4-dinitrophenyl group) IgG (first solid phase) were incubated overnight simultaneously with anti-thyroglobulin IgG in human serum (20 μL) and 15 fmol of 2,4-dinitrophenyl-thyroglobulin in the presence of excess nonspecific rabbit IgG and, after washing, was incubated for 1 h with excess ϵN-2,4-dinitrophenyl-L-lysine to elute the immune complex of the two components. The eluate was incubated for 3 h with a polystyrene bead coated with affinity-purified rabbit (anti-human IgG γ-chain) IgG (second solid phase). Finally, the second solid phase was washed and was incubated for 3 h with 600 fmol (50 ng) of rabbit anti-thyroglobulin Fab'-horseradish peroxidase conjugate to measure 2,4-dinitrophenyl-thyroglobulin bound to human anti-thyroglobulin IgG.

The detection limit of anti-thyroglobulin IgG in serum by immune complex transfer enzyme immunoassay III was 2 ng/mL. This was 3000- to 10,000-fold lower than that by the hemagglutination method and the conventional enzyme immunoassay, in which a thyroglobulin-coated polystyrene bead was incubated with serum samples for 3 h and, after washing, was incubated with 600 fmol of rabbit (anti-human IgG γ-chain) Fab'-peroxidase conjugate for 3 h or an affinity-purified rabbit (anti-human IgG γ-chain) IgG-coated polystyrene bead was incubated with serum samples for 3 h and, after washing, was incubated with 50 fmol of thyroglobulin-peroxidase conjugate for 3 h (Table 6.1).

Anti-thyroglobulin IgG was demonstrated in 38% of healthy subjects (Kohno et al., 1988e) and in all patients with Graves' disease and chronic thyroiditis (Kohno et al., 1988d) by immune complex transfer enzyme immunoassay III, but in only 0.9–1.3% of the healthy subjects (Kohno et al., 1988e) and 38–75% of the same patients (Kohno et al., 1988d) by the hemagglutination method and conventional enzyme immunoassays (Table 6.2 and Fig. 6.1) (Kohno et al., 1988d, e).

6.1.4. Immune complex transfer enzyme immunoassay IV

Immune complex transfer enzyme immunoassay IV (Fig. 5.4) was evaluated using anti-insulin IgG in guinea pig serum (Kohno and Ishikawa, 1988b).

Anti-insulin IgG in guinea pig serum (10 μL) was incubated for 3 h with 15 fmol of 2,4-dinitrophenyl-bovine serum albumin-insulin-peroxidase conjugate and two colored polystyrene beads coated with affinity-purified rabbit (anti-2,4-dinitrophenyl group) IgG (first solid phase). After washing, the first solid phase was incubated for 3 h with excess ϵN-2,4-dinitrophenyl-L-lysine and two white polystyrene beads coated with affinity-purified rabbit (anti-guinea pig IgG) IgG (second solid phase) in a test tube. Peroxidase activity bound to the white polystyrene beads distinguished from the colored ones was correlated with the amount or concentration of anti-insulin IgG.

The detection limit of anti-insulin IgG was 14 pg/assay. This was similar to that (20 pg/assay) by conventional enzyme immunoassays, in which a polystyrene bead coated with insulin-bovine serum albumin was incubated with guinea pig anti-insulin serum for 3 h and, after washing, with 600 fmol (50 ng) of (anti-guinea pig IgG) Fab'-peroxidase conjugate for 3 h, or alternatively, a polystyrene bead coated with affinity-purified rabbit (anti-guinea pig IgG) IgG was incubated with guinea pig anti-insulin serum for 3 h and, after washing, with 600 fmol (50 ng) of insulin-peroxidase conjugate for 3 h.

However, the detection limit of anti-insulin IgG in serum by immune complex transfer enzyme immunoassay IV was 1.4 ng/mL, which was 1000- to 10,000-fold lower than that by the conventional enzyme immunoassay (Table 6.1).

6.1.5. Immune complex transfer enzyme immunoassay V

Immune complex transfer enzyme immunoassay V (Fig. 5.5) has been evaluated using antibody IgGs to various antigens including thyroglobulin (Kohno et al., 1989b, c; 1991b; Hirota et al., 1993; Yogi et al., 1993a, b, c), insulin (Hirota et al., 1991), T-cell leukemia virus type I (Kohno et al., 1990a; 1991a, d, e; 1992a, b, c; Hashida et al., 1994b; Ishikawa S. et al., 1995b, c), angiotensin I (Kohno et al., 1990b), β-D-galactosidase (Kohno et al., 1991b) and HIV-1 (Hashida et al., 1993; 1994a; 1995b, c; 1996a, b; 1997; 1998a; Hashinaka et al., 1994a, b; Hirota et al., 1994; Ishikawa et al., 1998; Ishikawa S. et al., 1995a; 1996; 1997; 1998a, b). Evaluations of immune complex transfer enzyme immunoassay V are described in some detail below.

Anti-thyroglobulin IgG in human serum (20 μL) was incubated for 3 h simultaneously with 100 fmol each of 2,4-dinitrophenyl-thyroglobulin and thyroglobulin-β-D-galactosidase conjugate and subsequently overnight with two colored polystyrene beads coated with affinity-purified (anti-2,4-dinitrophenyl group) IgG (first solid phase). After washing, the first solid phase was incubated for 3 h with excess ϵN-2,4-dinitrophenyl-L-lysine and two white polystyrene beads coated with affinity-purified (anti-human IgG γ-chain) IgG (second solid phase).

The detection limit of anti-thyroglobulin IgG with β-D-galactosidase from *E. coli* as label was lowered approximately 50-fold over that by immune complex transfer enzyme immunoassay II (Fig. 5.2) to 2 pg/assay and 0.1 ng/mL of serum (Table 6.1) (Kohno et al., 1989b). The detection limit of anti-thyroglobulin IgG with horseradish peroxidase as label was three times larger (Kohno et al., 1989b).

Anti-thyroglobulin IgG was detected not only in all patients with Graves' disease and chronic thyroiditis (Kohno et al., 1989c) but also in almost all healthy subjects (Kohno et al., 1991c) by immune complex transfer enzyme immunoassay V (Fig. 5.5), but in only 0.9–1.3% of the healthy subjects and 38–75% of the same patients by the hemagglutination method and conventional enzyme immunoassays (Kohno et al., 1989b) (Table 6.2 and Fig. 6.1).

Immune complex transfer enzyme immunoassay V (Fig. 5.5) was also evaluated using anti-insulin IgG in human serum (Hirota et al., 1991). The sensitivity to anti-insulin IgG in serum was improved approximately 30-fold as compared with that in immune complex transfer enzyme immunoassay I (Fig. 5.1) and 30,000- to 300,000- fold as compared with that in the conventional enzyme immunoassay using insulin-bovine serum albumin-coated polystyrene beads and rabbit (anti-human IgG γ-chain) Fab'-peroxidase conjugate (Table 6.1).

Antibody IgGs to HIV-1 p17 antigen and reverse transcriptase antigens were also subjected to immune complex transfer enzyme immunoassay V (Fig. 5.5) (Ishikawa et al., 1998). Incubation with the solid phase was performed with shaking throughout.

Table 6.3 shows the effect of immune complex transfer on the detection limit of antibody IgG to HIV-1 p17 antigen. Serum from an HIV-1 seropositive subject (asymptomatic carrier) was diluted 1×10^4-fold with buffer, and 10 μL of the diluted serum was incubated simultaneously with 100 fmol each of 2,4-dinitrophenyl-maltose binding protein-recombinant HIV-1 p17 (rp17) fusion protein and rp17-β-D-galactosidase conjugate for 0.5 h to form the immune complex consisting of the three components. The reaction mixture was incubated with two colored polystyrene beads coated with affinity-purified (anti-2,4-dinitrophenyl group) IgG (first solid phase) for 1 h to trap the immune complex. After washing, the first solid phase was incubated with ϵN-2,4-dinitrophenyl-L-lysine for 0.5 h, and the eluate was incubated with two white polystyrene beads coated with affinity-purified (anti-human IgG γ-chain) IgG (second solid phase) for 1 h.

By the immune complex transfer process, the signal in the presence of antibody IgG to HIV-1 p17 antigen was reduced only 2.2-fold, while the nonspecific signal in the absence of antibody IgG to HIV-1 p17 antigen was reduced 720-fold. Consequently, the detection limit of antibody IgG to HIV-1 p17 antigen was lowered

TABLE 6.3

Effects of immune complex transfer, contact between the first and second solid phases and serum samples on signals in immune complex transfer enzyme immunoassay V (Fig. 5.5) for antibody IgG to HIV-1 p17 antigen

Addition of serum	Fluorescence intensity of β-D-galactosidase activity						
	For rp17-β-D-galactosidase conjugate used	In the absence of antibodies to p17 antigen			In the presence of antibodies to p17 antigen		
		Bound to the first solid phase	Bound to the second solid phase		Bound to the first solid phase	Bound to the second solid phase	
			Contact between the first and second solid phases			Contact between the first and second solid phases	
			No	Yes		No	Yes
—	1.76×10^7	192	0.27	0.53	20,540	9,240	11,360
	(9.2×10^4)	(1.0)	–	–	–	–	–
	(6.6×10^7)	(720)	(1.0)	(2.0)	(2.2)	(1.0)	(1.2)

Serum (10 μL)	1.76×10^7	208	0.56	1.22	20,780	8,540	10,440
from HIV-1			0.49	0.84	–	–	–
seronegative			1.0	1.38	–	–	–
subjects			0.31	0.58	–	–	–
			0.31	0.58	–	–	–
			0.40	0.58	–	–	–
			0.40	0.49	–	–	–

Serum from an HIV-1 seropositive subject (asymptomatic carrier) was diluted 1×10^4-fold with buffer and 10 μL of the diluted serum was incubated with 100 fmol each of 2,4-dinitrophenyl-maltose binding protein-recombinant p17 (rp17) fusion protein and rp17 β-D-galactosidase conjugate for 0.5 h and subsequently with two colored polystyrene beads of 3.2 mm diameter coated with affinity-purified (anti-2,4-dinitrophenyl group) IgG (first solid phase) for 1 h. After washing, the first solid phase was incubated with ϵN-2,4-dinitrophenyl-L-lysine for 0.5 h. The eluate was incubated with two white polystyrene beads of 3.2 mm diameter coated with affinity-purified (anti-human IgG γ-chain) IgG (second solid phase) for 1 h (contact between the first and second solid phases—No). Alternatively, the first solid phase was incubated with the second solid phase in the presence of ϵN-2,4-dinitrophenyl-L-lysine for 1 h (Contact between the first and second solid phases—Yes). The signals shown are expressed as those obtained by a 20-h assay, and the fluorescence intensity of 1×10^{-10} mol/L 4-methylumbelliferone was 1. Values in parentheses are the ratios of signals to those for β-D-galactosidase activity bound to the first solid phase before transfer of the immune complex and the second solid phase with no contact between the first and second solid phases. The maximal dilution of the positive serum with serum from an HIV-1 seronegative subject to give a positive HIV-1 p17 band on Western blotting was 2×10^2 (Ishikawa et al., 1998).

approximately 300-fold by immune complex transfer. This method was 3×10^4-fold more sensitive than Western blotting for the HIV-1 p17 band, when β-D-galactosidase activity was assayed for 1 h and was 3×10^5-fold more sensitive, when assayed for 20 h.

Table 6.4 shows the effect of immune complex transfer on the detection limit of antibody IgG to HIV-1 reverse transcriptase (RT). Serum from an HIV-1 seropositive subject (asymptomatic carrier) was diluted 2×10^3-fold with buffer and 10 μL of the diluted serum was incubated simultaneously with 100 fmol each of 2,4-dinitrophenyl-bovine serum albumin-recombinant RT (rRT) conjugate and rRT-β-D-galactosidase conjugate for 4 h. The immune complex consisting of the three components formed was trapped and was transferred as described above for antibody IgG to HIV-1 p17 antigen.

Two different preparations of rRT-β-D-galactosidase conjugate, that is, less polymerized and highly polymerized forms, were tested.

On immune complex transfer, the signal of the less polymerized conjugate in the presence of antibody IgG to RT was reduced 1.8-fold, while the nonspecific signal in its absence was reduced 1913-fold. Thus, the detection limit of antibody IgG to RT was lowered 1000-fold by immune complex transfer. This method was thus 1×10^4-fold more sensitive than Western blotting for the HIV-1 p66 band, when β-D-galactosidase activity was assayed for 1 h and was 1×10^5-fold more sensitive when assayed for 20 h. (RT consists of two subunits: p51 and p66.)

With the highly polymerized conjugate, the signal in the presence of antibody IgG to RT was reduced 2.7-fold by immune complex transfer, but the nonspecific signal in its absence, which was 32-fold higher than that with the less polymerized conjugate, was reduced 15,138-fold. Thus, the detection limit of antibody IgG to RT was lowered 5600-fold by immune complex transfer, and the method was 3×10^3-fold more sensitive than Western blotting for the HIV-1 p66 band when β-D-galactosidase activity was assayed for 1 h and 3×10^4-fold more sensitive when assayed for 20 h.

TABLE 6.4

Effects of immune complex transfer, contact between the first and second solid phases and serum samples on signals in immune complex transfer enzyme immunoassay V (Fig. 5.5) for antibody IgG to HIV-1 reverse transcriptase

rRT-β-D-galactosidase conjugate	Fluorescence intensity of β-D-galactosidase activity					
	For rRT-β-D-galactosidase conjugate used	In the absence of antibodies to RT			In the presence of antibodies to RT		
		Bound to the first solid phase	Bound to the second solid phase		Bound to the first solid phase	Bound to the second solid phase	
			Contact between the first and second solid phases			Contact between the first and second solid phases	
			No	Yes		No	Yes
Nonpolymeric	1.87×10^7	612	0.32	0.55	28,080	15,600	16,200
	(3.1×10^4)	(1.0)	–	–	–	–	–
	(5.8×10^7)	(1,913)	(1.0)	(1.7)	(1.8)	(1.0)	(1.0)

Polymeric	1.62×10^7	19,680	1.3	26	62,400	16,080	16,080
	(823)	(1.0)	–	–	–	–	–
	(1.25×10^7)	(15,138)	(1.0)	(20)	(2.7)	(1.0)	(1.0)

Serum from an HIV-1 seropositive subject (asymptomatic carrier) was diluted 2×10^3-fold with buffer and 10 μL of the diluted serum was incubated with 100 fmol each of 2,4-dinitrophenyl-bovine serum albumin-recombinant RT (rRT) and rRT β-D-galactosidase conjugate for 3.5–4 h and subsequently with two colored polystyrene beads of 3.2 mm diameter coated with affinity-purified (anti-2,4-dinitrophenyl group) IgG (first solid phase) for 1 h. After washing, the first solid phase was incubated with ϵN-2,4-dinitrophenyl-L-lysine for 0.5 h. The eluate was incubated with two white polystyrene beads of 3.2 mm diameter coated with affinity-purified (anti-human IgG γ-chain) IgG (second solid phase) for 1 h (contact between the first and second solid phases—No). Alternatively, the first solid phase was incubated with the second solid phase in the presence of ϵN-2,4-dinitrophenyl-L-lysine for 1 h (contact between the first and second solid phases—Yes). The signals shown are expressed as those obtained by a 20 h assay. The fluorescence intensity of 1×10^{-10} mol/L 4-methylumbelliferone was 1. Values in parentheses are ratios of signals to those for β-D-galactosidase activity bound to the first solid phase before transfer of the immune complex and the second solid phase with no contact between the first and second solid phases. The maximal dilution of the positive serum with serum from an HIV-1 seronegative subject to give a positive HIV-1 p66 band on Western blotting was 2×10^2 (Ishikawa et al., 1998).

In general, the effect of immune complex transfer tends to be greater when β-D-galactosidase activity bound to the first solid phase in the absence of analytes, that is the nonspecific signal, is higher.

Immune complex transfer enzyme immunoassay V for antibody IgG to HIV-1 reverse transcriptase has made the diagnosis of HIV-1 infection using 100 μL of urine samples (Hashinaka et al., 1994a) or 1 μL of whole saliva, collected by simple spitting without stimulation, more reliable (Ishikawa S. et al., 1995a).

Antibody IgM can also be measured with high sensitivity, provided that anti-IgM antibodies with sufficiently strong affinity are used (Hashida et al., 1998c).

6.1.6. Immune complex transfer enzyme immunoassay VI

Immune complex transfer enzyme immunoassay VI (Fig. 5.6) for antibodies to β-D-galactosidase from *E. coli* in human serum using 2,4-dinitrophenyl-biotinyl-β-D-galactosidase and β-D-galactosidase-peroxidase conjugate and streptavidin-coated polystyrene beads was as sensitive as immune complex transfer enzyme immunoassay V for antibody IgG to the enzyme using 2,4-dinitrophenyl-β-D-galactosidase and β-D-galactosidase-peroxidase conjugate and affinity-purified (anti-human IgG γ-chain) IgG-coated polystyrene beads (Fig. 6.2) (Kohno et al., 1991b).

In immune complex transfer enzyme immunoassay VI for antibody IgGs to HIV-1 reverse transcriptase and p24 antigen, the nonspecific signals with serum samples from HIV-1 seronegative subjects were considerably and significantly higher, respectively, than those in the corresponding immune complex transfer enzyme immunoassay V, although fairly low for antibody IgG to p17 antigen (unpublished).

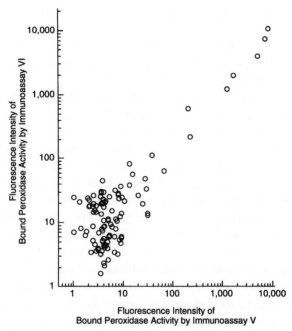

Fig. 6.2. Correlation between fluorescence intensities of bound peroxidase activity obtained by immune complex transfer enzyme immunoassays V and VI (Figs. 5.5 and 5.6) for antibodies to β-D-galactosidase from *E. coli*. Serum samples (20 μL) of 107 healthy subjects (57 males aged 18–79 years and 50 females aged 16–84 years) were subjected to the two immunoassays using horseradish peroxidase as label (Kohno et al., 1991b). Bound peroxidase activity was assayed by fluorometry.

It remains to be carefully evaluated whether, or not, immune complex transfer enzyme immunoassays V and VI are similarly sensitive.

6.1.7. Immune complex transfer enzyme immunoassay VII

Immune complex transfer enzyme immunoassay VII (Fig. 5.7) was evaluated using antibody IgG to β-D-galactosidase from *E. coli* in human urine (Ishikawa and Ishikawa, 1994).

Antibody IgG to the enzyme in urine (100 μL) was incubated for 3 h with 100 fmol of 2,4-dinitrophenyl-β-D-galactosidase and then overnight with two colored polystyrene beads coated with affinity-purified (anti-2,4-dinitrophenyl group) IgG (first solid phase). After washing, the first solid phase was incubated with excess ϵN-2,4-dinitrophenyl-L-lysine for 1 h, and the eluate was incubated first for 3 h with 100 fmol of biocytin-S—S-(anti-human IgG γ-chain) IgG and then overnight with two white polystyrene beads coated with streptavidin (second solid phase). After washing, the second solid phase was incubated for 3 h with 2-mercaptoethylamine and two colored polystyrene beads coated with affinity-purified (anti-human IgG γ-chain) IgG (the third solid phase). β-D-galactosidase activity bound to the third solid phase was assayed for 25 h. In immune complex transfer enzyme immunoassay IV, anti-β-D-galactosidase IgG in urine was incubated with 2,4-dinitrophenyl-β-D-galactosidase and subsequently with the first solid phase as described above. After washing, the first solid phase was incubated for 3 h with two white polystyrene beads coated with affinity-purified (anti-human IgG γ-chain) IgG (second solid phase) in the presence of excess ϵN-2,4-dinitrophenyl-L-lysine. β-D-galactosidase activity bound to the second solid phase was assayed for 1 h.

β-D-galactosidase activity nonspecifically bound in the absence of anti-β-D-galactosidase IgG, that is nonspecific binding, was 73-fold lower in immune complex transfer enzyme immunoassay VII than in immune complex transfer enzyme immunoassay IV. In contrast, β-D-galactosidase activity specifically bound, that is specific binding (the difference between the enzyme activities in the absence and presence of anti-β-D-galactosidase IgG), was only 2.1-fold lower in immune complex transfer enzyme immunoassay VII than in immune complex transfer enzyme immunoassay IV. Thus, the sensitivity was improved approximately 30-fold by double transfer of the immune complex in immune complex transfer enzyme immunoassay VII over that by single transfer in immune complex transfer enzyme immunoassay IV.

6.1.8. Immune complex transfer enzyme immunoassay VIII

Immune complex transfer enzyme immunoassay VIII (Fig. 5.8) has not yet been evaluated, although its increase in sensitivity over immune complex transfer enzyme immunoassay V (Fig. 5.5) may be similar to that achieved by immune complex transfer enzyme immunoassay VII (Fig. 5.7) described above (Ishikawa et al., 1993).

6.2. Improvement of sensitivity to antigens

Immune complex transfer enzyme immunoassays IX and X described in Chapter 5 (Figs. 5.9 and 5.10) have been evaluated using various antigens including human thyroid-stimulating hormone (hTSH), human growth hormone (hGH), human ferritin and HIV-1 p24 antigen.

6.2.1. Immune complex transfer enzyme immunoassay IX

Immune complex transfer enzyme immunoassay IX (Fig. 5.9) was evaluated using hTSH and hGH (Hashida et al., 1988c).

The antigens were incubated overnight simultaneously with 150 fmol of 2,4-dinitrophenyl-monoclonal mouse antibody IgG_1 and 200 fmol of rabbit antibody Fab'-β-D-galactosidase conjugates and then for 4 h with two colored polystyrene beads coated with affinity-purified rabbit (anti-2,4-dinitrophenyl group) IgG (first solid phase). After washing, the first solid phase was incubated for 4 h with two white polystyrene beads coated with affinity-purified rabbit (anti-mouse IgG) IgG (second solid phase) in the presence of excess ϵN-2,4-dinitrophenyl-L-lysine. In the conventional two-site enzyme immunoassay, a polystyrene bead coated with monoclonal mouse antibody IgG$_1$ was incubated overnight with the antigens and, after washing, was incubated for 4 h with rabbit antibody Fab'-β-D-galactosidase conjugate.

In the conventional enzyme immunoassays, β-D-galactosidase activities nonspecifically bound in the absence of the antigens (background) were 0.0011% (hTSH) and 0.0014% (hGH) of the β-D-galactosidase activity added. In immune complex transfer enzyme immunoassays IX, β-D-galactosidase activities nonspecifically bound to the first solid phases were 0.0026% (hTSH) and 0.012% (hGH), and those nonspecifically bound to the second solid phases (background) were 0.000017% (hTSH) and 0.00012% (hGH). Therefore, the backgrounds in immune complex transfer enzyme immunoassays IX were 65-fold (hTSH) and 12-fold (hGH) lower than those in the conventional two-site enzyme immunoassays.

β-D-galactosidase activities specifically bound to the first solid phases in immune complex transfer enzyme immunoassays IX were 2.7-fold (hTSH) and 7.1-fold (hGH) higher than those specifically bound in the conventional enzyme immunoassays. However, 55% (hTSH) and 41% (hGH) of the immune complexes were lost during the immune complex transfer process. Therefore, the specific bindings in immune complex transfer enzyme immunoassays IX were 1.5-fold (hTSH) and 2.9-fold (hGH) higher than those in the conventional two-site enzyme immunoassays.

Thus, the detection limits of hTSH and hGH were 30- to 100-fold lower than those by conventional enzyme immunoassays. Using affinity-purified anti-hCG Fab'-β-D-galactosidase conjugate, the detection limit of hTSH was 0.01 nU (0.02 amol), and, using anti-hGH Fab'-β-D-galactosidase conjugate without affinity-purification, the detection limit of hGH was 10 fg (0.5 amol) (Table 6.5).

TABLE 6.5

Detection limits of antigens by immune complex transfer enzyme immunoassays in comparison with that by the conventional two-site enzyme immunoassays

Antigen	Affinity purification of antibodies	Immune complex transfer enzyme immunoassay	Nonspecific signal 1st solid phase (%)	Nonspecific signal 2nd solid phase (%)	Specific signal 1st solid phase (%)	Specific signal 2nd solid phase (%)	Detection limit of antigen (zmol)	Detection limit of antigen by conventional two-site enzyme immunoassays (zmol)	Reference
hTSH	Yes	IX (Fig. 5.9)	100	0.65	100	45	20 (0.01 nU)	600 (0.3 nU)	Hashida et al. (1988c)
hGH	No	IX (Fig. 5.9)	100	0.01	100	59	500 (10 fg)	15,000 (300 fg)	Hashida et al. (1988c)
Ferritin	Yes	X (Fig. 5.10)	100	0.5–0.7	100	43–66	1	30	Hashida and Ishikawa (1990)
HBsAg	Monoclonal	X (Fig. 5.10)	–	–	–	–	2	100	Unpublished
Ornithine δ-aminotransferase	No	X (Fig. 5.10)	–	–	–	–	10	300	Hashida and Ishikawa (1990)
HIV-1 p24 antigen	Monoclonal	X (Fig. 5.10)	100	0.33	100	32	10	1,000	Ishikawa et al. (1998)

6.2.2. Immune complex transfer enzyme immunoassay X

Immune complex transfer enzyme immunoassay X (Fig. 5.10) was evaluated using human ferritin (Hashida and Ishikawa, 1990).

Ferritin was incubated for 2 h simultaneously with 50 fmol of 2,4-dinitrophenyl-biotinyl-affinity-purified anti-ferritin IgG and 5 fmol of affinity-purified anti-ferritin Fab'-β-D-galactosidase conjugate, and then overnight with two colored polystyrene beads coated with affinity-purified (anti-2,4-dinitrophenyl group) IgG (first solid phase). After washing, the first solid phase was incubated for 4 h with two white polystyrene beads coated with streptavidin (second solid phase) in the presence of excess ϵN-2,4-dinitrophenyl-L-lysine. β-D-galactosidase activity bound to the second solid phase was assayed by fluorometry for 20 h.

β-D-galactosidase activity nonspecifically bound to the second solid phase in the absence of ferritin (background) was 0.5–0.7% of that nonspecifically bound to the first solid phase. β-D-galactosidase activity specifically bound to the second solid phase in the presence of ferritin was 43–66% of that specifically bound to the first solid phase. Namely, the nonspecific binding (background noise) was lowered 143- to 200-fold with much less (34–57%) decrease in the specific binding. As a result, the detection limit of ferritin was lowered to 1 zmol/assay. This value was 30-fold less than that by the conventional two-site enzyme immunoassay, in which an anti-ferritin IgG-coated polystyrene bead was incubated with ferritin and, after washing, with affinity-purified anti-ferritin Fab'-β-D-galactosidase conjugate (Table 6.5).

From β-D-galactosidase activity specifically bound to the second solid phase in the presence of 1–10,000 zmol of ferritin, the average number of anti-ferritin Fab'-β-D-galactosidase conjugate molecules bound per ferritin molecule added was calculated to be 0.95–1.4. In addition, loss of specifically bound β-D-galactosidase activity during elution and transfer of the immune complex was only 34–57% as described above. Therefore, further transfer of the immune complex (double transfer) was strongly suggested to improve the sensitivity, although the sensitivity of assay of an enzyme label requires considerable improvement, and an efficient method for further transfer of the immune complex remains to be developed.

From the above results for ferritin, immune complex transfer enzyme immunoassay X may be capable of detecting zeptomole amounts of other antigens, which are measurable at attomole levels by conventional two-site enzyme immunoassays (Table 6.5). In a preliminary experiment, the detection limit of ornithine δ-aminotransferase from rat kidney was 10 zmol/assay by immune complex transfer enzyme immunoassay X using 2,4-dinitrophenyl-biotinyl-bovine serum albumin-anti-ornithine δ-aminotransferase Fab' conjugate and anti-ornithine δ-aminotransferase Fab'-β-D-galactosidase conjugate without affinity-purification. On the other hand, the detection limit of this enzyme by the conventional two-site enzyme immunoassay was 300 zmol. Affinity-purification may further lower the detection limit. In the same way, the detection limit of hepatitis B surface antigen (HBs Ag) was 2 zmol/assay using 2,4-dinitrophenyl-biotinyl-mouse monoclonal anti-HBs Ag IgG_3 and mouse monoclonal anti-HBs Ag Fab'-β-D-galactosidase conjugate, but 100 zmol by the conventional two-site enzyme immunoassay using the same antibody.

Immune complex transfer enzyme immunoassay X (Fig. 5.10) was also evaluated using HIV-1 p24 antigen (Ishikawa et al., 1998).

The antigen was incubated for 3 h simultaneously with 100 fmol of 2,4-dinitrophenyl-biotinyl-bovine serum albumin-affinity-purified rabbit anti-p24 Fab' conjugate and 5 fmol of monoclonal mouse anti-p24 Fab'-β-D-galactosidase conjugate and then for 1 h with two colored polystyrene beads coated with affinity-purified (anti-2,4-dinitrophenyl group) IgG (first solid phase). After washing, the first solid phase was incubated with excess ϵN-2,4-dinitrophenyl-L-lysine for 0.5 h to elute the immune complex. The eluate was incubated for 1 h with two white polystyrene beads coated with streptavidin (second solid phase). The incubations with solid phases were performed with shaking. β-D-galactosidase activity bound to the second solid phase was assayed by fluorometry using 4-methylumbelliferyl-β-D-galactosidase as a substrate.

Table 6.6 shows the effect of immune complex transfer on the detection limit of HIV-1 p24 antigen. In the presence of HIV-1 p24 antigen, the signal, that is the fluorescence intensity of β-D-galactosidase activity bound to the second solid phase, was 3.1-fold less than that bound to the first solid phase. Namely, the fraction of the immune complex transferred was 32%. In contrast, the signal of β-D-galactosidase activity bound to the second solid phase in the absence of the antigen was 300-fold lower than that bound to the first solid phase. Namely, the nonspecific signal was reduced 300-fold by the immune complex transfer process. Thus, by immune complex transfer, the detection limit of HIV-1 p24 antigen was lowered 100-fold to 0.1 amol when β-D-galactosidase activity was assayed for 1 h and to 10 zmol when assayed for 20 h (Table 6.6). The detection limit on a 1-h assay of β-D-galactosidase activity was 400- to 1700-fold lower than those obtained with currently available commercial kits and the detection limit on a 20-h assay was 4000- to 17,000-fold lower.

6.3. Simultaneous detection of antigens and antibodies by the immune complex transfer enzyme immunoassay

HIV infection has been diagnosed by detecting HIV antibodies in serum and other body fluids. Following HIV infection, however, there is a window period of 6–8 weeks, during which HIV antibodies are not detectable in the circulation and infection cannot be diagnosed by conventional methods for detecting HIV antibodies. In contrast, HIV antigens are detectable in the circulation before the detection of HIV antibodies in the latter part of the window period, although the level of HIV antigens declines as the level of HIV antibodies increases. Therefore, simultaneous detection of HIV antigens and HIV antibodies shortens the window period, minimizing risk of HIV infection by blood transfusion (Fig. 6.3).

TABLE 6.6

Effects of immune complex transfer, contact between the first and second solid phases and serum samples on signals in the immune complex transfer enzyme immunoassay X (Fig. 5.10) for HIV-1 p24 antigen

Addition of serum	Fluorescence intensity of β-D-galactosidase activity						
	For anti-p24 Fab'-β-D-galactosidase conjugate used	In the absence of p24 antigen			In the presence of p24 antigen (100 amol)		
		Bound to the first solid phase	Bound to the second solid phase		Bound to the first solid phase	Bound to the second solid phase	
			Contact between the first and second solid phases			Contact between the first and second solid phases	
			No	Yes		No	Yes
–	1.28×10^6	60	0.20	0.23	7,160	2,320	2,880
	(2.13×10^4)	(1.0)	–	–	–	–	–
	(6.4×10^6)	(300)	(1.0)	(1.15)	(3.1)	(1.0)	(1.24)
Serum (10 μL) from HIV-1 seronegative subjects	1.28×10^6	–	–	0.18–0.5 ($n = 10$)	–	–	–

The antigen, p24, (100 amol) was incubated simultaneously with 5 fmol of monoclonal anti-p24 Fab'-β-D-galactosidase conjugate and 100 fmol of 2,4-dinitrophenyl-biotinyl-bovine serum albumin-affinity-purified rabbit anti-p24 Fab' conjugate in the presence of 10 μL nonspecific rabbit serum for 3 h and subsequently with two colored polystyrene beads of 3.2 mm diameter coated with affinity-purified (anti-2,4-dinitrophenyl group) IgG (first solid phase) for 1 h. The first solid phase was incubated with ϵN-2,4-dinitrophenyl-L-lysine for 0.5 h, and the eluate was incubated with two white polystyrene beads of 3.2 mm diameter coated with streptavidin (second solid phase) for 1 h (contact between the first and second solid phases—No). Alternatively, the first solid phase was incubated with the second solid phase in the presence of ϵN-2,4-dinitrophenyl-L-lysine for 1 h (contact between the first and second solid phases—Yes). The signals shown were as those obtained by a 20 h assay. The fluorescence intensity of 1×10^{-10} mol/L 4-methylumbelliferone was 1. Values in parentheses are ratios of signals to those for β-D-galactosidase activity bound to the first solid phase before transfer of the immune complex and the second solid phase after transfer of the immune complex without contact between the first and second solid phases (Ishikawa et al., 1998).

TABLE 6.7

Assay variations of immune complex transfer enzyme immunoassays

Immune complex transfer enzyme immunoassay	Antibody or antigen assayed	Number of determinations	Variation coefficient	
			Within-assay (%)	Between-assay (%)
I	Anti-insulin IgG	15	4.2–9.2	6.8–9.8
	Anti-insulin IgG	15	10	8.4–12
II	Anti-thyroglobulin IgG	10	8.6–11	9.0–12
III	Anti-thyroglobulin IgG	10	8.5–13	9.1–12
IV	Anti-insulin IgG	15	8.1–11	6.3–11
V	Anti-thyroglobulin IgG	15	7.4–9.8	9.1–12
	Anti-HIV-1 p17 IgG	10	4.9–8.5	6.8–9.6
	Anti-HIV-1 p24 IgG	10	4.7–7.0	4.7–8.0
	Anti-HTLV-I IgG	10	3.9–6.3	6.1–8.7
X	Ferritin	10	3.6–7.6	8.4–13
	HIV-1 p24 antigen	20	5.1–7.3	6.2–8.8

On the basis of these considerations, an immune complex transfer enzyme immunoassay for simultaneous detections of HIV-1 p24 antigen and antibody IgGs to HIV-1 reverse transcriptase and p17 antigen was developed (Fig. 5.11) (Hashida et al., 1996a).

Serum samples (10 μL) were incubated for 3 h simultaneously with 2,4-dinitrophenyl-biotinyl-bovine serum albumin-affinity-purified rabbit anti-p24 Fab' conjugate, monoclonal mouse anti-p24 Fab'-β-D-galactosidase conjugate, 2,4-dinitrophenyl-bovine serum albumin-recombinant HIV-1 p17 (rp17) conjugate, 2,4-dinitrophenyl-bovine serum albumin-recombinant HIV-1 reverse transcriptase (rRT) conjugates, rp17-β-D-galactosidase conjugate and rRT-β-D-galactosidase conjugate and then overnight with two colored polystyrene beads coated with affinity-purified (anti-2,4-

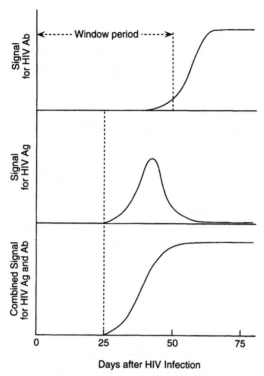

Fig. 6.3. Shortening of the window period in the diagnosis of HIV infection by simultaneous detection of HIV antigens and antibodies (Fig. 5.11).

dinitrophenyl group) IgG (first solid phase). After washing, the first solid phase was incubated for 3 h with two white polystyrene beads coated with both streptavidin and affinity-purified (anti-human IgG γ-chain) IgG (second solid phase) in the presence of excess ϵN-2,4-dinitrophenyl-L-lysine.

Eleven HIV-1 seroconversion serum panels were tested. The test results were positive 6–42 days (average 14 days) earlier than those by conventional methods such as conventional enzyme immunoassays and the gelatin particle agglutination test for HIV antibodies. Thus, the simultaneous detection of HIV-1 p24 antigen and antibody IgGs to HIV-1 reverse transcriptase and p17 antigen by immune complex transfer enzyme immunoassay shortened the window period by making diagnosis of HIV-1 infection possible as early as the time of appearance of p24 antigen in the circulation.

6.4. Further improvement of sensitivity

Most of the immune complex transfer enzyme immunoassays described in this chapter were performed by incubation of polystyrene beads of 3.2 mm diameter in a volume of 150 μL without shaking. The periods required were rather long. However, the immune complex transfer enzyme immunoassays can be performed not only more rapidly, but also with higher sensitivities as described in Chapter 7.

6.5. Assay variation

The assay variations in immune complex transfer enzyme immunoassays I–V and X (Figs. 5.1–5.5 and 5.10) were examined using various antigens including human ferritin (Hashida and Ishikawa, 1990) and HIV-1 p24 (Hashida et al., 1995a) and antibody IgGs to various antigens including insulin (Kohno and Ishikawa, 1987; 1988a, b; Kohno et al., 1988a), human thyroglobulin (Kohno et al., 1988b, c, d, e; 1989a, b, c), HTLV-I antigens (Kohno et al., 1991a, d, e; 1992a, b, c) and HIV-1 antigens (Hashida et al., 1993; 1994a; 1995b) (Table 6.7). The within- and between-assay variation coefficients were 4–10 and 6–12%, respectively, in most cases.

In our recent experience, immune complex transfer enzyme immunoassays for both antigens and antibodies have been highly reproducible. The between-assay variation coefficients in immune complex transfer enzyme immunoassays V (Fig. 5.5) for antibody IgGs to HIV-1 reverse transcriptase, p24 and p17 antigens were 4.7–9.6% (Hashida et al., 1993; 1994a), and that in immune complex transfer enzyme immunoassay X for HIV-1 p24 antigen was 6.2–8.8% (Hashida et al., 1995a). However, the between-assay variation coefficients by immune complex transfer enzyme immunoassay X for ferritin at 1–3 zmol levels were 26–36%, although they were 8.4–13% at levels of above 12 zmol.

6.6. Factors limiting improvement in sensitivity of the immune complex transfer enzyme immunoassay

6.6.1. Nonspecific adsorption and desorption of labeled reactants

Theoretically, the sensitivities of immune complex transfer enzyme immunoassays V, VI, IX and X (Figs. 5.5, 5.6, 5.9 and 5.10) can be infinitely improved provided that the immune complexes consisting of the three components are eluted from the first solid phase efficiently and specifically without desorption of labeled reactants (antigens and antibodies) nonspecifically bound to the first solid phase and efficiently transferred to the second solid phase. However, during the immune complex transfer process, labeled reactants nonspecifically bound to the first solid phase are released to various extents and nonspecifically bind to the second solid phase to various extents, limiting the effect of immune complex transfer. Therefore, actual improvements in the sensitivities are limited, as shown in Tables 6.1 and 6.3–6.6 (Ishikawa et al., 1998).

6.6.2. Direct contact of the first solid phase from which the immune complex is eluted and the second solid phase to which the immune complex is transferred

In immune complex transfer enzyme immunoassays V (Fig. 5.5) and X (Fig. 5.10) described above, the immune complexes consisting of the three components are trapped on polystyrene beads coated with affinity-purified (anti-2,4-dinitrophenyl group) IgG (first solid phase) and are transferred to polystyrene beads coated with streptavidin or affinity-purified (anti-human IgG γ-chain) IgG (second solid phase) in two different ways (Tables 6.3, 6.4 and 6.6) (Ishikawa et al., 1998).

First, to avoid direct contact between the first and second solid phases, the first solid phase after washing is incubated with excess ϵN-2,4-dinitrophenyl-L-lysine for 0.5 h to elute the immune complexes and, then, the eluates are incubated with the second solid phase to transfer the immune complexes. This requires longer incubations for elution and transference. Second, the first solid phase after washing is incubated with the second solid phase in the presence of excess ϵN-2,4-dinitrophenyl-L-lysine in a test tube. The immune complexes tend to be transferred more efficiently in shorter periods of time. However, the nonspecific signals are enhanced to various extents by direct contact between the first and second solid phases during the incubation (Tables 6.3, 6.4 and 6.6). Notably, when highly polymerized recombinant HIV-1 reverse transcriptase-β-D-galactosidase conjugate was used, the nonspecific signal was enhanced 20-fold by direct contact between the first and second solid phases (Table 6.4).

6.6.3. Affinities of antibodies used or measured

The immune complexes of antigens and antibodies with sufficiently high affinities are fairly stable at neutral pH. However, immune complexes containing low affinity antibodies may dissociate to various extents, resulting in loss of the immune complexes during the immune complex transfer process described in Chapters 5 and 6 and limiting the sensitivity of the immune complex transfer enzyme immunoassays.

For example, the immune complex consisting of 2,4-dinitrophenyl-bovine serum albumin-HIV-1 gp41 peptide (28 amino acids), antibodies from an HIV-1 seropositive subject (asymptomatic carrier) and HIV-1 gp41 peptide (28 amino acids) β-D-galactosidase conjugate dissociated 48% within 0.5 h and

TABLE 6.8

Decrease in β-D-galactosidase activity bound to polystyrene beads coated with affinity-purified (anti-2,4-dinitrophenyl group) IgG (first solid phase) when stood in buffer

Time in buffer	Fluorescence intensity of β-D-galactosidase activity bound to the first solid phase		
	Anti-RT	Anti-p17	Anti-gp41
min	(%)	(%)	(%)
0	100	100	100
30	96	85	52
60	94	76	33

Polystyrene beads of 6.35 mm diameter coated with affinity-purified (anti-2,4-dinitrophenyl group) IgG (first solid phase) were incubated sequentially with 2,4-dinitrophenyl-HIV-1 antigen conjugates for 5 min, with serum samples containing antibody IgGs to HIV-1 for 5 min and with HIV-1 antigen-β-D-galactosidase conjugates for 10 min as in immune complex transfer enzyme immunoassay V (Fig. 5.5) and, after washing, were stood in buffer at room temperature for the indicated periods of time (Ishikawa S. et al., 1998b). The HIV-1 antigens used were recombinant reverse transcriptase (RT), recombinant p17 antigen and synthetic peptide (28 amino acids) of gp41.

67% within 1 h, whereas the immune complex consisting of 2,4-dinitrophenyl-bovine serum albumin-recombinant HIV-1 reverse transcriptase (rRT), antibodies from an HIV-1 seropositive subject (asymptomatic carrier) and rRT-β-D-galactosidase conjugate and the immune complex consisting of 2,4-dinitrophenyl-maltose binding protein-HIV-1 p17 fusion protein, antibodies from an HIV-1 seropositive subject (asymptomatic carrier) and recombinant HIV-1 p17 (rp17)-β-D-galactosidase conjugate dissociated only 6 and 24%, respectively, within 1 h (Table 6.8) (Ishikawa S. et al., 1998b).

This is consistent with the general concept that antibodies to proteins tend to be less reactive with peptides as parts of the proteins than with the proteins themselves.

Immune complexes of antigens and antibodies with low affinities are formed slowly, hampering rapid performance of sensitive immunoassays.

For example, in immune complex transfer enzyme immunoassay V for antibody IgG to HIV-1 p17 antigen using 2,4-dinitrophenyl-bovine serum albumin-rp17 conjugate and rp17-β-D-galactosidase conjugate, the immune complex of the three components with serum samples from subjects shortly after HIV-1 infection continued to be formed for more than 2 h, while the formation of the immune complex with serum samples from subjects long after infection was almost completed within 30 min (Hashida et al., 1998a).

This is consistent with the general concept that the affinity of antibodies synthesized at early stages of immunization is low.

6.6.4. Detection limit of enzyme labels

Immune complex transfer markedly reduces the nonspecific binding of labeled reactants, requiring high sensitivities of methods for the detection of the labels. In other words, the detection limit of labels limits the sensitivity of immune complex transfer enzyme immunoassays.

In immune complex transfer enzyme immunoassay V (Fig. 5.5) for antibody IgG to HIV-1 p17 antigen, β-D-galactosidase activity nonspecifically bound to polystyrene beads coated with affinity-purified (anti-2,4-dinitrophenyl group) IgG (first solid phase), on which the immune complex was trapped, was 9.2×10^4-fold lower, equivalent to 1.1 amol, than that of recombinant-HIV-1 p17-β-D-galactosidase conjugate (100 fmol) used. On immune complex transfer, β-D-galactosidase activity nonspecifically bound to polystyrene beads coated with affinity-purified (anti-human IgG γ-chain) IgG (second solid phase) was 720-fold lower, equivalent to 1.5 zmol, than that nonspecifically bound to the first solid phase (Table 6.3) (Ishikawa et al., 1998).

Similarly, in immune complex transfer enzyme immunoassay V (Fig. 5.5) for antibody IgG to HIV-1 reverse transcriptase (RT), β-D-galactosidase activity nonspecifically bound to the first solid phase was 3.1×10^4-fold lower, equivalent to 3.2 amol, than that of the nonpolymeric recombinant RT-β-D-galactosidase (100 fmol) used, and β-D-galactosidase activity nonspecifically bound to the second solid phase was 1913-fold lower, equivalent to 1.7 zmol, than that nonspecifically bound to the first solid phase (Table 6.4) (Ishikawa et al., 1998). With the polymeric conjugate, β-D-galactosidase activity nonspecifically bound to the first solid phase was 823-fold lower, equivalent to 121 amol, and that nonspecifically bound to the second solid phase was 1.5×10^4-fold lower, equivalent to 8 zmol (Table 6.4).

In immune complex transfer enzyme immunoassay X (Fig. 5.10) for HIV-1 p24 antigen, β-D-galactosidase activity nonspecifically bound to the first solid phase was 2.13×10^4-fold lower, equivalent to 235 zmol, than that of anti-p24 Fab'-β-D-galactosidase conjugate (5 fmol) used, and that nonspecifically bound to the second solid phase was 300-fold lower, equivalent to 0.8 zmol, than that nonspecifically bound to the first solid phase (Table 6.6) (Ishikawa et al., 1998).

Thus, β-D-galactosidase activities nonspecifically bound to the second solid phases were extremely low (equivalent to 0.8–8 zmol). To make use of the immune complex transfer effect as efficient as possible, detections of these low activities required 20 h fluorometric assay of β-D-galactosidase (Tables 6.3, 6.4 and 6.6). Therefore, immune complex transfer enzyme immunoassay V for antibody IgG to HIV-1 reverse transcriptase using β-D-galactosidase from E. coli is 30-fold more sensitive than that using horseradish peroxidase, when the enzyme labels are assayed for up to 2.5 h (Hashinaka et al., 1994b). The difference in the sensitivities with the two enzyme labels may be larger when the enzyme labels are assayed for a longer time, since horseradish peroxidase, not β-D-galactosidase, tends to be inactivated during assay by incubation for more than 1 h. These small quantities of β-D-galactosidase conjugates nonspecifically bound to the second solid phases (0.8–8 zmol) appear to be slightly smaller than the smallest quantity of alkaline phosphatase detectable by chemiluminescent assay using a derivative of adamantyl-1,2-dioxetane phosphate as substrate (10 zmol) (Bronstein et al., 1989).

6.6.5. Antibodies to enzyme labels

Human serum samples may contain antibodies to various proteins including enzymes used as labels in enzyme immunoassays. In fact, antibody IgG to β-D-galactosidase from *E. coli* is present in a significant portion of healthy subjects (Fig. 6.2) (Kohno et al., 1991b).

In immune complex transfer enzyme immunoassay V for antibodies (Fig. 5.5), serum samples containing the specific antibodies to be measured are incubated simultaneously with 2,4-dinitrophenyl-antigens and antigen-enzyme conjugates. The immune complexes consisting of the three components formed are trapped on the first solid phase coated with affinity-purified (anti-2,4-dinitrophenyl group) IgG. After washing, the immune complexes are eluted from the first solid phase with excess ϵN-2,4-dinitrophenyl-L-lysine and are transferred to the second solid phase coated with anti-immunoglobulin IgG. When serum samples contain antibodies to enzyme labels, these bind to antigen-enzyme conjugates. The immune complexes formed consisting of the two components may be nonspecifically adsorbed to the first solid phase, partially and spontaneously desorbed during elution of the immune complexes of the three components and specifically bound to the second solid phase, enhancing the nonspecific signal in the absence of the specific antibodies to be measured and limiting the sensitivity of immune complex transfer enzyme immunoassay V (Fig. 5.5).

This is the case in immune complex transfer enzyme immunoassay V for antibody IgG to thyroglobulin using β-D-galactosidase from *E. coli* as an enzyme label (Kohno et al., 1991c).

Serum samples (20 μL) from 231 healthy subjects (123 males aged 18–83 years and 108 females aged 16–86 years) were incubated with an excess amount (10 μg) of thyroglobulin and were subjected to immune complex transfer enzyme immunoassay V (Fig. 5.5) for antibody IgG to thyroglobulin as described above. The conjugates and solid phase used were 2,4-dinitrophenyl-thyroglobulin, thyroglobulin-β-D-galactosidase conjugate and polystyrene beads of 3.2 mm diameter (two beads per assay). β-D-galactosidase activity bound to the second solid phase was assayed by fluorometry. The fluorescence intensity of bound β-D-galactosidase activity varied widely: 13 ± 128 (SD) (range, 0.3–1940) (Table 6.9). This was due to the presence of anti-β-D-galactosidase antibodies as shown by the following experiments.

Serum samples (20 μL) from three healthy subjects were preincubated with both thyroglobulin (10 μg) and increasing amounts (0–50 μg) of inactive β-D-galactosidase (Boehringer Mannheim, GmbH, Mannheim, Germany) and were subjected to immune complex transfer enzyme immunoassay V (Fig. 5.5) for anti-thyroglobulin IgG. Bound β-D-galactosidase activity decreased with increase in the amount of inactive β-D-galactosidase added, reaching a minimum with 50 μg (Fig. 6.4).

On the basis of this result, the 231 serum samples (20 μL) were preincubated with thyroglobulin and/or inactive β-D-galactosidase in three different ways: with 50 μg of inactive β-D-galactosidase alone, with 10 μg of thyroglobulin alone and with both 10 μg of thyroglobulin and 50 μg of inactive β-D-galactosidase. Then, they were tested by immune complex transfer enzyme immunoassay V (Fig. 5.5) for anti-thyroglobulin IgG. In most of the serum samples, β-D-galactosidase activities bound after preincubation with both 50 μg of inactive β-D-galactosidase and 10 μg of thyroglobulin were significantly lower than those after preincubation with 10 μg of thyroglobulin alone (Fig. 6.5 and Table 6.9), indicating

TABLE 6.9

Effects of inactive β-D-galactosidase and thyroglobulin on specific and nonspecific signals in immune complex transfer enzyme immunoassay V (Fig. 5.5) for antibody IgG to human thyroglobulin in serum using β-D-galactosidase from *E. coli* as a label

Sample No. of serum	Sex	Fluorescence intensity of β-D-galactosidase activity bound to the second solid phase after preincubation with			
		No addition	Inactive β-D-galacto-sidase	Thyro-globulin	Thyro-globulin plus inactive β-D-galactosidase
1–214	M, F	1.7–15,600	1.1–12,200	0.3–46	0.1–1.8
215	M	94	83	6.9	2.6
216	F	790	770	5.4	3.6
217	M	1,320	1,410	3.1	2.6
218	F	17,200	17,400	24	23
219	F	20,400	19,900	18	7.1
220	F	47,100	53,600	5.8	2.7
221	F	72,500	85,900	6.0	3.9
222	F	74,100	76,000	8.8	7.1
223	F	102,000	102,000	25	24
224	F	103,000	98,100	14	10
225	F	186,000	214,000	14	8.8
226	M	209,000	202,000	12	8.0
227	M	235,000	246,000	16	11
228	F	275,000	260,000	21	17
229	F	312,000	335,000	13	11
230	F	1,590,000	1,740,000	193	184
231	F	4,460,000	4,620,000	1,940	1,250

The volume of serum used was 20 μL. β-D-galactosidase activity bound was assayed for 2.5 h. The fluorescence intensity of 1×10^{-10} mol/L 4-methylumbelliferone was 1. M: male. F: female (Kohno et al., 1991c).

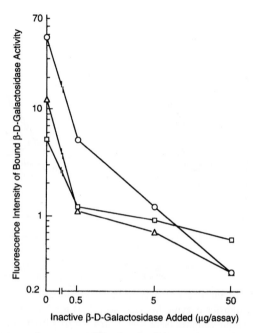

Fig. 6.4. Effect on the nonspecific signal of increasing amounts of inactive β-D-galactosidase during preincubation with serum samples in immune complex transfer enzyme immunoassay V (Fig. 5.5) for antibody IgG to thyroglobulin. Serum samples (20 μL) from three healthy subjects were preincubated with 10 μg of thyroglobulin and increasing amounts (0–50 μg) of inactive β-D-galactosidase and were subjected to immune complex transfer enzyme immunoassay V for anti-thyroglobulin IgG (Kohno et al., 1991c).

that the preincubation with excess inactive β-D-galactosidase reduced the adverse effect of anti-β-D-galactosidase IgG present in most healthy subjects as described above (Fig. 6.2). In almost all the serum samples, β-D-galactosidase activities bound after preincubation with both 50 μg of inactive β-D-galactosidase and 10 μg of thyroglobulin were markedly or significantly lower than those after preincubation with 50 μg of inactive β-D-galactosidase alone, indicating the presence of anti-thyroglobulin IgG in almost all the healthy subjects (Fig. 6.6 and Table 6.9). Thus, the pres-

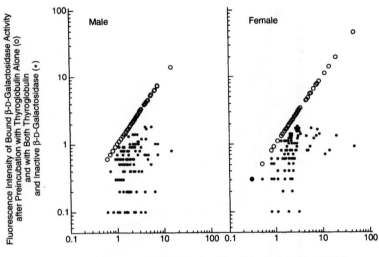

Fluorescence Intensity of Bound β-D-Galactosidase Activity
after Preincubation with Thyroglobulin Alone

Fig. 6.5. Effect of inactive β-D-galactosidase on the nonspecific signal in immune complex transfer enzyme immunoassay V (Fig. 5.5) for antibody IgG to thyroglobulin. Serum samples (sera Nos. 1–214, 20 μL) from 214 of 231 healthy subjects (119 males aged 18–83 years and 95 females aged 16–86 years) were preincubated with 10 μg of thyroglobulin alone (open circles) and with both 10 μg of thyroglobulin and 50 μg of inactive β-D-galactosidase (closed smaller circles) and were subjected to immune complex transfer enzyme immunoassay V for anti-thyroglobulin IgG (Kohno et al., 1991c). See Table 6.9 for the other 17 of the 231 serum samples.

ence of anti-thyroglobulin IgG in almost all healthy subjects can be demonstrated more clearly by using inactive β-D-galactosidase.

The value of inactive β-D-galactosidase to reduce the adverse effect of antibody IgG to the enzyme was tested by immune complex transfer enzyme immunoassay V for antibody IgG to HIV-1 reverse transcriptase (RT) antigen, which is completely absent in serum samples from HIV-1 seronegative subjects (Table 6.10). Aliquots (10 μl) of serum samples from HIV-1 seronegative subjects were incubated for 2 h with a mixture of inactive β-D-galactosidase, 2,4-dinitrophenyl-maltose binding protein-RT fusion protein and

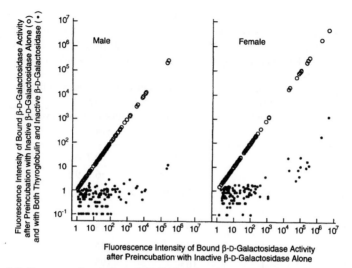

Fig. 6.6. Presence of anti-thyroglobulin IgG in serum of healthy subjects. Serum samples (sera Nos. 1–231, 20 μL) from 231 healthy subjects (123 males aged 18–83 years and 108 females aged 16–86 years) were preincubated with 50 μg of inactive β-D-galactosidase alone (open circles) or with both 10 μg of thyroglobulin and 50 μg of inactive β-D-galactosidase (closed smaller circles) and subjected to immune complex transfer enzyme immunoassay V (Fig. 5.5) for anti-thyroglobulin IgG (Kohno et al., 1991c).

recombinant RT-β-D-galactosidase conjugate (simultaneous incubation), for 1 h with two colored polystyrene beads of 3.2 mm diameter coated with affinity-purified (anti-2,4-dinitrophenyl group) IgG (first solid phase). After washing, the colored polystyrene beads were incubated for 1 h with two white polystyrene beads coated with affinity-purified (anti-human IgG γ-chain) IgG (second solid phase) in the presence of excess ϵN-2,4-dinitrophenyl-L-lysine. β-D-galactosidase activity bound to the white polystyrene beads (nonspecific signal) was assayed for 20 h. In all, 500 serum samples from HIV-1 seronegative subjects were tested.

In 375 serum samples (75%), nonspecific signals were reduced more or less in the presence of inactive β-D-galactosidase. Taking a fluorescence intensity for bound β-D-galactosidase activity of 10

TABLE 6.10

Effect of inactive β-D-galactosidase on the nonspecific signal in immune complex transfer enzyme immunoassay V (Fig. 5.5) for antibody IgG to HIV-1 reverse transcriptase (RT) antigen using β-D-galactosidase from *Escherichia coli* as a label

Sample Nos. of sera	Number of serum samples	Signal (fluorescence intensity of bound β-D-galactosidase activity)	
		Addition of inactive β-D-galactosidase	
		No	Yes
1–450	450	1.6–10	0.7–6.0
451–463	13	3.6–9.7	6.1–9.5
464–496	33	11–50	1.7–8.1
497	1	545	2.4
498	1	93	13
499	1	40	15
500	1	163	195

Serum samples (10 μL) from 500 HIV-1 seronegative subjects were incubated simultaneously with 50 μg of inactive β-D-galactosidase, 100 fmol of 2,4-dinitrophenyl-maltose binding protein-HIV-1 RT fusion protein and 30 fmol of recombinant HIV-1 RT antigen-β-D-galactosidase conjugate for 2 h and subsequently with two colored polystyrene beads coated with affinity-purified (anti-2,4-dinitrophenyl group) IgG (first solid phase) for 1 h. After washing, the first solid phase was incubated with two white polystyrene beads coated with affinity-purified (anti-human IgG γ-chain) IgG (second solid phase) in the presence of excess ϵN-2,4-dinitrophenyl-L-lysine for 1 h. Incubations with the solid phases were performed at room temperature with shaking. β-D-galactosidase activity bound to the second solid phase was assayed by fluorometry for 20 h. The fluorescence intensity of 1×10^{-10} mol/L 4-methylumbelliferone was 1.

as a tentative cut-off value, the specificity was improved from 92.6 to 99.4% in the presence of inactive β-D-galactosidase.

Alternatively, serum samples from HIV-1 seronegative samples were incubated first for 1 h with inactive β-D-galactosidase (preincubation) and then for 2 h with the two conjugates and finally processed as described above. Nonspecific signals obtained by the preincubation with inactive β-D-galactosidase were lower than

TABLE 6.11

Effect of preincubation of serum samples with inactive β-D-galactosidase on nonspecific signals in immune complex transfer enzyme immunoassay V (Fig. 5.5) for antibody IgG to HIV-1 reverse transcriptase (RT)

Sample Nos. of sera	Signal (fluorescence intensity of bound β-D-galactosidase activity)			
	Addition of inactive β-D-galactosidase			
	No		Yes	
	Preincubation		Preincubation	
	No	Yes	No	Yes
1	12	6.3	2.1	1.9
2	2.2	1.2	2.1	1.3
3	5.3	1.8	4.0	1.5
4	19	2.6	4.0	1.8
5	21	15	7.5	6.0
6	14	3.7	7.5	2.5
7	18	7.7	8.1	3.3
8	11	2.5	12	1.6
9	40	27	17	8.4
10	163	131	195	137

Serum samples (10 μL) from HIV-1 seronegative subjects were subjected to immune complex transfer enzyme immunoassay V for antibody IgG to HIV-1 RT in two different ways. First, serum samples were incubated simultaneously with inactive β-D-galactosidase and the two conjugates as described in Table 6.10. Second, serum samples were incubated first with inactive β-D-galactosidase for 1 h (preincubation) and subsequently with the two conjugates for 2 h.

those obtained by the simultaneous incubation described above. Notably, nonspecific signals were significantly reduced simply by 1 h incubation of serum samples with 10 mmol/L sodium phosphate buffer, pH 7.0, containing 0.4 mol/L NaCl, 1 mmol/L $MgCl_2$, 0.1% bovine serum albumin and 0.1% NaN_3 (Table 6.11).

6.6.6. Antibodies to IgG from other species of animals

A significant proportion of human serum samples contain antibodies to mouse IgG, for example, which enhance the nonspecific
signal in two-site enzyme immunoassays of antigens by bridging
monoclonal mouse antibody-coated solid phases and monoclonal
mouse antibody-enzyme conjugates, although a high nonspecific
signal is avoided simply by addition of nonspecific mouse IgG
(Yone et al., 1990; Hashida et al., 1991b). Similarly in some serum
samples, the nonspecific signal is enhanced in immune complex
transfer enzyme immunoassays IX and X (Figs. 5.9 and 5.10)
for antigens using 2,4-dinitrophenyl-(biotinyl)-monoclonal mouse
antibodies and monoclonal mouse antibody-enzyme conjugates.

6.6.7. Unknown factors

The sensitivity of immune complex transfer enzyme immunoassays is limited more or less by nonspecific signals due to unknown
factors in test samples such as serum and plasma.

In immune complex transfer enzyme immunoassay X (Fig.
5.10) of HIV-1 p24 antigen using 2,4-dinitrophenyl-biotinyl-bovine
serum albumin-affinity-purified anti-HIV-1 p24 Fab′ conjugate and
affinity-purified anti-HIV-1 p24 β-D-galactosidase conjugate, high
nonspecific signals were observed with serum samples which had
been stored at $-20°C$ for 29–30 months. This problem was overcome by substitution of monoclonal mouse anti-HIV-1 p24 Fab′-
β-D-galactosidase conjugate for affinity-purified rabbit anti-HIV-1
p24 Fab′-β-D-galactosidase conjugate (Fig. 6.7) (Hashida et al.,
1996c).

However, nonspecific signals with monoclonal mouse anti-HIV-
1 p24 Fab′-β-D-galactosidase conjugate in the presence of serum
samples from HIV-1 seronegative subjects were still slightly higher
than those in their absence (Table 6.6) (Ishikawa et al., 1998).
The detection limit of HIV-1 p24 antigen by a 1-h assay of β-D-
galactosidase assay using 10 μL serum samples was 0.1 amol (2.4

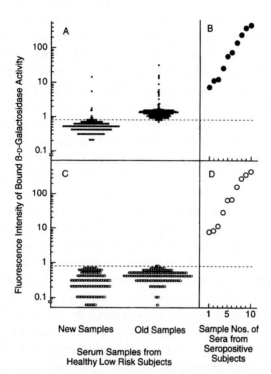

Fig. 6.7. Signals (fluorescence intensities of bound β-D-galactosidase activity) for serum samples from healthy subjects at low risk of HIV infection and HIV-1 seropositive subjects by immune complex transfer enzyme immunoassay X (Fig. 5.10) for HIV-1 p24 antigen using affinity-purified rabbit anti-p24 Fab'-β-D-galactosidase conjugate (A and B) and monoclonal mouse anti-p24 Fab'-β-D-galactosidase conjugate (C and D). Serum samples were collected from 229 healthy subjects (168 males aged 32–63 years and 61 females aged 21–68 years) at low risk of HIV infection three months before use (new samples), from 276 healthy subjects (157 males aged 19–77 years and 119 females aged 20–69 years) at low risk of HIV infection 29–30 months before use (old samples) and from seven HIV-1 seropositive subjects (seroconversion serum panels) 17–72 months before use and were stored at −20°C until use (Hashida et al., 1996c).

fg)/assay or 10 amol (0.24 pg)/mL of serum, since the nonspecific signal was almost zero and was 40- to 80-fold lower than those obtained with currently available commercial kits using 100–200 μL serum samples (10–20 pg/mL of serum). However, the highest nonspecific signal in the presence of 10 μL serum samples from HIV-1 seronegative subjects on a 20-h assay of β-D-galactosidase activity was almost equal to the specific signal corresponding to 20 zmol of HIV-1 p24 antigen in the absence of human serum samples (Table 6.6). Therefore, a 20-h assay of β-D-galactosidase activity improved the detection limit of HIV-1 p24 antigen only 5-fold in the presence of human serum samples over that on a 1-h assay, although the detection limit was improved approximately 10-fold to 10 zmol in the absence of human serum samples.

Similarly, the nonspecific signal in immune complex transfer enzyme immunoassay V (Fig. 5.5) for antibody IgG to HIV-1 p17 antigen was also enhanced to various extents by the presence of human serum samples from HIV-1 seronegative subjects, allowing only limited improvement of the sensitivity on a 20-h assay of β-D-galactosidase activity over that on a 1-h assay (Table 6.3) (Ishikawa et al., 1998). The detection limits of antibody IgG to p17 antigen in 1- and 20-h assays of β-D-galactosidase activity using 10 μL serum samples were 3×10^4- and 1×10^5-fold, respectively, lower than those by Western blotting for the HIV-1 p17 band.

The adverse effect of serum samples from HIV-1 seronegative subjects in immune complex transfer enzyme immunoassay X (Fig. 5.10) for HIV-1 p24 antigen might be due to the presence in serum samples of a protein(s) that reacts with the anti-p24 antibodies used and/or the presence of an antibody or antibodies other than anti-p24 antibodies in the preparation of anti-p24 antibodies used. The adverse effect of serum samples in immune complex transfer enzyme immunoassay V (Fig. 5.5) for antibody IgGs to HIV-1 p17 antigen and reverse transcriptase (RT) might be due to the presence of another protein(s) in the preparations of recombinant HIV-1 p17 (rp17) and RT (rRT) used and/or the presence of antibody IgG(s) reactive with rp17 and rRT in serum samples.

CHAPTER 7

Ultrasensitive and rapid enzyme immunoassay

In most of the immune complex transfer enzyme immunoassays described in Chapter 6, the periods of time used for immunoreactions are rather long.

In the typical immune complex transfer enzyme immunoassay V (Fig. 5.5), for example, the specific antibody IgG to be measured is allowed to react simultaneously with 2,4-dinitrophenyl-antigen and antigen-enzyme conjugate for 3 h. The immune complex consisting of the three components formed is trapped on two colored polystyrene beads of 3.2 mm diameter coated with affinity-purified (anti-2,4-dinitrophenyl group) IgG (first solid phase) by overnight incubation and is transferred to two white polystyrene beads of 3.2 mm diameter coated with affinity-purified (anti-human IgG γ-chain) IgG (second solid phase) in the presence of excess ϵN-2,4-dinitrophenyl-L-lysine by a 3-h incubation. Thus, the total time required for the immunoreactions is more than 20 h.

This chapter describes some methods for performing immune complex transfer enzyme immunoassays rapidly with high sensitivity.

7.1. Shaking for immunoreactions on solid phases

Shortening of incubation times for immunoreactions on solid phases is important for rapid performance of immune complex transfer enzyme immunoassays.

In the immune complex transfer enzyme immunoassays described in Chapter 6, the immune complexes consisting of 2,4-

dinitrophenyl-antigens or antibodies are trapped on solid phases coated with affinity-purified (anti-2,4-dinitrophenyl group) IgG (first solid phase). For testing this process more simply, 2,4-dinitrophenyl-β-D-galactosidase was prepared, and the time courses of its binding to affinity-purified (anti-2,4-dinitrophenyl group) IgG immobilized on various solid phases were examined. The solid phases used were small polystyrene beads of 3.2 mm diameter (two beads/assay), polystyrene sticks (one stick/microplate well) (Fig. 7.1) and polystyrene microplate wells. These solid phases coated with affinity-purified (anti-2,4-dinitrophenyl group) IgG were incubated with 2,4-dinitrophenyl-β-D-galactosidase (200 fmol) in a total volume of 150 μL for up to 60 min with and without shaking (Fig. 7.2).

On incubation without shaking, the fractions of 2,4-dinitrophenyl-β-D-galactosidase bound continued to increase for 60 min and reached only 16–37% after 60 min incubation. In contrast, when incubation was performed with rather vigorous shaking, the fractions of 2,4-dinitrophenyl-β-D-galactosidase bound to the coated polystyrene sticks and microplates reached maxima (70–90%) within 30–40 min, although the fraction bound to the small polystyrene beads continued to increase for 60 min and reached only 55% even after 60 min incubation.

Thus, the binding of 2,4-dinitrophenyl-β-D-galactosidase to affinity-purified (anti-2,4-dinitrophenyl group) IgG immobilized on solid phases occurs much more efficiently with shaking.

Similar time dependence of the signal by immune complex transfer enzyme immunoassay V (Fig. 5.5) of antibody IgG to HIV-1 p17 antigen is shown in Table 7.1 (Ishikawa S. et al., 1997).

As in the typical immune complex transfer enzyme immunoassay V (Fig. 5.5), serum containing antibody IgG to HIV-1 p17 antigen from an HIV-1 seropositive subject (asymptomatic carrier) was incubated for 0.5 h simultaneously with 2,4-dinitrophenyl-maltose binding protein-HIV-1 p17 fusion protein and recombinant HIV-1 p17 (rp17)-β-D-galactosidase conjugate and subsequently overnight with two colored polystyrene beads of 3.2 mm diame-

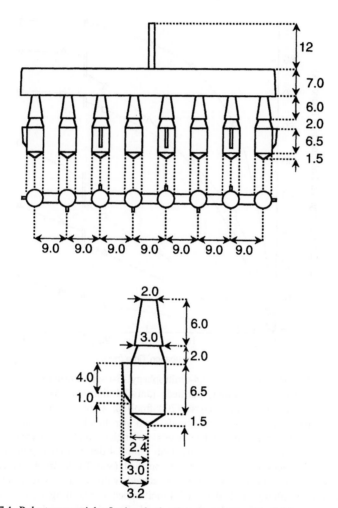

Fig. 7.1. Polystyrene sticks for incubation in microplate wells (Ishikawa S. et al., 1997). Values indicate the sizes of various parts in mm.

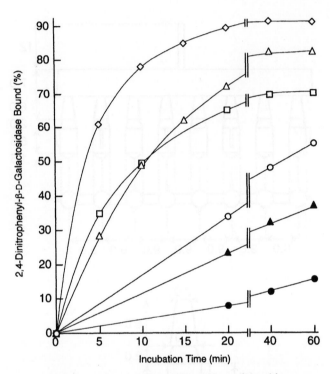

Fig. 7.2. Binding of 2,4-dinitrophenyl-β-D-galactosidase to solid phases coated with affinity-purified (anti-2,4-dinitrophenyl group) IgG. 2,4-dinitrophenyl-β-D-galactosidase (200 fmol) in a total volume of 150 μL was incubated with polystyrene beads (two per tube) of 3.2 mm diameter (circles), polystyrene microplate wells (triangles) and polystyrene sticks (Fig. 7.1) coated with affinity-purified (anti-2,4-dinitrophenyl group) IgG. Polystyrene sticks coated with affinity-purified (anti-2,4-dinitrophenyl group) IgG were used in microplate wells coated with bovine serum albumin (squares) or affinity-purified (anti-2,4-dinitrophenyl group) IgG (rhombuses). Incubations were performed with (open symbols) and without (closed symbols) shaking. The rate and width of shaking were 180/min and 2.5 cm.

ter coated with affinity-purified (anti-2,4-dinitrophenyl group) IgG (first solid phase) to trap the immune complex consisting of the three components formed. For transfer of the immune complex, the first solid phase after washing was incubated for 3 h with two white polystyrene beads of 3.2 mm diameter coated with affinity-purified (anti-human IgG γ-chain) IgG (second solid phase) in the presence of excess ϵN-2,4-dinitrophenyl-L-lysine (immunoassay V-1-1). Incubations were performed without shaking.

For comparison with these long incubations, the immune complex formed was trapped on the first solid phase of 3.2 mm diameter beads by incubation for 0.5–1 h and was transferred to the second solid phase of 3.2 mm diameter beads by incubation for 0.5–1 h. Incubations were performed with (immunoassays V-2-1 and V-2-2) and without (immunoassay V-1-2) shaking.

β-D-galactosidase activity bound to the second solid phase was assayed by fluorometry.

The signals (fluorescence intensities of bound β-D-galactosidase activity) of serum samples from the seropositive subject (positive signals) by immunoassay V-1-2 with 1 h trapping and 1 h transference of the immune complex without shaking were only 21–24% of those by immunoassay V-1-1 with overnight trapping and 3 h transference without shaking. Thus, shortening the incubation time for trapping and transference from 18 to 2 h results in serious (4- to 5-fold) decrease in the positive signal. However, the positive signals by immunoassays V-2-1 and V-2-2 with 0.5–1 h trapping and 0.5–1 h transference with shaking were enhanced to 167–366% of those by immunoassay V-1-1 with overnight trapping and 3 h transference without shaking. Since the nonspecific signals were not significantly different with and without shaking, the sensitivity of immune complex transfer enzyme immunoassay V was improved 1.7- to 3.7-fold simply by shaking even with 0.5–1 h trapping and 0.5–1 h transference over that with overnight trapping and 3 h transference without shaking and was improved 6.9- to 17-fold over that with 1 h trapping and 1 h transference without shaking.

TABLE 7.1

Signals by immune complex transfer enzyme immunoassays V (Fig. 5.5) of antibody IgG to HIV-1 p17 antigen using different sample volumes and various solid phases incubated with and without shaking

Immune complex transfer enzyme immunoassay No.	First solid phase (diameter, surface area)	Volume of serum sample	Incubation time for trapping the immune complex	transferring the immune complex	Signal (fluorescence intensity of bound β-D-galactosidase activity) with serum samples from		
					Seronegative subject(s)	A seropositive subject diluted 10^5-fold	diluted 10^4-fold
		(μL)	(h)	(h)			
Without shaking							
V-1-1	Two beads per tube	10	overnight	3	0.3 ± 0.1 (0.1–0.9)	12	103
V-1-2	(3.2 mm, 64 mm²)	10	1	1	0.5	2.9	22
V-1-4	Four beads per well (3.2 mm, 129 mm²)	10	1	1	–	–	107
V-1-6	One bead per well (5.0 mm, 79 mm²)	10	1	1	0.5	4.9	59
V-1-7	One bead per well (6.3 mm, 127 mm²)	10	1	1	–	–	113
V-1-8	One stick per well (120 mm²)	10	1	1	0.5	6.9	54
With shaking							
V-2-1	Two beads per tube	10	0.5	0.5	0.0	20	193
V-2-2	(3.2 mm, 64 mm²)	10	1	1	0.1 ± 0.1 (0.1–0.4)	38	377
V-2-3		100	1	1	0.2 ± 0.3 (0.0–1.4)	310	–
V-2-4	Four beads per well	10	0.5	0.5	0.2	59	572
V-2-5	(3.2 mm, 129 mm²)	100	0.5	0.5	0.0	457	–
V-2-6	One bead per well (5.0 mm, 79 mm²)	10	0.5	0.5	–	–	448
V-2-7	One bead per well (6.3 mm, 127 mm²)	10	0.5	0.5	0.0	44	472
V-2-8	One stick per well (120 mm²)	10	0.25	0.25	0.2	22	180
V-2-9		10	0.5	0.5	0.2	40	359
V-2-10		10	1	1	0.5	53	465
V-2-11		100	0.5	0.5	0.4	255	–
V-2-12		100	1	1	0.2	403	–

Serum from an HIV-1 seropositive subject (asymptomatic carrier) was diluted 10^4- and 10^5-fold with pooled serum from HIV-1 seronegative subjects. Bound β-D-galactosidase activity was assayed at room temperature for 1 h. The fluorescence intensity of 1×10^{-10} mol/L 4-methylumbelliferone was 1. Some signals for HIV-1 seronegative subjects are expressed as means ±SD and ranges in parentheses ($n = 50$) (Ishikawa S. et al., 1997).

The effects of shaking on signals with other solid phases are also shown in Table 7.1. The first solid phases used were small polystyrene beads (3.2 mm in diameter, four beads/microplate well), larger polystyrene beads (5.0 and 6.35 mm in diameter, one bead/microplate well) and polystyrene sticks (one stick/microplate well) (Fig. 7.1), and the second solid phase used was microplate wells (immunoassays V-1-4 to 8 and V-2-4 to 10). The positive signals were enhanced 4.2- to 8.6-fold by 0.5–1 h trapping and 0.5– 1 h transference with shaking and 3.2- to 3.3-fold even by 0.25 h trapping and 0.25 h transference with shaking over those by 1 h trapping and 1 h transference without shaking, increasing the sensitivity to similar extents, since the nonspecific signals were similar with and without shaking.

Thus, much higher signals are obtained within much shorter periods by shaking solid phases in immunoreactions, considerably improving the sensitivity of immune complex transfer enzyme immunoassay V, since the nonspecific signals in the absence of antibody IgG to HIV-1 p17 antigen are similar for different solid phases with and without shaking. For example, immune complex transfer enzyme immunoassay V (Fig. 5.5) of antibody IgG to HIV-1 p17 antigen using polystyrene beads of 6.35 mm diameter as a solid phase and serum samples of 10 μL with 0.5 h trapping and 0.5 h transference and with shaking (immunoassays V-2-7) is 10,000- to 20,000-fold more sensitive than Western blotting for the HIV-1 p17 band.

7.2. Use of larger sample volumes

The detection limit of analytes may be expressed as moles or grams per assay. However, a practically important detection limit of analytes is moles or grams per unit volume of samples such as serum and plasma. A simple way to improve the sensitivity in terms of moles or grams per unit volume of samples is to use larger sample volumes.

When the volume of serum samples used was increased from 10 to 100 μL in immune complex transfer enzyme immunoassay V (Fig. 5.5) for antibody IgG to HIV-1 p17 antigen described above, the sensitivity in terms of dilution of positive serum samples with negative serum was improved 6.4- to 8.2-fold (immunoassays V-2-2 to 5 and V-2-9 to 12) (Table 7.1) (Ishikawa S. et al., 1997). The sensitivity did not improve proportionally with increase in the sample volume due to serum interference. Immune complex transfer enzyme immunoassay V of antibody IgG to HIV-1 p17 antigen using 100 μL of serum samples were 50,000- to 100,000-fold more sensitive than Western blotting for the HIV-1 p17 band, even when both trapping and transferring of the immune complex were performed for only 0.5 h (the immunoassays V-2-5 and 11) (Table 7.1).

7.3. Use of solid phases with larger surfaces

The time courses of immunoreactions on solid phase surfaces depend on the sizes of the surfaces. The effects of solid phase surface areas on the time courses of the binding of 2,4-dinitrophenyl-β-D-galactosidase to solid phases coated with affinity-purified (anti-2,4-dinitrophenyl group) IgG as a model immunoreaction on a solid phase are shown in Fig. 7.2. The solid phases used are polystyrene beads of 3.2 mm diameter, microplate wells and polystyrene sticks (Fig. 7.1). The total surface area of the two polystyrene beads used per assay was 64 mm^2, and the surface areas of the microplate wells and polystyrene sticks covered with 150 μL were 125 and 130 mm^2, respectively (Table 7.2). The binding rate increased with increase in the solid phase surface area, being highest with polystyrene sticks coated with the IgG used in combination with microplate wells coated with the IgG.

The effect of the solid phase surface area on specific signals in immune complex transfer enzyme immunoassay V (Fig. 5.5) of antibody IgG to HIV-1 p17 antigen is also shown in Table 7.1 (Ishikawa S. et al., 1997). The solid phases used were polystyrene

TABLE 7.2

Surface areas of various solid phases

Solid phase	Surface area (mm^2)
Polystyrene beads	
3.2 mm in diameter	32
5.0 mm in diameter	79
6.35 mm in diameter	127
Microplate well covered with 150 μL of solution	125
Polystyrene stick (Fig. 7.1) covered with 150 μL of solution in microplate well	130
Polystyrene cup (Fig. 7.4) covered with 5 mL of solution	1100

beads of 3.2, 5.0 and 6.35 mm diameter. The total surface areas of two and four polystyrene beads of 3.2 mm diameter used per assay were 64 and 128 mm^2, respectively, and the surface areas of single polystyrene beads of 5.0 and 6.35 mm diameter were 79 and 127 mm^2, respectively (Table 7.2).

Positive signals were higher with larger solid phase surfaces, irrespective of whether the immunoreactions were performed with or without shaking. However, the positive signals with polystyrene sticks of 130 mm^2 surface area were lower than those with four polystyrene beads of 3.2 mm diameter and one polystyrene bead of 5.0 or 6.3 mm diameter, which have surface areas similar to or less than those of polystyrene sticks. This might be because the surface of polystyrene sticks was smooth, but those of other solid phases are rough.

7.4. Use of circulating thin aqueous layers covering solid phase surfaces

The results with solid phases of different surface areas shown in Fig. 7.2 and Table 7.1 indicate that the period required for immunoreactions on solid phases decreases with the increase in the size of the solid phase surfaces used. In these conditions, the solid phase surfaces always remained in solution as in most of the immunoassays described in Chapter 6. Therefore, the size of solid phase surfaces that can be used is limited by the solution volume used.

However, it must not be essential to always keep solid phase surfaces in solution, provided that all parts of solid phase surfaces are in even contact with solutions during incubations, even if only small parts of them are in contact at any given time, so as to continuously mix thin aqueous layers covering solid phase surfaces with solutions. Therefore, solid phases with larger surface areas can be used under appropriate conditions, so that immunoreactions on solid phases take place rapidly. This is evident from the results with different solid phase surface areas and different solution volumes described below (Ishikawa S. et al., 1998a).

First, single polystyrene beads of 6.35 mm diameter coated with affinity-purified (anti-2,4-dinitrophenyl group) IgG were incubated with 150 μL of 2,4-dinitrophenyl-β-D-galactosidase solution (7.7 amol/μL) by shaking in test tubes of three different sizes (10 $\times$ 75, 13.3 $\times$ 54 and 18 $\times$ 100 mm) (Fig. 7.3A, B and C). The shaking rate was 180 per min, and the shaking width was 25 mm. In a test tube of 10 $\times$ 75 mm, the whole surface of the polystyrene bead always remained in the 2,4-dinitrophenyl-β-D-galactosidase solution during incubation with shaking. In other test tubes, only a small part of the polystyrene bead surface was in the solution at any given time, but the polystyrene bead was rotated randomly by shaking, so that the solution contacted all parts of the polystyrene bead surface evenly during incubation continuously mixing the thin aqueous layer covering the polystyrene bead surface with the rest of the solution.

The fraction of 2,4-dinitrophenyl-β-D-galactosidase bound to the polystyrene bead after 2.5 min incubation increased from 16 to 70% with increase in the size of the test tube from 10 $\times$ 75 to 18 $\times$ 100 mm (Table 7.3).

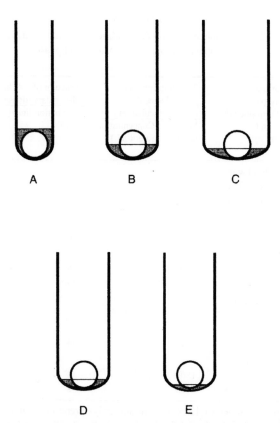

Fig. 7.3. Incubation of polystyrene beads of 6.35 mm diameter in different volumes of solution in test tubes of different sizes. The solution volumes and sizes of test tubes used were 150 μL and 10 $\times$ 75 mm (A), 150 μL and 13.3 $\times$ 54 mm (B), 150 μL and 18 $\times$ 100 mm (C), 50 μL and 13.3 $\times$ 54 mm (D) and 15 μL and 13.3 $\times$ 54 mm (E).

Second, a polystyrene bead of 6.35 mm diameter coated with affinity-purified (anti-2,4-dinitrophenyl group) IgG was incubated with different volumes (15, 50 and 150 μL) of 2,4-dinitrophenyl-β-D-galactosidase solution in a test tube (13.3 $\times$ 54 mm) with shaking (Fig. 7.3B, D and E).

TABLE 7.3

Binding of 2,4-dinitrophenyl-β-D-galactosidase to affinity-purified (anti-2,4-dinitrophenyl group) IgG-coated solid phases

Solid phase coated with affinity-purified (anti-2,4-dinitrophenyl group) IgG and test tube for incubation	2,4-Dinitrophenyl-β-D-galactosidase used for incubation		Fraction of 2,4-dinitrophenyl-β-D-galactosidase bound (%)	
			Incubation time (min)	
	Volume (μL)	Concentration (amol/μL)	1.25	2.5
Polystyrene bead with a diameter of 6.35 mm incubated in test tube of				
10 × 75 mm	150	0.77	12	19
	150	7.7	11	16
13.3 × 54 mm	150	7.7	30	51
18 × 100 mm	150	7.7	–	70
13.3 × 54 mm	50	7.7	58	77
13.3 × 54 mm	15	7.7	78	100
Polystyrene test tube				
12 × 75 mm	150	7.7	–	51
	50	7.7	57	77
	15	7.7	84	96
Polystyrene cup of				
25 × 100 mm	1500	770	13	25
	150	7700	58	81

Polystyrene test tubes of 12 × 75 mm and polystyrene cups of 25 × 100 mm were coated with 0.4 mL and 5 mL, respectively, of affinity-purified (anti-2,4-dinitrophenyl group) IgG, and the coated inner surface areas are 220 and 1100 mm^2, respectively (Ishikawa S. et al., 1998a).

The fraction of 2,4-dinitrophenyl-β-D-galactosidase bound to the polystyrene bead increased from 30 to 78% after 1.25 min incubation and from 51 to 100% after 2.5 min incubation with decrease in the solution volume from 150 to 15 μL (Table 7.3).

Third, polystyrene test tubes (12 × 75 mm) and polystyrene cups (25 × 100 mm) (Fig. 7.4) coated with 0.4 and 5 mL, respectively, of affinity-purified (anti-2,4-dinitrophenyl group) IgG were

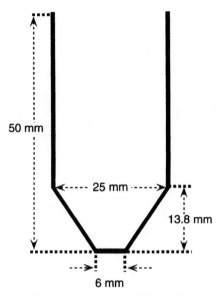

Fig. 7.4. Polystyrene cup of 25 × 100 cm.

incubated with different volumes (15, 50, 150 and 1500 μL) of 2,4-dinitrophenyl-β-D-galactosidase solution with rotation, so that the 2,4-dinitrophenyl-β-D-galactosidase solution evenly contacted all parts of the coated polystyrene tube and cup surfaces during incubation. The rotation rate was 40 per min.

The fraction of 2,4-dinitrophenyl-β-D-galactosidase bound to a test tube of 12 × 75 mm after 2.5 min incubation increased from 51 to 96% with decrease in the solution volume from 150 to 15 μL and that bound to a polystyrene cup of 25 × 100 mm after 2.5 min incubation increased from 25 to 81% with decrease in the solution volume from 1500 to 150 μL (Table 7.3 and Fig. 7.5).

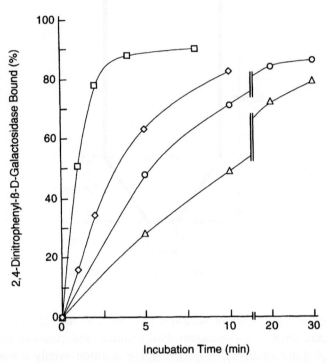

Fig. 7.5. Binding of 2,4-dinitrophenyl-β-D-galactosidase to solid phases coated with affinity-purified (anti-2,4-dinitrophenyl group) IgG. 2,4-dinitro-phenyl-β-D-galactosidase was incubated with solid phases coated with affin-ity-purified (anti-2,4-dinitrophenyl group) IgG for up to 30 min. The amount of 2,4-dinitrophenyl-β-D-galactosidase, the total volume of solution and the solid phase used for the incubation were 200 fmol, 150 μL and one microplate well (triangles), 200 fmol, 150 μL and one polystyrene bead of 6.35 mm diameter (rhombuses), 1 pmol, 150 μL and one polystyrene cup of 25 × 100 mm (Fig. 7.4) (squares) and 1 pmol, 1500 μL and one polystyrene cup of 25 × 100 mm (Fig. 7.4) (circles). The incubations of microplate wells and polystyrene beads in test tubes of 13.3 × 54 mm were performed with shaking. Polystyrene cups were rotated so that the solution evenly contacted all parts of the surface coated with the IgG. The rotation rate was 40/min.

7.5. Advantages of circulating thin aqueous layer immunoassay

7.5.1. Rapid solid phase immunoassay

As evident from the above results, immunoreactions on solid phases take place efficiently by continuously mixing thin aqueous layers covering solid phase surfaces with solutions for incubation, even when the whole solid phase surfaces are not always kept in solutions. The higher the ratio of the solid phase surface area to the solution volume, the faster is the immunoreaction on a solid phase. This makes possible rapid solid phase immunoassays that may be called *circulating thin aqueous layer immunoassays.*

7.5.2. Saving of expensive reagents

In the circulating thin aqueous layer immunoassays described above, it is possible to save expensive reagents including labeled reactants (antigens and antibodies) by using smaller solution volumes, since the rates of immunoreactions on solid phases depend on the concentrations of reactants and the fractions of reactants bound are much smaller than the total amounts used.

7.5.3. Sensitive detection of label enzymes

Under appropriate conditions, it is possible to incubate solid phases of larger surface areas with smaller solution volumes for rapid immunoreactions on solid phases as described above. This is also applicable to the assay of label enzymes bound to solid phase surfaces. Namely, solid phases on which enzyme activities are bound may be incubated with smaller volumes of substrate solutions. In this way, enzyme activities bound to solid phases can be assayed with higher sensitivities, since the backgrounds of enzyme assays are reduced proportionally with decrease in the amount of substrate used, and the sensitivities of enzyme assays are improved proportionally with decrease in the background.

7.6. Circulating thin aqueous layer immunoassay for antibodies

7.6.1. Immunoassay processes

On the basis of the above results and considerations, antibody IgG to HIV-1 p17 antigen was measured in two different ways (circulating thin aqueous layer immune complex transfer enzyme immunoassays V-I and V-II abbreviated as simultaneous and sequential immunoassays V-I and V-II) (Fig. 7.6) (Ishikawa S. et al., 1998a).

In simultaneous immunoassay V-I (Fig. 5.5), aliquots (10 μL) of serum samples containing antibody IgG to HIV-1 p17 antigen were incubated simultaneously with 100 fmol each of 2,4-dinitrophenyl-maltose binding protein-HIV-1 p17 fusion protein and recombinant HIV-1 p17 (rp17)-β-D-galactosidase conjugate in a total volume of 22 μL in a styrol test tube (13.3 × 54 mm and 2.1 g). After addition of a polystyrene bead of 6.35 mm diameter coated with affinity-purified (anti-2,4-dinitrophenyl group) IgG (first solid phase), the styrol test tube was shaken, so that the polystyrene bead was rotated randomly and a small drop of the reaction mixture (22 μL) became in even contact with all parts of the polystyrene bead surface during incubation to continuously mix the thin aqueous layer covering the polystyrene bead surface with the rest of the reaction mixture, although only a small part of the polystyrene bead surface was in contact with the mixture at any given time. After washing. the polystyrene bead and 30 μL of ϵN-2,4-dinitrophenyl-L-lysine solution were put in a polystyrene tube (12 × 75 mm) coated with affinity-purified (anti-human IgG γ-chain) IgG (second solid phase), and the polystyrene tube was shaken with slow rotation in a box (15 × 35 mm × 20 mm depth) to elute and transfer the immune

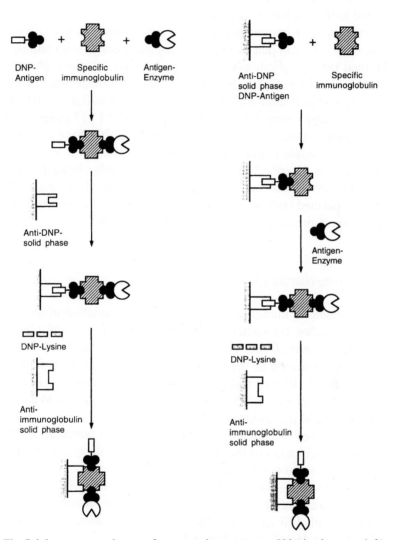

Fig. 7.6. Immune complex transfer enzyme immunoassays V-I (simultaneous, left) and V-II (sequential, right). DNP: 2,4-dinitrophenyl group.

complex to the polystyrene tube surface. β-D-galactosidase activity bound to the test tube was assayed by fluorometry.

In sequential immunoassay V-II, a polystyrene bead with a diameter of 6.35 mm that had been coated successively with affinity-purified (anti-2,4-dinitrophenyl group) IgG and 2,4-dinitrophenyl-maltose binding protein-HIV-1 p17 fusion protein (first solid phase), was incubated with a mixture of 6 μL of buffer and 10 μL of serum sample containing antibody IgG to HIV-1 p17 antigen and subsequently with 10 μL of buffer containing 200 fmol of rp17-β-D-galactosidase conjugate in a styrol test tube (13.3 × 54 mm and 2.1 g) as described above. The immune complex formed on the first solid phase was transferred to a polystyrene tube coated with affinity-purified (anti-human IgG γ-chain) IgG (second solid phase) as in simultaneous immunoassay V-I described above.

7.6.2. Time courses of immunoreactions

In simultaneous immunoassay V-I (Fig. 7.6), formation of the immune complex consisting of the three components was almost complete within 10 min on incubation of serum samples (10 μL) with 100 fmol each of the two conjugates in a total volume of 22 μL, while 30–40 min was required when serum samples (10 μL) were incubated with 100 fmol each of the two conjugates in a total volume of 150 μL, as described in Chapter 6.

Trapping of the immune complex was almost complete within 3 min on incubation of the first solid phase (a polystyrene bead of 6.35 mm diameter) with 22 μL of reaction mixture containing the immune complex, while 1–1.5 h was required when the first solid phase (two colored polystyrene beads of 3.2 mm diameter) was incubated with 150 μL of reaction mixture containing the immune complex, as described in Chapter 6.

Transference of the immune complex was almost complete within 10 min on incubation of the first solid phase with 30 μL of ϵN-2,4-dinitrophenyl-L-lysine in a test tube of 12 × 75 mm as the second solid phase, while 1–1.5 h was required when the first and second solid phases (two colored and two white polystyrene beads of 3.2 mm diameter) were incubated with ϵN-2,4-dinitrophenyl-L-lysine in a total volume of 150 μL, as described in Chapter 6.

In sequential immunoassay V-II (Fig. 7.6), the binding of antibody IgG against HIV-1 p17 antigen to the first solid phase (a polystyrene bead of 6.35 mm diameter) was almost complete within 5 min when the first solid phase was incubated with serum samples (10 μL) in a total volume of 16 μL. The binding to the first solid phase of recombinant HIV-1 p17 (rp17)-β-D-galactosidase conjugate, which was added at a final concentration of 200 fmol/26 μL, continued to increase for 30 min. Transference of the immune complex was almost complete within 10 min as in simultaneous immunoassay V-I.

Thus, in immunoassays V-I and V-II (Fig. 7.6) using a polystyrene bead of 6.35 mm diameter and a total solution volume of 16–30 μL, the times required for completion of the immunoreactions (15–25 min) are much shorter than that (150 min) in immune complex transfer enzyme immunoassay V using two polystyrene beads of 3.2 mm diameter and a total solution volume of 150 μL (Table 7.4).

7.6.3. Sensitivity

Based on the time courses of immunoreactions described above, simultaneous and sequential (circulating thin aqueous layer immune complex transfer enzyme) immunoassays V-I and V-II (Fig. 7.6) using polystyrene beads of 6.35 mm diameter and smaller solution volumes (16–30 μL) were performed in shorter times (15–25 min for immunoreactions) as described below. The sensitivities achieved are shown in comparison with that of immune complex transfer enzyme immunoassay V using polystyrene beads of 3.2 mm diameter (two beads per assay) and a solution volume of 150 μL in Table 7.4.

In simultaneous immunoassay V-I, the immune complex was allowed to form for 10 min, trapped for 5 min and transferred for 10 min. Then, β-D-galactosidase activity bound to the second solid phase was assayed for 60 min. Under these conditions using 25 min for immunoreactions, simultaneous immunoassay V-I was as sensitive as simultaneous immune complex transfer enzyme immunoassay V using 150 min for immunoreactions, in which the immune complex was formed in 30 min, trapped for 60 min and transferred for 60 min using two polystyrene beads of 3.2 mm diameter per tube in a total volume of 150 μL and bound β-D-galactosidase activity was assayed for 60 min (Table 7.4). The simultaneous immunoassay V-I was approximately 20,000-fold more sensitive than Western blotting of the HIV-1 p17 band.

In sequential immunoassay V-II, the first solid phase was incubated with serum samples for 5 min and then with rp17-β-D-galactosidase conjugate for 5 min, and the immune complex formed was transferred for 5 min. Under these conditions using only 15 min for the immunoreactions, the sequential immunoassay V-II was slightly more sensitive than the simultaneous immune complex transfer enzyme immunoassay V using 150 min for the immunoreactions described above (Table 7.4) and was 20,000-fold more sensitive than Western blotting of the HIV-1 p17 band.

The sensitivity of sequential immunoassay V-II did not change significantly when the assay time of bound β-D-galactosidase activity was reduced to 30 min, when incubation with rp17-β-D-galactosidase conjugate and transference of the immune complex were both performed for 10 min (Table 7.4). Thus, the sequential immunoassay V-II performed within 55 min (25 min for immunoreactions and 30 min for β-D-galactosidase assay) was as sensitive as the immune complex transfer enzyme immunoassay V requiring 210 min (150 min for immunoreactions and 60 min for β-D-galactosidase assay) and was 20,000-fold more sensitive than Western blotting of the HIV-1 p17 band.

Finally, in sequential immunoassay V-II, the first solid phase was incubated with serum samples for 5 min and with rp17-β-D-

TABLE 7.4

Signal (fluorescence intensity of bound β-D-galactosidase activity) by immune complex transfer enzyme immunoassays V, V-I (Fig. 5.5) and V-II (Fig. 7.6) of antibody IgG to HIV-1 p17 antigen in comparison with test results by Western blotting of the HIV-1 p17 band

Immune complex transfer enzyme immunoassay	Diameter of polystyrene beads (number per assay) (mm)	Total volume of immunoreaction (μL)	Incubation time for						Signal				
			formation of the immune complex	trapping of the immune complex	reaction with antibody IgG to p17 (min)	reaction with rp17-β-D-galactosidase	transfer of the immune complex	β-D-galactosidase assay	Serum from an HIV-1 sero-negative subject	Dilution of serum from an HIV-1 sero-positive subject with serum from an HIV-1 seronegative subject			
										2×10^6	2×10^4	10^3	3×10^2
V	3.2 (2/assay)	150	30	60	–	–	60	60	0.0	4.1	365	–	–
V-I	6.35 (1/assay)	22–30	10	5	–	–	10	60	0.0	3.9	373	–	–
V-II		16–30	–	–	5	5	5	60	0.0	4.7	439	–	–
V-II		16–30	–	–	5	10	10	30	0.0	3.5	328	–	–
Western blotting for the HIV-1 p17 band								–				NG	PS

The volumes of serum samples used were 10 μL in all immunoassays except Western blotting. Immunoassay V was performed as described in Table 6.3. In immunoassay V-I, 10 μL of serum sample was incubated for 10 min simultaneously with 100 fmol each of 2,4-dinitrophenyl-maltose binding protein-HIV-1 p17 fusion protein and recombinant HIV-1 p17 (rp17)-β-D-galactosidase conjugate in a total volume of 22 μL and subsequently for 5 min with a polystyrene bead coated with affinity-purified (anti-2,4-dinitrophenyl group) IgG. In immunoassay V-II, a polystyrene bead coated successively with affinity-purified (anti-2,4-dinitrophenyl group) IgG and 2,4-dinitrophenyl-maltose binding protein-HIV-1 p17 fusion protein (800 fmol) was incubated for 5 min with 10 μL of serum samples in a total volume of 16 μL, and incubation was continued for 5–10 min after addition of rp17-β-D-galactosidase conjugate (200 fmol) in a volume of 10 μL. For immune complex transfer, the polystyrene bead after washing was incubated with ϵN-2,4-dinitrophenyl-L-lysine in a polystyrene test tube (12 × 75 mm) coated with affinity-purified (anti-human IgG γ-chain) IgG for 5–10 min. The fluorescence intensity of 1×10^{-10} mol/L 4-methylumbelliferone was 1. NG: negative. PS: positive (Ishikawa S. et al., 1998a).

TABLE 7.5

Signal (fluorescence intensity of bound β-D-galactosidase activity) by immune complex transfer enzyme immunoassays V (Fig. 5.5) and V-II (Fig. 7.6) of antibody IgG to HIV-1 p17 antigen with prolonged assay of bound β-D-galactosidase activity

Immune complex transfer enzyme immuno-assay	Diameter of poly-styrene beads (number per assay) (mm)	Total volume for immuno-reaction (µL)	Incubation time for				transfer of the immune complex	β-D-galacto-sidase assay	Signal	
			formation of the immune complex	trapping of the immune complex	reaction with antibody IgG to p17	reaction with rp17-β-D-galacto-sidase			Serum samples from 8 HIV-1 sero-negative subjects Mean ±SD (range)	Serum from an HIV-1 seropositive subject diluted 2×10^7-fold with serum from an HIV-1 sero-negative subject
			(min)				(min)			
V	3.2 (2/assay)	150	30	60	—	—	60	600	0.94 ± 0.24 (0.63–1.3)	4.9
V-II	6.35 (1/assay)	16–30	—	—	5	10	10	600	0.66 ± 0.27 (0.4–1.2)	7.9

Immunoassays V and V-II were performed as described in Table 7.4. The fluorescence intensity of 1×10^{-10} mol/L 4-methylumbelliferone was 1 (Ishikawa S. et al., 1998a).

galactosidase conjugate for 10 min. Then, after 10 min transfer of the immune complex, β-D-galactosidase activity bound to the second solid phase was assayed for 10 h. The fluorescence intensities of bound β-D-galactosidase activity in the presence of serum samples from HIV-1 seronegative subjects were 0.66 ± 0.27 (SD) (range, 0.4–1.2; $n = 8$) (Table 7.5). This was only 0.14% of that of β-D-galactosidase activity bound to the first solid phase and was as low as in immune complex transfer enzyme immunoassay V using two polystyrene beads of 3.2 mm diameter and a total solution volume of 150 μL. In contrast, the fluorescence intensity in the presence of serum from an HIV-1 seropositive subject (asymptomatic carrier) increased proportionally with increase in the assay time of β-D-galactosidase activity from 1 h to 10 h, and was approximately 35% of that of β-D-galactosidase activity bound to the first solid phase. Thus, the sensitivity of the sequential immunoassay V-II by a 10-h assay of β-D-galactosidase activity was approximately 10-fold higher than that by a 1-h assay of β-D-galactosidase activity and was approximately 250-fold higher than that when β-D-galactosidase activity bound to the first solid phase was assayed without transference of the immune complex. The improved sensitivity was 200,000-fold higher than that by Western blotting of the HIV-1 p17 band.

7.6.4. Advantages and disadvantages

Sequential immunoassay V-II is superior to simultaneous immunoassay V-I. The specific signal by sequential immunoassay V-II was higher than that by simultaneous immunoassay V-I, while the nonspecific signals by the two immunoassays were similar (Table 7.4). This is consistent with the theoretical consideration described in Chapter 4. The amount of the immune complex consisting of the three components formed by sequential immunoassay V-II must theoretically be twice as much as that formed by simultaneous immunoassay V-I, provided that there is no steric hindrance (Fig. 4.16).

Both immunoassays V-I and V-II have three disadvantages. First, the nonspecific signal to make full use of immune complex transfer can be measured only by a 10-h assay. Namely, the highest sensitivity that is achieved by immune complex transfer enzyme immunoassay V required 10 h (600 min) assay of the label enzyme, as described in Chapter 6. Therefore, the sensitivity of this assay method for the label enzyme remains to be improved at least 25- to 40-fold, since the immunoreactions are performed within 15–25 min. Second, the fractions of the immune complex transferred in 5 and 10 min were only 26 and 35%, respectively. Third, direct contact of the first and second solid phases during transfer of the immune complex enhances the nonspecific signal, limiting the sensitivity, as described in Chapter 6 (Tables 6.3, 6.4 and 6.6).

The last two disadvantages could be overcome by an alternative immune complex transfer process (sequential circulating thin aqueous layer immune complex transfer enzyme immunoassay V-III abbreviated as sequential immunoassay V-III). For this, the first solid phase (a polystyrene bead of 6.35 mm diameter) after washing was incubated with 35 μL of 2 mmol/L ϵN-2,4-dinitrophenyl-L-lysine in a styrol test tube (13.3 × 54 mm and 2.1 g) for 15 min (first eluate) and, after removal of the first eluate, with another 35 μL of 2 mmol/L ϵN-2,4-dinitrophenyl-L-lysine for 1 min (second eluate) to elute the immune complex. The first and second eluates were incubated for 15 min in a polystyrene test tube (12 × 75 mm) coated with affinity-purified (anti-human IgG γ-chain) IgG (second solid phase), which was rotated slowly, so that all parts of the coated surface became in even contact with the combined eluate as described above. The fraction of the immune complex transferred increased to 54%, while the nonspecific signal was reduced 835-fold by the immune complex transfer process (Table 7.6) (Ishikawa S. et al., 1998b).

7.6.5. Characteristics of different antibodies

Sequential (circulating thin aqueous layer immune complex transfer enzyme) immunoassay V-III (Fig. 7.6) was evaluated using two more different antibody IgGs (antibody IgGs to HIV-1 reverse transcriptase (RT) and gp41 antigens) in comparison with antibody IgG to HIV-1 p17 antigen described above (Tables 7.6–7.8) (Ishikawa S. et al., 1998b). The first and second solid phases used were polystyrene beads of 6.35 mm diameter coated with affinity-purified (anti-2,4-dinitrophenyl group) IgG and (anti-human IgG γ-chain) IgG, respectively (one bead per assay). The amounts of 2,4-dinitrophenyl-HIV-1 antigens used were those giving the maximal specific bindings. HIV-1 antigen-β-D-galactosidase conjugates were used at high concentrations (100–200 fmol/26 μL).

For formation of the immune complex containing antibody IgG to HIV-1 p17 antigen, the first solid phase coated with 800 fmol of 2,4-dinitrophenyl-maltose binding protein-HIV-1 p17 fusion protein in a total volume of 15 μL was incubated with 10 μL of serum samples in a total volume of 16 μL for 5 min, and the incubation was continued for 10 min after addition of recombinant HIV-1 p17-β-D-galactosidase conjugate (200 fmol in 10 μL) (Table 7.6).

For formation of the immune complex containing antibody IgG to HIV-1 gp41 antigen, the first solid phase coated with 200 fmol of 2,4-dinitrophenyl-bovine serum albumin synthetic HIV-1 gp41 peptide conjugate in a total volume of 20 μL was incubated with 10 μL of serum samples in a total volume of 21 μL for 5 min, and the incubation was continued for 10 min after addition of synthetic HIV-1 gp41 peptide-β-D-galactosidase conjugate (100 fmol/5 μL) (Table 7.7).

For formation of the immune complex containing antibody IgG to HIV-1 reverse transcriptase (RT) antigen, the first solid phase coated with 400 fmol of 2,4-dinitrophenyl-bovine serum albumin-recombinant HIV-1 RT conjugate in a total volume of 20 μL was incubated with 10 μL of serum samples in a total volume of 21 μL for 5 min, and the incubation was continued for 10 min after ad-

TABLE 7.6

Effects of immune complex transfer on signals (fluorescence intensities of bound β-D-galactosidase activity) in the absence and presence of antibodies to HIV-1 p17 antigen in immune complex transfer enzyme immunoassays V (Fig. 5.5) and V-III (Fig. 7.6)

| Immune complex transfer enzyme immuno-assay | Total volume for immuno-reaction (μL) | Incubation time for | | | | transfer of the immune complex | β-D-galacto-sidase assay | Signal for rp17-β-D-galacto-sidase conjugate used | Signal in the absence of antibodies to p17 antigen | | Signal in the presence of antibodies to p17 antigen | |
		formation of the immune complex	trapping of the immune complex	reaction with antibody IgG to p17	reaction with rp17-β-D-galacto-sidase conjugate (min)				before transfer of the immune complex	after transfer of the immune complex	before transfer of the immune complex	after transfer of the immune complex
V	150	30	60	–	–	60	1,200	1.98×10^7 (9.52×10^4) (2.08×10^7)	208 (1.0) (219)	0.95 – (1.0)	10,387 – (2.0)	5,217 – (1.0)
V-III	16–70	–	–	5	10	30	1,200	3.97×10^7 (4.32×10^4) (3.61×10^7)	918 (1.0) (835)	1.1 – (1.0)	28,440 – (1.9)	15,260 – (1.0)

Serum from an HIV-1 seropositive subject (asymptomatic carrier) was diluted 2×10^4-fold with serum from an HIV-1 seronegative subject, and 10 μL of the diluted serum was used. Immunoassay V was performed using polystyrene beads of 3.2 mm diameter as described in Table 6.3. Immunoassay V-III was performed essentially in the same way as immunoassay V-II described in Table 7.4, except that the immune complex was transferred as follows. After incubation with serum samples and recombinant HIV-1 p17 (rp17)-β-D-galactosidase conjugate, the polystyrene bead of 6.35 mm diameter was incubated with 35 μL of ϵ N-dinitrophenyl-L-lysine for 15 min (first eluate) and, after removal of the first eluate, with another 35 μL of ϵ N-2,4-dinitrophenyl-L-lysine for 1 min (second eluate). The first and second eluates were incubated with a polystyrene test tube (12 × 75 mm) coated with affinity-purified (anti-human IgG γ-chain) IgG for 15 min. The signals shown (fluorescence intensities of bound β-D-galactosidase activity) are expressed as those assayed for 20 h. The fluorescence intensity of 1×10^{-10} mol/L 4-methylumbelliferone was 1. Values in parentheses are ratios of signals to those for β-D-galactosidase activity bound to the first and second solid phases before and after transfer of the immune complex (Ishikawa S. et al., 1998b).

TABLE 7.7

Effects of immune complex transfer on signals in the absence and presence of antibodies to HIV-1 gp41 antigen in immune complex transfer enzyme immunoassays V (Fig. 5.5) and V-III (Fig. 7.6)

Immune complex transfer enzyme immunoassay	Total volume for immuno-reaction (μL)	Incubation time for					β-D-galacto-sidase assay	Signal for gp41-β-D-galacto-sidase conjugate used	Signal in the absence of antibodies to gp41		Signal in the presence of antibodies to gp41	
		formation of the immune complex	trapping of the immune complex	reaction with antibody IgG to gp41	reaction with gp41-β-D-galacto-sidase conjugate (min)	transfer of the immune complex			before transfer of the immune complex	after transfer of the immune complex	before transfer of the immune complex	after transfer of the immune complex
V	150	30	60	–	–	60	1,200	1.91×10^7 (4.03×10^4) (8.30×10^6)	474 (1.0) (206)	2.3 – (1.0)	15,540 – (2.6)	6,000 – (1.0)
V-III	21–70	–	–	5	10	30	1,200	1.91×10^7 (6.37×10^3) (4.06×10^6)	3,000 (1.0) (638)	4.7 – (1.0)	61,260 – (5.8)	10,596 – (1.0)

Serum from an HIV-1 seropositive subject (asymptomatic carrier) was diluted 2×10^2-fold with serum from an HIV-1 seronegative subject, and 10 μL of the diluted serum was used. Immunoassay V was performed using polystyrene beads of 3.2 mm diameter as described in Table 6.3, except that 2,4-dinitrophenyl-bovine serum albumin-synthetic HIV-1 gp41 peptide conjugate and synthetic HIV-1 gp41 peptide-β-D-galactosidase conjugate were substituted for the two HIV-1 p17 conjugates and that serum samples were incubated with the two conjugates in the presence of 10 μL nonspecific rabbit serum. Immunoassay V-III was performed essentially in the same way as immunoassay V-III described in Table 7.6, except for the following conditions. Individual polystyrene beads of 6.35 mm diameter coated successively with affinity-purified (anti-2,4-dinitrophenyl group) IgG and 2,4-dinitrophenyl-bovine serum albumin-synthetic HIV-1 gp41 peptide conjugate (200 fmol) were incubated with 10 μL of serum samples in the presence of 2.5 μL nonspecific rabbit serum in a total volume of 21 μL for 5 min, and the incubation was continued for 10 min after addition of 100 fmol of synthetic HIV-1 gp41 peptide-β-D-galactosidase conjugate in a volume of 5 μL. The signals shown (fluorescence intensities of bound β-D-galactosidase activity) are expressed as those assayed for 20 h. The fluorescence intensity of 1×10^{-10} mol/L 4-methylumbelliferone was 1. Values in parentheses are ratios of signals to those for β-D-galactosidase activity bound to the first and second solid phases before and after transfer of the immune complex (Ishikawa S. et al., 1998b).

dition of recombinant HIV-1 RT conjugate (100 fmol/5 μL) (Table 7.8).

The immune complexes consisting of antibody IgGs to HIV-1 antigens and the two conjugates were eluted from the first solid phase with 35 μL volumes of ϵN-2,4-dinitrophenyl-L-lysine first for 15 min (first eluate) and, after removing the first eluate, then for 1 min (second eluate). The first and second eluates were incubated in a polystyrene test tube (12 × 75 mm) coated with affinity-purified (anti-human IgG γ-chain) IgG (second solid phase) for 15 min as described above.

The β-D-galactosidase activities bound to the first solid phases for antibody IgGs to HIV-1 p17, gp41 and RT antigens were 2.7-, 3.9- and 0.55-fold, respectively, as high as those by simultaneous immune complex transfer enzyme immunoassays V, in which serum samples (10 μL) were incubated simultaneously with the two conjugates in a total volume of 150 μL for 0.5 h for antibody IgGs to p17 and gp41 antigens and for 4 h for antibody IgG to RT and subsequently for 1 h with two colored polystyrene beads of 3.2 mm diameter coated with affinity-purified (anti-2,4-dinitrophenyl group) IgG (Tables 7.6–7.8).

The amount of β-D-galactosidase activity bound to the second solid phase for antibody IgG to HIV-1 gp41 antigen after the transfer was 5.8-fold lower than that bound to the first solid phase before the transfer, although the amounts for antibody IgGs to HIV-1 p17 and RT antigens were only 1.9- and 1.6-fold, respectively, lower (Tables 7.6–7.8). The immune complex with the synthetic HIV-1 gp41 peptide conjugates might have been dissociated to a greater extent than those with recombinant p17 and RT conjugates. This possibility was supported by the fact that β-D-galactosidase activity bound to the first solid phase for antibody IgG to HIV-1 gp41 antigen decreased more rapidly (48 and 67% within 30 and 60 min, respectively) when it was allowed to stand in a neutral buffer than those for antibody IgGs to HIV-1 p17 and RT antigens (4–15 and 6–24% within 30 and 60 min, respectively) (Table 6.8). Notably, β-D-galactosidase activity bound to a polystyrene bead of 6.35 mm

TABLE 7.8

Effects of immune complex transfer on signals in the absence and presence of antibodies to HIV-1 reverse transcriptase (RT) antigen in immune complex transfer enzyme immunoassays V (Fig. 5.5) and V-III (Fig. 7.6)

Immune complex transfer enzyme immunoassay	Total volume for immunoreaction (μL)	Incubation time for (min)					β-galactosidase assay	Signal of rRT-β-D-galactosidase conjugate used	Signal in the absence of antibodies to RT		Signal in the presence of antibodies to RT	
		formation of the immune complex	trapping of the immune complex	reaction with antibody IgG to RT	reaction with rRT-β-D-galactosidase conjugate	transfer of the immune complex			before transfer of the immune complex	after transfer of the immune complex	before transfer of the immune complex	after transfer of the immune complex
V	150	240	60	–	–	60	1,200	1.87×10^7 (3.05×10^4) (2.92×10^6)	612 (1.0) (96)	3.3 (1.0)	28,080 – (1.7)	14,946 – (1.0)
V-III	21–70	–	–	5	10	30	1,200	1.87×10^7 (1.41×10^4) (1.56×10^7)	1,326 (1.0) (1,105)	1.2 (1.0)	15,330 (1.6)	9,408 (1.0)

Serum from an HIV-1 seropositive subject (asymptomatic carrier) was diluted 2×10^3-fold with serum from an HIV-1 seronegative subject, and 10 μL of the diluted serum was used. Immunoassay V was performed using polystyrene beads of 3.2 mm diameter as described in Table 6.3 except for the following conditions. 2,4-dinitrophenyl-bovine serum albumin-recombinant HIV-1 reverse transcriptase (rRT) conjugate and rRT-β-D-galactosidase conjugate were substituted for the two HIV-1 p17 conjugates, and serum samples were incubated with the two conjugates in the presence of 10 μL nonspecific rabbit serum for 4 h. Immunoassay V-III was performed essentially in the same way as immunoassay V-III described in Table 7.6 except for the following conditions. Individual polystyrene beads of 6.35 mm diameter coated successively with affinity-purified (anti-2,4-dinitrophenyl group) IgG and 2,4-dinitrophenyl-bovine serum albumin-recombinant HIV-1 reverse transcriptase (rRT) conjugate (400 fmol) were incubated with 10 μL of serum samples in the presence of 2.5 μL nonspecific rabbit serum in a total volume of 21 μL for 5 min, and the incubation was continued for 10 min after addition of rRT-β-D-galactosidase conjugate (100 fmol) in a volume of 5 μL. The signals shown (fluorescence intensities of bound β-D-galactosidase activity) are expressed as those assayed for 20 h. The fluorescence intensity of 1×10^{-10} mol/L 4-methylumbelliferone was 1. Values in parentheses are ratios of signals to those for β-D-galactosidase activity bound to the first and second solid phase before and after transfer of the immune complex (Ishikawa S. et al., 1998b).

diameter for antibody IgG to HIV-1 gp41 antigen decreased to a greater extent (67% within 60 min) than that bound to polystyrene beads of 3.2 mm diameter (35% within 60 min), suggesting that the immune complex formed with the β-D-galactosidase conjugate at a high concentration of 100 fmol/26 μL was dissociated to a greater extent than that formed with the same conjugate at a low concentration of 100 fmol/150 μL.

The β-D-galactosidase activities bound to the second solid phase for antibody IgGs to HIV-1 p17, gp41 and RT antigens were 2.9, 1.8 and 0.63 times, respectively, as high as those obtained by the simultaneous immune complex transfer enzyme immunoassay V, in which the immune complexes containing antibody IgGs to HIV-1 were transferred from the two colored polystyrene beads (3.2 mm in diameter) described above to two white polystyrene beads (3.2 mm in diameter) coated with affinity-purified (anti-human IgG γ-chain) IgG by incubating the four polystyrene beads in 150 μL of ϵN-2,4-dinitrophenyl-L-lysine for 1 h. The nonspecific signals were not very different in immunoassays V and V-III. Thus, the sensitivities to antibody IgGs to HIV-1 p17 and gp41 antigens achieved by the sequential (circulating thin aqueous layer immune complex transfer enzyme) immunoassay V-III in a much shorter time (45 min for the immunoreactions) were higher than those obtained by the simultaneous immune complex transfer enzyme immunoassay V involving 150–360 min for immunoreactions, but the sensitivity to antibody IgG to RT by the sequential immunoassay V-III was lower. This may be explained at least partly by a possible difference in steric hindrance, as described in Chapter 4.

7.7. Circulating thin aqueous layer immunoassay for antigens

7.7.1. Immunoassay processes

The circulating thin aqueous layer immune complex transfer enzyme immunoassay X (Fig. 5.10) was evaluated in three different ways (simultaneous, sequential and semi-sequential immunoassays X-I, X-II and X-III) (Figs. 4.15 and 5.10) using HIV-1 p24 antigen (Ishikawa S. et al., 1998c).

In simultaneous immunoassay X-I, an aliquot (2.5 μL) of non-specific rabbit serum was mixed successively with 5 fmol of mon-oclonal mouse anti-p24 Fab$'$-β-D-galactosidase conjugate and 100 fmol of 2,4-dinitrophenyl-biotinyl-bovine serum albumin-affinity-purified rabbit anti-p24 Fab$'$ conjugate in a total volume of 7 μL and was incubated with 10 μL of serum from an HIV-1 seronegative subject and recombinant p24 (rp24) antigen in a volume of 2 μL in a styrol test tube (13.3 $\times$ 54 mm and 2.1 g) to allow formation of an immune complex consisting of the three components. Subsequently, the reaction mixture (19 μL) was incubated with a polystyrene bead of 6.35 mm diameter coated with affinity-purified (anti-2,4-dinitrophenyl group) IgG (first solid phase) to trap the immune complex. Incubation with the first solid phase was performed by shaking the styrol test tube in a box (16 $\times$ 16 mm $\times$ 20 mm depth). The shaking rate and width were 180/min and 25 mm, respectively. As a result, the first solid phase was rotated randomly in the styrol test tube, and a small drop (19 μL) of the reaction mixture became in even contact with all parts of the first solid phase surface dur-ing incubation continuously mixing the thin aqueous layer covering the first solid phase surface with the rest of the reaction mixture, although only a small part was in contact at any given time. After washing, the first solid phase was incubated with 35 μL of ϵN-2,4-dinitrophenyl-L-lysine in a styrol test tube (13.3 $\times$ 54 mm and 2.1 g) (first eluate) and, after removal of the first eluate, with another 35 μL of ϵN-2,4-dinitrophenyl-L-lysine (second eluate) as described above to elute the immune complex. The first and second eluates were put into a polystyrene test tube (12 $\times$ 75 mm) coated with streptavidin (second solid phase), which was rotated slowly so that all parts of its surface became in even contact with the combined eluate as described above.

In sequential immunoassay X-II, a polystyrene bead of 6.35 mm diameter coated successively with affinity-purified (anti-2,4-

dinitrophenyl group) IgG and 2,4-dinitrophenyl-biotinyl-bovine serum albumin-affinity-purified rabbit anti-p24 Fab′ conjugate (first solid phase) was incubated sequentially with rp24 antigen in the presence of 2.5 μL of nonspecific rabbit serum and 10 μL of serum from an HIV-1 seronegative subject in a total volume of 20 μL and with 5 fmol of monoclonal mouse anti-p24 Fab′-β-D-galactosidase conjugate in a volume of 5 μL with shaking as described above. The immune complex was transferred as described above.

In semi-sequential immunoassay X-III, rp24 antigen was incubated with 5 fmol of monoclonal mouse anti-p24 Fab′-β-D-galactosidase conjugate in the presence of 2.5 μL of nonspecific rabbit serum and 10 μL of human serum from an HIV-1 seronegative subject in a total volume of 19 μL and subsequently with a polystyrene bead of 6.35 mm diameter coated successively with affinity-purified (anti-2,4-dinitrophenyl group) IgG and 2,4-dinitrophenyl-biotinyl-bovine serum albumin-affinity-purified rabbit anti-p24 Fab′ conjugate (first solid phase) with shaking as described above. The immune complex was transferred as described above.

7.7.2. Time courses of immunoreactions

The time courses of the immunoreactions in simultaneous, sequential and semi-sequential immunoassays X-I, X-II and X-III are described below.

In simultaneous immunoassay X-I, the formation of the immune complex was almost complete within 15 min, and trapping of the immune complex on the first solid phase was almost complete within 3 min.

In sequential and semi-sequential immunoassays X-II and X-III, β-D-galactosidase activities bound to the first solid phase were maximal when the first solid phases were coated with 200 and 400 fmol, respectively, of 2,4-dinitrophenyl-biotinyl-bovine serum albumin-affinity-purified rabbit anti-p24 Fab′ conjugate.

TABLE 7.9

Signals (fluorescence intensities of β-D-galactosidase activity) by immune complex transfer enzyme immunoassays X, X-I (Fig. 5.10), X-II and X-III of HIV-1 p24 antigen

Immune complex transfer enzyme immunoassay	Total volume for immunoreaction	Incubation time for		reaction with rp24	reaction with anti-p24 Fab'-β-D-galactosidase conjugate	formation of the immune complex of rp24 and anti-p24 Fab'-β-D-galactosidase conjugate	trapping of the immune complex of rp24 and anti-p24 Fab'-β-D-galactosidase conjugate	transferring of the immune complex	assay of β-D-galactosidase	Signal rp24 (amol)		Serum samples from HIV-1 seronegative subjects
		formation of the immune complex of the three components	trapping of the immune complex of the three components			(min)				0	100	
	(μL)											
X	150	240	60	–	–	–	–	60	60	0.0	144	–
X-I	19–70	15	5	–	–	–	–	30	60	0.0	353	0.0–0.59
X-II	20–70	–	–	5	20	–	–	30	60	0.0	126	–
X-III	19–70	–	–	–	–	10	20	30	60	0.0	424	0.0–0.27

Immunoassay X was performed using polystyrene beads of 3.2 mm diameter (two beads per tube) as described in Table 6.6. The procedures for formation of the immune complex in immunoassays X-I, X-II and X-III are shown schematically in Fig. 4.15. In immunoassay X-I, HIV-1 p24 antigen in 10 μL serum was incubated simultaneously with 5 fmol of monoclonal mouse anti-p24 Fab'-β-D-galactosidase conjugate and 100 fmol of 2,4-dinitrophenyl-biotinyl-bovine serum albumin-affinity-purified rabbit anti-p24 Fab' conjugate in the presence of 2.5 μL nonspecific rabbit serum in a total volume of 19 μL for 15 min and then with a polystyrene bead of 6.35 mm diameter coated with affinity-purified (anti-2,4-dinitrophenyl group) IgG (first solid phase) for 5 min. In immunoassay X-II, the first solid phase coated with 200 fmol of the 2,4-dinitrophenyl-conjugate was incubate with HIV-1 p24 antigen in 10 μL serum in the presence of 2.5 μL nonspecific rabbit serum in a total volume of 20 μL for 5 min and then with 5 fmol of the β-D-galactosidase conjugate in 5 μL for 20 min. In immunoassay X-III, HIV-1 p24 antigen in 10 μL serum was incubated with 5 fmol of the β-D-galactosidase conjugate in the presence of 2.5 μL nonspecific rabbit serum in a total volume of 20 μL for 10 min and then with the first solid phase coated with 400 fmol of the 2,4-dinitrophenyl-conjugate for 20 min. The immune complex of the three components was transferred to a polystyrene bead coated successively with biotinyl-bovine serum albumin and streptavidin as described in Table 7.6. The fluorescence intensity of 1×10^{-10} mol/L 4-methylumbelliferone was 1. The volumes of nonspecific rabbit serum used were 10 μL in the immunoassay X and 2.5 μL in the other immunoassays. See text for immunoassays X, X-I (simultaneous), X-II (sequential) and X-III (semi-sequential) (Ishikawa S. et al., 1998c).

In sequential immunoassay X-II, the binding of β-D-galactosidase activity to the first solid phase was almost maximal within 30 min after addition of monoclonal mouse anti-p24 Fab'-β-D-galactosidase conjugate, when the first solid phase was incubated with rp24 antigen for 5 min followed by addition of the conjugate.

In semi-sequential immunoassay X-III, formation of the immune complex of rp24 antigen and monoclonal mouse anti-p24 Fab'-β-D-galactosidase conjugate was almost complete within 10–15 min, and the binding of the immune complex to the first solid phase continued to increase for 30 min, possibly reaching a maximum within 50–60 min.

A total of 70–75% of the immune complex was eluted from the first solid phase with ϵN-2,4-dinitrophenyl-L-lysine within 10–15 min, and its transfer to the second solid phase was almost complete within 15 min.

7.7.3. Sensitivity

On the basis of the above results, simultaneous, sequential and semi-sequential immunoassays X-I, X-II and X-III were performed as follows (Table 7.9) (Ishikawa S. et al., 1998c). In simultaneous immunoassay X-I, rp24 antigen was incubated with the two conjugates for 15 min and subsequently with the first solid phase for 5 min, and the immune complex was eluted for 15 min and was transferred for 15 min. In sequential immunoassay X-II, the first solid phase was incubated with rp24 antigen for 5 min and subsequently with monoclonal mouse anti-p24 Fab'-β-D-galactosidase conjugate for 20 min, and the immune complex was transferred as described above. In semi-sequential immunoassay X-III, rp24 antigen was incubated with monoclonal mouse anti-p24 Fab'-β-D-galactosidase conjugate for 10 min and subsequently with the first solid phase for 20 min, and the immune complex was transferred as described above.

In simultaneous immunoassay X-I, the detection limit of rp24 antigen was 0.1 amol/assay on a 1-h assay of bound β-D-

TABLE 7.10

Effects of immune complex transfer on signals (fluorescence intensities of bound β-D-galactosidase activity) in the absence and presence of HIV-1 p24 antigen in immune complex transfer enzyme immunoassays X (Fig. 5.10) and X-III for HIV-1 p24 antigen

Immune complex transfer enzyme immunoassay	Total volume of immuno-reaction (μL)	Incubation time for (min)						Signal for anti-p24 Fab'-β-D-galactosidase conjugate used	Signal in the absence of p24 antigen		Signal in the presence of p24 antigen (100 amol)	
		formation of the immune complex of the three components	trapping of the immune complex of the three components	formation of the immune complex of rp24 and anti-p24 Fab'-β-D-galactosidase conjugate	trapping of the immune complex of rp24 and anti-p24 Fab'-β-D-galactosidase conjugate	transfer of the immune complex	assay of β-D-galactosidase		before transfer of the immune complex	after transfer of the immune complex	before transfer of the immune complex	after transfer of the immune complex
X	150	180	60	–	–	60	1,200	1.28×10^6 (2.13×10^4) (5.57×10^6)	60 (1.0) (261)	0.23 – (1.0)	7,160 – (2.5)	2,880 – (1.0)
X-III	19–70	–	–	10	20	30	1,200	1.28×10^6 (5.33×10^3) (3.20×10^6)	240 (1.0) (600)	0.40 – (1.0)	17,760 – (1.9)	9,288 – (1.0)

Immunoassay X was performed using polystyrene beads of 3.2 mm diameter (two beads per tube) as described in Table 6.6. Immunoassay X-III was performed using polystyrene beads of 6.35 mm diameter (one bead per tube) as described in Table 7.9. The signals shown (fluorescence intensities of bound β-D-galactosidase activity) are expressed as those assayed for 20 h. The fluorescence intensity of 1×10^{-10} mol/L 4-methylumbelliferone was 1. Values in parentheses are ratios of signals to those for β-D-galactosidase activity bound to the first and second solid phases (Ishikawa S. et al., 1998b).

galactosidase activity and was lowered to 10 zmol/assay by a 20-h assay of bound β-D-galactosidase activity.

In sequential immunoassay X-II, the detection limit of rp24 antigen was 0.2 amol/assay on a 1-h assay of bound β-D-galactosidase activity.

In semi-sequential immunoassay X-III, β-D-galactosidase activity bound to the first solid phase in the absence of p24 antigen was 5330-fold lower than that of the monoclonal mouse anti-p24 Fab'-β-D-galactosidase conjugate used, and β-D-galactosidase activity bound to the second solid phase in the absence of p24 antigen was 600-fold lower than that bound to the first solid phase. In contrast, β-D-galactosidase activity bound to the second solid phase in the presence of p24 antigen was only 1.9-fold lower than that bound to the first solid phase. The amounts of the immune complex bound to the first and second solid phases were 2.5- to 3.2-fold larger than those by immunoassay X, in which the immune complex was formed for 3–4 h, trapped on the first solid phase (two polystyrene beads of 3.2 mm diameter) for 1 h and transferred to the second solid phase (two polystyrene beads of 3.2 mm diameter) for 1 h in a total volume of 150 μL as described in Chapter 6, while β-D-galactosidase activities bound to the second solid phases in the absence of the antigen were similar in both immunoassays X and X-III (Table 7.10) (Ishikawa S. et al., 1998c). Thus, the detection limit of p24 antigen was lowered 300-fold on transfer of the immune complex and was 0.1 amol/assay by a 1-h assay of bound β-D-galactosidase activity. This was further lowered to 3 zmol/assay by a 20-h assay of bound β-D-galactosidase activity.

However, the highest bound β-D-galactosidase activity in the presence of serum samples from HIV-1 seronegative subjects was only slightly lower than that corresponding to 0.2 amol/assay of rp24 antigen in simultaneous immunoassay X-I and 0.1 amol/assay of rp24 antigen in semi-sequential immunoassay X-III. Namely, the sensitivities of immunoassays X-I and X-III were limited by an unknown reaction(s) of the conjugate(s) with serum samples from HIV-1 seronegative subjects.

CHAPTER 8

Protocol of immune complex transfer enzyme immunoassay

Reproducible methods are described below. However, unexpected results may be observed in some cases. Favorable results may be obtained by changing conditions, such as the concentration of reagents, pH, time, temperature etc.

8.1. Choice of enzymes as labels

The enzymes used as labels must be stable and detectable with sufficiently high sensitivities. For effective immune complex transfer, zeptomole quantities of label enzymes have to be detected not only easily but also rapidly as described in Chapter 6 (Tables 6.3, 6.4 and 6.6). In addition, label enzymes should be chosen to minimize not only the nonspecific binding of enzyme conjugates but also serum interference, which varies depending on the enzymes used as labels (Figs. 4.9 and 4.17).

8.2. Choice of enzyme-labeling methods

Enzyme-labeled antibodies should provide not only sufficiently high specific bindings but also sufficiently low nonspecific bindings. This is possible with Fab′-enzyme conjugates prepared by hinge methods, in which thiol groups in the hinge of Fab′ are allowed to selectively react with maleimide groups introduced into enzyme molecules as described in Chapters 4, 11 and 13 (Table 4.2 and Figs. 4.2, 4.3, 4.7, 11.3 and 11.9).

Enzyme-labeled antigens may be prepared by various methods. Recommended are maleimide methods, in which the reaction between maleimide and thiol groups is used for conjugation as described in Chapters 15 and 16, since the maleimide and thiol groups are fairly stable under conditions for enzyme-labeling and highly reactive with each other but not with most proteins. For preparation of useful conjugates, it is important to control the number of maleimide and thiol groups introduced into antigen and enzyme molecules to be conjugated carefully in order to reduce the formation of heteropolymers and homopolymers.

8.3. Use of inactive forms of enzyme labels

Serum samples contain antibodies to various proteins of microorganisms, plants and animals. An example is antibody IgG to β-D-galactosidase from *E. coli* (Fig. 6.2). This causes high nonspecific signals in immune complex transfer enzyme immunoassay V for antibodies (Fig. 5.5) using β-D-galactosidase as a label as described in Chapter 6. The adverse effect of antibodies to β-D-galactosidase from *E. coli* can be reduced using inactive β-D-galactosidase (Tables 6.9, 6.10 and Figs. 6.4, 6.5).

Inactive β-D-galactosidase also reduces the nonspecific bindings of antigen- and antibody-β-D-galactosidase conjugates in some cases (Table 4.4 and Fig. 4.5).

8.4. Preparation of 2,4-dinitrophenyl-bovine serum albumin for immunization

2,4-dinitrophenyl-bovine serum albumin is used for obtaining (anti-2,4-dinitrophenyl group) IgG by immunization.

1. Prepare 20 mg (0.3 μmol) of bovine serum albumin [mol wt = 66,200 (Peters, 1975); E_{280} = 0.63 g^{-1} L cm^{-1} (Webster, 1970)] in 0.8 mL of 0.1 mol/L sodium carbonate buffer, pH 9.5, containing 0.1 mol/L NaCl.

2. Incubate the albumin solution with 0.2 mL of 0.35 mol/L 2,4-dinitrobenzene sulfonic acid in deionized water and 25 μL of 1 mol/L NaOH at 37°C overnight. The reaction mixture must be kept at pH 9.5 during incubation.

3. Subject the incubated mixture to gel filtration by centrifugation (Penefsky, 1979) using a column (5–10 mL) of Sephadex G-50 fine (Amersham Pharmacia Biotech, Uppsala, Sweden) in 0.1 mol/L sodium phosphate buffer, pH 7.0, containing 0.1 mol/L NaCl.

4. Measure the content of 2,4-dinitrophenyl groups [E_{360} = 17,400 mol^{-1} L cm^{-1} and E_{360}/E_{280} = 1/0.32 (Eisen et al., 1954)] in bovine serum albumin, and calculate the average number of 2,4-dinitrophenyl groups introduced per bovine serum albumin molecule which is 30–35.

8.5. Preparation of biotinyl- and 2,4-dinitrophenyl-bovine serum albumin for immunoassays

Biotinyl-bovine serum albumin is used for preparation of streptavidin-coated solid phases. Solid phases are coated first with biotinyl-bovine serum albumin by physical adsorption and subsequently allowed to react with streptavidin for use in immune complex transfer enzyme immunoassays X for antigens (Fig. 5.10).

2,4-dinitrophenyl-bovine serum albumin is used for preparations of 2,4-dinitrophenyl-bovine serum albumin-antigen conjugates, 2,4-dinitrophenyl-bovine serum albumin-antibody Fab' conjugates and affinity-purified (anti-2,4-dinitrophenyl group) IgG.

Biotinyl-bovine serum albumin is prepared by reaction of mercaptoacetyl-bovine serum albumin with 6-maleimidohexanoyl-biocytin (Fig. 8.1). 2,4-dinitrophenyl-bovine serum albumin is prepared by substitution of ϵN-2,4-dinitrophenyl-L-lysine for biocytin (Fig. 8.1).

1. Prepare 10 mg of bovine serum albumin [mol wt = 66,200 (Peters, 1975); $E_{280} = 0.63$ g^{-1} L cm^{-1} (Webster, 1970)] in 0.9 mL of 0.1 mol/L sodium phosphate buffer, pH 7.0.

2. Incubate the albumin solution with 0.1 mL of 22 mmol/L N-succinimidyl-S-acetylmercaptoacetate (mol wt 231) (Pierce, Rockford, IL) in N,N-dimethylformamide at 30°C for 30 min.

3. Incubate the mixture with 0.1 mL of 1 mol/L Tris-HCl buffer, pH 7.0, and 0.1 mL of 0.1 mol/L EDTA at 30°C for 10 min.

4. Incubate the mixture with 0.15 mL of 1 mol/L hydroxylamine-HCl, pH 7.0, at 30°C for 10 min to release free thiol groups from S-acetyl groups.

5. Incubate the mixture at 30°C for 60 min with 0.25 mL of 6-maleimidohexanoyl-biocytin solution, prepared by incubating 0.2 mL of 50 mmol/L biocytin (mol wt 372.5) with 0.05 mL of 100 mmol/L N-succinimidyl-6-maleimidohexanoate (mol wt 308.3) in N,N-dimethylformamide at 30°C for 60 min.

6. Subject the incubated mixture to gel filtration by centrifugation (Penefsky, 1979) using a column (10 mL) of Sephadex G-50 fine (Amersham Pharmacia Biotech, Uppsala, Sweden) in 0.1 mol/L sodium phosphate buffer, pH 7.0.

    It is difficult to estimate the number of biocytin residues introduced per bovine serum albumin molecule. Therefore, assess it from the number of 2,4-dinitrophenyl groups introduced in the same way as described below.

7. Introduce 2,4-dinitrophenyl groups into bovine serum albumin using ϵN-2,4-dinitrophenyl-L-lysine in place of biocytin (Fig. 8.1). The average number of 2,4-dinitrophenyl groups [$E_{360} = 17,400$ mol^{-1} L cm^{-1} and $E_{360}/E_{280} = 1/0.32$ (Eisen et al., 1954)] introduced per bovine serum albumin molecule was approximately 6. This must be similar to the number of biocytin residues introduced per bovine serum albumin molecule as described above.

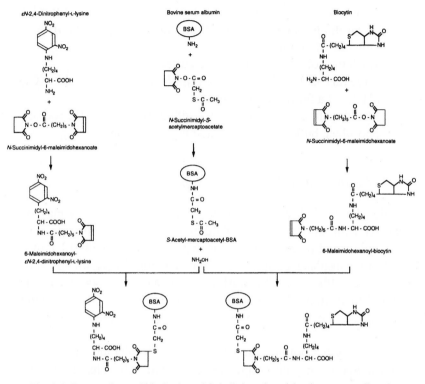

Fig. 8.1. Preparations of biotinyl- and 2,4-dinitrophenyl-bovine serum albumin.

8.6. Affinity-purification of (anti-2,4-dinitrophenyl group) IgG

1. Prepare 2,4-dinitrophenyl-bovine serum albumin by coupling ϵN-2,4-dinitrophenyl-L-lysine to bovine serum albumin as described above.

2. Couple 10 mg of the preparation to 1 g of CNBr-activated Sepharose 4B (3.5 mL in wet volume) following the instructions of the manufacturer.

3. Prepare 400 mg of (anti-2,4-dinitrophenyl group) IgG in 10 mL of 0.1 mol/L sodium phosphate buffer, pH 7.0.

4. Apply the IgG solution to a column (1.2 × 2.7 cm, 3.0 mL) of 2,4-dinitrophenyl-bovine serum albumin-Sepharose 4B at a flow rate of 10 mL/h.
5. Wash the column with the same buffer.
6. Elute (anti-2,4-dinitrophenyl group) IgG with 3.2 mmol/L HCl, pH 2.5 at a flow rate of 80 mL/h.
7. Mix the eluate (45 mg/15 mL) with 2 mL of 1 mol/L sodium phosphate buffer, pH 7.0, containing 1 g/L NaN$_3$.

8.7. Coating of solid phases with proteins

Solid phases such as polystyrene beads and microplates may be coated with antigens and antibodies by physical adsorption. For example, solid phases may be incubated overnight with 0.1 mol/L sodium phosphate buffer, pH 7.0, containing 10 μg/mL of antigens and antibodies. After washing, the coated solid phases may be stored in 10 mmol/L sodium phosphate buffer, pH 7.0, containing 0.1 mol/L NaCl, 0.1% bovine serum albumin and 0.1% NaN$_3$ at 4°C.

In many but not all cases, the nonspecific bindings of antigen- and antibody-enzyme conjugates to coated solid phases and the degrees of serum interference decrease as days, weeks or months pass after coating solid phases with antigens and antibodies and vary depending on the conditions used (Chapter 4).

8.8. Preparations of 2,4-dinitrophenyl-(biotinyl)-antigens and antibodies and antigen- and antibody-enzyme conjugates

Antigens and antibodies may be directly 2,4-dinitrophenylated and biotinylated as described above or conjugated with 2,4-dinitrophenyl-(biotinyl)-bovine serum albumin as described in Chapters 11–16. The average number of 2,4-dinitrophenyl groups and biocytin residues introduced per antigen, antibody or bovine serum albumin molecule should be 3–5.

Antigens and antibodies may be conjugated with enzymes as described in Chapters 11–16.

Alternatively, 2,4-dinitrophenyl-(bovine serum albumin-)avidin conjugate and avidin-enzyme conjugate prepared as described in Chapter 14 may be allowed to react with biotinyl-antigens and antibodies for use in immune complex transfer enzyme immunoassay V for antibodies and antigens, respectively (Fig. 5.5) (Kohno et al., 1990b).

Immune complex transfer enzyme immunoassays of antigens and antibodies may be slightly more sensitive with β-D-galactosidase from *E. coli* detected by fluorometry using 4-methylumbelliferyl-β-D-galactoside as substrate than with alkaline phosphatase from calf intestine detected by luminometry using a derivative of adamantyl-1,2-dioxetane phosphate as substrate (Bronstein et al., 1989) and much more sensitive than with peroxidase from horseradish detected by fluorometry using *p*-hydroxyphenylpropionic acid as a hydrogen donor. The sensitivity of the immune complex transfer enzyme immunoassay for antibody IgG to HIV-1 reverse transcriptase was 30-fold more sensitive with β-D-galactosidase from *E. coli* than with horseradish peroxidase, since the detection limits of β-D-galactosidase and peroxides are at zeptomole and attomole levels, respectively (Hashinaka et al., 1994b).

8.9. Typical protocol of immune complex transfer enzyme immunoassay V for antibody IgG

1. Prepare 0.1 mL of a mixture of serum samples and 10 mmol/L sodium phosphate buffer, pH 7.0, containing 0.1 mol/L NaCl, 1 mmol/L MgCl$_2$, 0.1% bovine serum albumin and 0.1% NaN$_3$ (buffer A).

   The serum volume for test may be increased up to 0.1 mL, although serum interference may become more serious with increase in the serum volume. In some cases, the nonspecific bindings of antigen-enzyme conjugates and the extents of serum interference are reduced at high salt concentrations such as 0.4–0.5 mol/L NaCl and/or in the presence of serum from some species of animals (Chapter 4).

Use of higher or lower pH values may be favorable for obtaining higher sensitivity, as described in Chapter 4 (Fig. 4.8).

2. Prepare 0.05 mL of buffer A containing 50 μg of inactive β-D-galactosidase (Boehringer Mannheim GmbH, Mannheim, Germany) and 100 fmol each of 2,4-dinitrophenyl-antigen and antigen-β-D-galactosidase conjugate.

Addition of serum from some species of animals significantly reduces the nonspecific signal in some cases, as described in Chapter 4 (Table 4.5).

3. Incubate the two solutions together to allow formation of an immune complex of the three components.

Under this condition, the formation of the immune complex consisting of 2,4-dinitrophenyl-bovine serum albumin-recombinant HIV-1 p17 (rp17) conjugate, rp17-β-D-galactosidase and antibody IgG to HIV-1 p17 antigen from HIV-1 asymptomatic carriers is almost complete within 30 min. However, immune complex formations with antibody IgG and IgM from subjects shortly after HIV-1 infection required longer times (Hashida et al., 1998a, c). With recombinant HIV-1 reverse transcriptase in place of HIV-1 rp17 antigen, almost 4 h is required for completion of the reaction (Hashida et al., 1998a).

The incubation time is shortened at higher temperatures and at higher concentrations of the two conjugates, but depends upon the properties of antigens and antibodies involved.

However, conjugate concentrations must not exceed the capacities of solid phases coated with affinity-purified (anti-2,4-dinitrophenyl group) IgG to trap 2,4-dinitrophenylated proteins. The trapping capacity depends on the surface areas of the solid phases, which are listed in Table 7.2. The time courses of binding of 2,4-dinitrophenyl-β-D-galactosidase to various solid phases coated with affinity-purified (anti-2,4-dinitrophenyl group) IgG and its amounts and fractions trapped are shown in Figs. 7.2, 7.5 and 8.2.

4. Incubate the incubated mixture with the first solid phase coated with 10 μg/mL of affinity-purified (anti-2,4-dinitrophenyl group) IgG with shaking.

When two polystyrene beads of 3.2 mm diameter are used as a solid phase, 1–2 h is required for complete trapping of the immune complex (Hashida et al., 1998a). However, the incubation time can be shortened by using solid phases of larger surface areas, and 10–20 min incubation may be sufficient with polystyrene beads of 6.35 mm diameter (one bead/150 μL) as described in Chapter 7 (Fig. 7.5).

The amount of the immune complex consisting of the three components trapped on the first solid phase increases with the increase in the concentration of affinity-purified (anti-2,4-dinitrophenyl group) IgG used for coating. However, the fraction of the immune complexes eluted from the first solid phase with ϵN-2,4-dinitrophenyl-L-lysine and transferred to the second solid phase decreases with the increase in its concentration used for coating, and serum interference becomes more serious (Table 8.1).

5. Wash the first solid phase with buffer A.
6. Incubate the first solid phase in 0.15 mL of buffer A containing 1–2 mmol/L ϵN-2,4-dinitrophenyl-L-lysine with shaking for 10–20 min to elute the immune complexes.

Approximately 75–85% of the immune complexes are eluted within 10–20 min, although the amounts eluted vary depending on the properties of the immune complexes.

7. Incubate the eluate with the second solid phase coated with 10 μg/mL of affinity-purified (anti-human IgG γ-chain) IgG with shaking.

When two polystyrene beads of 3.2 mm diameter are used as a solid phase, 1–2 h is required for complete transference of the immune complexes (Hashida et al., 1998a). However,

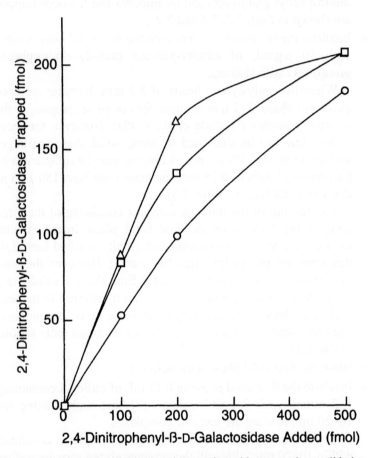

Fig. 8.2. Binding of 2,4-dinitrophenyl-β-D-galactosidase to various solid phases coated with affinity-purified (anti-2,4-dinitrophenyl group) IgG. The indicated amounts of 2,4-dinitrophenyl-β-D-galactosidase in 150 μL were incubated with polystyrene beads of 3.2 mm diameter (two beads/assay) (circles), polystyrene sticks (Fig. 7.1) (squares) and microplate wells (triangles) coated with affinity-purified (anti-2,4-dinitrophenyl group) IgG.

the incubation time can be shortened by using solid phases of larger surface area, and 10–20 min incubation may be sufficient with polystyrene beads of 6.35 mm diameter (one bead/assay) as described in Chapter 7 (Fig. 7.5).

8. Wash the second solid phase with buffer A.

9. Incubate the second solid phase with a mixture of 0.05 mL of 0.3 mmol/L 4-methylumbelliferyl-β-D-galactoside (4MUG) and 0.1 mL of buffer A containing 0.01% bovine serum albumin for 1–20 h. For preparation of 0.3 mmol/L 4MUG, mix 1 volume of 15 mmol/L 4MUG in N,N-dimethylformamide with 49 volumes of water. Stop the enzyme reaction by addition of 2.5 mL of 0.1 mol/L glycine-NaOH buffer, pH 10.3. Measure the fluorescence intensity using 360 nm for excitation and 450 nm for emission analysis by adjusting the fluorescence intensity of 10^{-8} mol/L 4-methylumbelliferone in 0.1 mol/L glycine-NaOH buffer, pH 10.3 to 100.

As described in Chapters 6 and 7, a 1-h assay of bound β-D-galactosidase activity provides much higher sensitivities of the immune complex transfer enzyme immunoassays than that of conventional immunoassays, but a 5–20-h assay is required for the highest sensitivity.

8.10. Typical protocols of immune complex transfer enzyme immunoassays IX and X for antigens

1. Prepare 0.1 mL of a mixture of serum samples and 10 mmol/L sodium phosphate buffer, pH 7.0, containing 0.1 mol/L NaCl, 1 mmol/L $MgCl_2$, 0.1% bovine serum albumin and 0.1% NaN_3 (buffer A).

The serum volume for tests may be increased up to 0.1 mL, although this may result in more serious serum interference. Use of a higher or lower pH value may increase sensitivity as described in Chapter 4.

TABLE 8.1

Effect of the concentration of affinity-purified (anti-2,4-dinitrophenyl group) IgG for coating the first solid phase in immune complex transfer enzyme immunoassay X (Fig. 5.10) of HIV-1 p24 antigen

Concentration of (anti-2,4-dinitro-phenyl group) IgG for coating polystyrene beads (μg/mL)	Addition of serum (50 μL)	Fluorescence intensity of β-D-galactosidase activity bound to		
		the first solid phase	the first solid phase after elution	the second solid phase
5	No	339 (100)	31 (9.1)	147 (43)
	Yes	303 (100)	11 (3.6)	126 (42)
10	No	832 (100)	299 (36)	237 (28)
	Yes	495 (100)	124 (25)	154 (31)
20	No	871 (100)	384 (44)	218 (25)
	Yes	441 (100)	105 (24)	140 (32)
50	No	963 (100)	523 (54)	207 (21)
	Yes	370 (100)	80 (22)	117 (32)
100	No	1096 (100)	748 (68)	146 (13)
	Yes	307 (100)	60 (20)	95 (31)

HIV-1 p24 antigen (100 amol) was incubated simultaneously with 2,4-dinitrophenyl-biotinyl-bovine serum albumin-affinity-purified rabbit anti-p24 Fab' conjugate (100 fmol) and monoclonal mouse anti-p24 Fab'-β-D-galactosidase conjugate (10 fmol) and subsequently with two colored polystyrene beads of 3.2 mm diameter coated with affinity-purified (anti-2,4-dinitrophenyl group) IgG (first solid phase). The first solid phase after washing was incubated with two white polystyrene beads coated with streptavidin (second solid phase) in the presence of ϵN-2,4-dinitrophenyl-L-lysine. Values in parentheses are expressed as percentages of the fluorescence intensities of β-D-galactosidase activity bound to the first solid phase. Bound β-D-galactosidase activity was assayed for 1 h. The fluorescence intensity of 1×10^{-10} mol/L 4-methylumbelliferone was 1.

2. Prepare 0.05 mL of buffer A containing 50 μg of inactive β-D-galactosidase and 100 fmol each of 2,4-dinitrophenyl-biotinyl-antibody IgG and antibody Fab'-β-D-galactosidase conjugate.

   2,4-dinitrophenyl-biotinyl-bovine serum albumin-antibody Fab' conjugate or 2,4-dinitrophenyl antibody IgG may be sub-stituted for 2,4-dinitrophenyl-biotinyl-antibody IgG. Addition of serum from some species of animals significantly reduces nonspecific signals in some cases, as described in Chapter 4 (Table 4.5). When monoclonal mouse antibodies are used, non-specific mouse IgG should be added in excess to reduce non-specific signals, since serum samples often contain antibodies to mouse IgG.

3. Incubate the two solutions together to allow formation of the immune complex.

   Under this condition, the formation of the immune complex consisting of 2,4-dinitrophenyl-biotinyl-bovine serum albumin-affinity-purified rabbit (anti-HIV-1 p24) Fab' conjugate, mono-clonal mouse anti-HIV-1 p24 Fab'-β-D-galactosidase and HIV-1 p24 antigen is complete at room temperature within 4 h, but at 37°C within 2 h (Hashida et al., 1998b). The incubation time may be shortened at higher temperatures and higher concen-trations of the conjugates but depends upon the properties of antigens and antibodies involved. The conjugate concentration must not exceed the capacity of the solid phase coated with affinity-purified (anti-2,4-dinitrophenyl group) IgG to trap 2,4-dinitrophenylated protein as described above. The formation of the immune complex is complete within 10–15 min at 10-fold higher concentrations of the two conjugates.

4. Incubate the incubated mixture with the first solid phase coated with 10 μg/mL of affinity-purified (anti-2,4-dinitrophenyl group) IgG with shaking.

   When two polystyrene beads of 3.2 mm diameter are used as a solid phase, 1–2 h is required for complete trapping of the immune complex (Hashida et al., 1998b). However, the incu-bation time can be shortened by using solid phases of larger surface areas, and 10–20 min incubation may be sufficient with polystyrene beads of 6.35 mm diameter (one bead/assay) as described in Chapter 7 (Fig. 7.5).

The amount of the immune complexes consisting of the three components trapped on the first solid phase increases with the increase in the concentration of affinity-purified (anti-2,4-dinitrophenyl group) IgG used for coating, but the fraction of the immune complexes eluted from the first solid phase with ϵN-2,4-dinitrophenyl-L-lysine and transferred to the second solid phase decreases with the increase in the concentration, and serum interference becomes more serious (Table 8.1).

5. Wash the first solid phase with buffer A.
6. Incubate the first solid phase with 0.15 mL of buffer A containing 1–2 mmol/L ϵN-2,4-dinitrophenyl-L-lysine with shaking for 10–20 min to elute the immune complex.
7. Incubate with shaking the eluate with the second solid phase coated first with 30 μg/mL of biotinyl-bovine serum albumin by physical adsorption and then with 30 μg/mL of streptavidin when 2,4-dinitrophenyl-biotinyl-antibody IgG or 2,4-dinitrophenyl-biotinyl-bovine serum albumin-antibody Fab′ is used. For 2,4-dinitrophenyl-antibody IgG, the second solid phase is coated with 20 μg/mL of affinity-purified (anti-IgG) IgG.

   When two polystyrene beads of 3.2 mm diameter are used as a solid phase, 1–2 h is required for complete transfer of the immune complex (Hashida et al., 1998b). However, the incubation time can be shortened by using solid phases of larger surface areas, and 10–20 min incubation may be sufficient with polystyrene beads of 6.35 mm diameter (one bead/assay) as described in Chapter 7 (Fig. 7.5).

8. Wash the second solid phase with buffer A.
9. Incubate the second solid phase with a mixture of 0.05 mL of 0.3 mmol/L 4-methylumbelliferyl-β-D-galactoside (4MUG) and 0.1 mL of buffer A containing 0.01% bovine serum albumin for 1–20 h. For preparation of 0.3 mmol/L 4MUG, mix 1 vol-

ume of 15 mmol/L 4MUG in N,N-dimethylformamide with 49 volumes of water. Stop the enzyme reaction by addition of 2.5 mL of 0.1 mol/L glycine-NaOH buffer, pH 10.3. Measure the fluorescence intensity using 360 nm for excitation and 450 nm for emission analysis by adjusting the fluorescence intensity of 10^{-8} mol/L 4-methylumbelliferone in 0.1 mol/L glycine-NaOH buffer, pH 10.3 to 100. As described in Chapters 6 and 7, a 1-h assay of bound β-D-galactosidase activity provides much higher sensitivities of the immune complex transfer enzyme immunoassays than that of conventional immunoassays, but a 5–20-h assay is required for the highest sensitivity.

CHAPTER 9

Ultrasensitive immunoassay for haptens

9.1. Introduction

The sensitivity of noncompetitive solid phase two-site enzyme immunoassay of antigens has been improved to attomole levels without immune complex transfer and to zeptomole levels with immune complex transfer, as described in the previous chapters.

The two-site immunoassay technique without immune complex transfer can measure 10 amol (30 fg) of α-human atrial natriuretic peptide, a 28 amino acid single chain peptide with an intramolecular disulfide bridge, secreted from the atrium (Fig. 9.1) (Hashida et al., 1988a, b). The detection limit of the peptide in plasma is 0.6 ng/L using 0.05 mL plasma. Thus, it is possible to measure the lowest level of the peptide in plasma of healthy subjects (about 5 ng/L) directly (without extraction), whereas extraction and concentration are essential for its assay by competitive radioimmunoassay (Mukoyama et al., 1988).

Three antibodies were used to measure this peptide by two-site enzyme immunoassay: one was specific for the C-terminus of the peptide (C-terminus antibody); the second was specific for the N-terminus (N-terminus antibody); and the third recognized the N-terminal half of the ring structure of the peptide (ring antibody). The combined use of the C-terminus antibody labeled with horseradish peroxidase by the hinge method (Chapters 11–13) and the ring antibody or the N-terminus antibody immobilized on polystyrene beads by physical adsorption was successful. The distance between the two epitopes, recognized by the C-terminus antibody and the ring antibody or the N-terminus antibody, is equivalent to a single chain

193

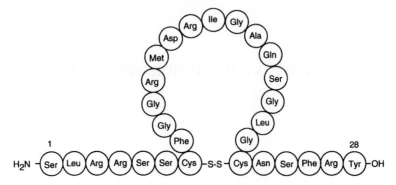

Fig. 9.1. Primary structure of α-atrial natriuretic peptide.

peptide consisting of approximately 12–15 amino acids. These findings strongly suggest that single chain peptides, consisting of more than 12–15 amino acids, can be measured at attomole levels by the above technique.

However, it is obviously impossible by two-site immunoassays to measure smaller haptens that cannot be bound simultaneously by two different antibodies specific for two different epitopes on hapten molecules. For the last 40 years, such smaller haptens have been measured mainly by competitive radioimmunoassays and partly by competitive nonisotopic immunoassays. The detection limits of these smaller haptens by competitive immunoassays are at femtomole levels.

In this chapter, ultrasensitive noncompetitive (hetero-two-site) immunoassays to measure attomole amounts of these small haptens carrying amino groups are described with emphasis on peptides.

9.2. Principle of noncompetitive (hetero-two-site) immunoassay

The principle described here for sensitive measurement of small hapten molecules carrying amino groups, which cannot be simultaneously bound by two different antibody molecules specific for the corresponding two different epitopes on the hapten molecules, is as follows (Ishikawa et al., 1990a).

First, the haptens to be measured should be labeled with an appropriate substance, so that one antibody molecule directed to the hapten molecules and another binding molecule for the label may be simultaneously bound to the labeled hapten molecules, thus allowing hetero-two-site assays. An appropriate label and its binding substance may be chosen from a variety of combinations, such as biotin-avidin, hapten-anti-hapten antibody (distinct from those to be measured), antigen-antibody, hormone-receptor and nucleotide-hybrids. Labeling of the haptens to be measured may be performed chemically using excess labels activated with appropriate functional groups, such as N-hydroxysuccinimide esters, anhydride groups, and aldehyde groups which are reactive with the haptens to be measured. Alternatively, the haptens to be measured may be labeled enzymatically.

Subsequently, excess labels partially unreacting and partially bound to substances other than the haptens to be measured, should be eliminated prior to two-site assay. This may be performed using solid phases coated with the antibodies directed to the structures of the haptens to be measured. For example, labeled haptens are trapped on solid phases coated with anti-hapten antibodies and, after washing, eluted at low pH.

Finally, hetero-two-site assay can be performed using anti-hapten antibodies and binding substances for labels. Anti-hapten antibodies are used for trapping labeled haptens on solid phases, and binding substances for labels are conjugated with enzymes. Alternatively, anti-hapten antibodies are conjugated with enzymes, and binding substances for labels are used for trapping labeled haptens on solid phases. Enzymes may be replaced by fluorescent or luminescent substances.

The haptens to be measured may also be labeled directly with fluorescent and luminescent substances, such as europium and acridinium, which can be measured with high sensitivity.

9.3. Feasibility of the principle

The feasibility of the principle described above has been tested in four different ways (methods I–IV) using angiotensin I (a 10-amino acid single chain peptide), [Arg[8]]-vasopressin (a nine amino acid single chain peptide with an intramolecular disulfide bridge) (Fig. 9.2), thyroxine (T_4) and α-atrial natriuretic peptide (Fig. 9.1). These peptides contain no L-lysine residue.

9.3.1. Method I using 2,4-dinitrophenyl-anti-peptide IgG and avidin-β-D-galactosidase conjugate

Angiotensin I was biotinylated by reaction with N-hydroxy-succinimidobiotin.

Biotinylated angiotensin I was separated from unreacted reagent and other biotinylated substances and measured using avidin-β-D-galactosidase conjugate, affinity-purified 2,4-dinitrophenyl-rabbit anti-angiotensin I IgG, affinity-purified (anti-2,4-dinitrophenyl group) IgG-coated polystyrene beads, and affinity-purified (anti-rabbit IgG) IgG-coated polystyrene beads (Fig. 9.3) (Ishikawa et al., 1990b).

Biotinylated angiotensin I was trapped on anti-angiotensin I IgG-coated polystyrene beads. The polystyrene beads were washed to eliminate unreacted reagent and other biotinylated substances and were treated at pH 1.0 to elute the biotinylated angiotensin I. The biotinylated angiotensin I eluted was neutralized and allowed to react with affinity-purified 2,4-dinitrophenyl-rabbit anti-angiotensin I IgG, and was trapped on affinity-purified (anti-2,4-dinitrophenyl group) IgG-coated polystyrene beads. The polystyrene beads were allowed to react with avidin-β-D-galactosidase conjugate. The complex consisting of affinity-purified 2,4-dinitrophenyl-rabbit anti-angiotensin I IgG, biotinylated angiotensin I and avidin-β-D-galactosidase conjugate was eluted from the polystyrene beads with excess ϵN-2,4-dinitrophenyl-L-lysine and transferred to affinity-

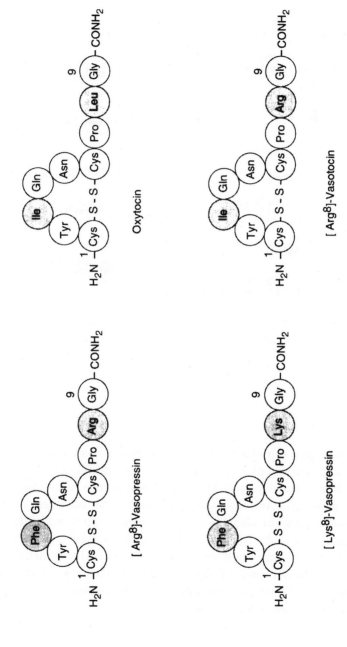

Fig. 9.2. Primary structures of [Arg8]-vasopressin and related peptides.

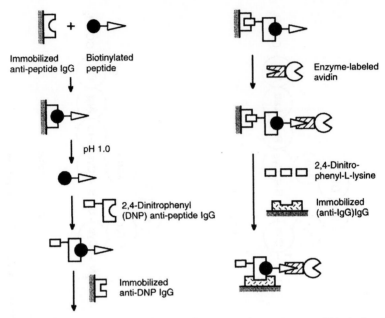

Fig. 9.3. Hetero-two-site complex transfer enzyme immunoassay of biotinylated peptides using enzyme-labeled avidin (method I).

purified goat (anti-rabbit IgG) IgG-coated polystyrene beads. In this step, the complex was transferred from affinity-purified (anti-2,4-dinitrophenyl group) IgG-coated polystyrene beads, to which avidin-β-D-galactosidase conjugate had been adsorbed nonimmunologically, to clean polystyrene beads coated with affinity-purified (anti-rabbit IgG) IgG. After washing the polystyrene beads, bound β-D-galactosidase activity was assayed by fluorometry.

The detection limit of angiotensin I was 10 amol (13 fg)/assay (Table 9.1). Since the procedure was time-consuming, a simpler method was developed as described below.

TABLE 9.1

Detection limits and assay ranges of haptens in plasma by hetero-two-site enzyme immunoassays (methods I–IV)

Method	Hapten	Detection limit	Volume of plasma (urine) used	Assay range in plasma	
		(amol (fg)/assay)	(μL)	(pmol (ng)/L)	
I	Angiotensin I	10 (13)	–	–	
II	Angiotensin I	10 (13)	5	2–2000	(2.6–2600)
			50	0.6–200	(0.8–260)
	α-atrial natriuretic peptide	20 (60)	75	0.27–400	(0.8–1,200)
	Arg^8-vasopressin	50 (54)	–	–	
III	Arg^8-vasopressin	10 (11)	(5)	2–2000	(2–2000)
			75	0.13–130	(0.14–140)
	T_4	100 (78)	–	–	
IV	Arg^8-vasopressin	1 (1.1)	75	0.013–40	(0.014–44)

9.3.2. Method II using streptavidin-coated solid phase and anti-peptide Fab'-peroxidase conjugate

Angiotensin I was biotinylated by reaction with sulfosuccinimidyl-6-(biotinamido)hexanoate.

Biotinylated angiotensin I was measured using affinity-purified anti-angiotensin I Fab'-peroxidase conjugate and streptavidin-coated polystyrene beads after removal of unreacted reagent and other biotinylated substances (Fig. 9.4) (Tanaka et al., 1989). Biotinylated angiotensin I was trapped on anti-angiotensin I IgG-coated polystyrene beads. The polystyrene beads were washed to eliminate unreacted reagent and other biotinylated substances and were treated at pH 1.0 to elute biotinylated angiotensin I. The biotinylated angiotensin I eluted was allowed to react with anti-angiotensin I Fab′-horseradish peroxidase conjugate and trapped on streptavidin-coated polystyrene beads. Peroxidase activity bound to the polystyrene beads was assayed by fluorometry using 3-(4-hydroxyphenyl)propionic acid as a hydrogen donor.

The detection limit of angiotensin I was 13 fg (10 amol)/assay. This value was 100-fold smaller than that by competitive radioimmunoassay using the same antiserum and ^{125}I-angiotensin I and 80- to 480-fold smaller than those by competitive radioimmunoassay (Fyhrquist et al., 1976) and competitive enzyme immunoassay (Scharpé et al., 1987; Aikawa et al., 1979).

The detection limit of α-atrial natriuretic peptide (Fig. 9.1) by the same method was 60 fg (20 amol)/assay (Table 9.1), which was 50-fold smaller than that by the competitive enzyme immunoassay using the same antibody (Hashida et al., 1991e).

The detection limit of arginine vasopressin, a nine amino acid single chain peptide with an intramolecular disulfide bridge (Fig. 9.2) by method II was 54 fg (50 amol)/assay (Table 9.1) (Tanaka et al., 1990a). There was little cross-reaction with oxytocin or [Arg^8]-vasotocin, but considerable cross-reaction with [Lys^8]-vasopressin. This indicated that the anti-arginine vasopressin IgG used was specific for the ring structure, including Phe^3 of arginine vasopressin (Fig. 9.2). Judging from the specificity of the anti-arginine vasopressin IgG used and the primary structure of the peptide (Fig. 9.2), the biotin residues introduced into the peptide molecules through N-terminal amino groups may have been located fairly close to the epitopic sites recognized by anti-arginine vasopressin Fab′-peroxidase conjugate. Therefore, due to steric hindrance, the biotinylated peptide molecules that bound to the conjugate molecules, may not have reacted efficiently with streptavidin-coated polystyrene beads.

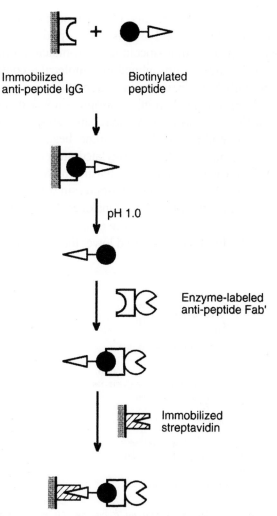

Immobilized
anti-peptide IgG

Biotinylated
peptide

pH 1.0

Enzyme-labeled
anti-peptide Fab'

Immobilized
streptavidin

Fig. 9.4. Hetero-two-site enzyme immunoassay of directly and indirectly biotinylated peptides using enzyme-labeled anti-peptide Fab' (methods II and III).

9.3.3. Method III by indirect biotinylation

On the basis of the above results, [Arg[8]]-vasopressin was biotinylated indirectly (Fig. 9.5). For this, the peptide molecules were
treated successively with N-succinimidyl-6-maleimidohexanoate to
introduce maleimide groups, glutathione molecules containing thiol
groups and with N-hydroxysuccinimidobiotin.

Indirectly biotinylated arginine vasopressin was measured using
affinity-purified anti-arginine vasopressin Fab'-peroxidase conjugate and streptavidin-coated polystyrene beads after removal of
unreacted reagents and other biotinylated substances as described
above for the measurement of angiotensin I by method II (Fig. 9.4).

The detection limit of arginine vasopressin was lowered 5-fold to
10 amol (11 fg)/assay (Table 9.1) (Tanaka et al, 1990a). This level is
50-fold lower than that by competitive enzyme immunoassay using
the same antibody, and 6- to 40-fold lower than those by competitive

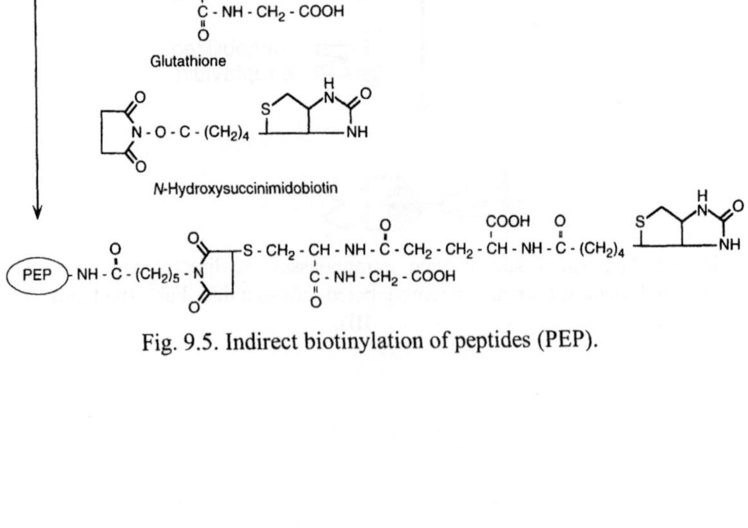

Fig. 9.5. Indirect biotinylation of peptides (PEP).

immunoassays (Morton et al., 1975; LaRochelle et al., 1980; Uno et al., 1982; Glänzer et al., 1984; Yamazaki et al., 1988; Watabe et al., 1987).

The detection limit of thyroxine (T_4) by method III was 78 fg (100 amol)/assay (Table 9.1), which was 50-fold lower than that by competitive enzyme immunoassay using the same antibody (Tanaka et al., 1990b).

9.3.4. Method IV

Arginine vasopressin was indirectly biotinylated using N-succinimidyl-6-maleimidohexanoate, glutathione and N-hydroxysuccinimidobiotin as described above (Fig. 9.5).

Indirectly biotinylated arginine vasopressin was trapped on anti-arginine vasopressin IgG-coated polystyrene beads and, after washing, eluted with HCl (Fig. 9.4). Indirectly biotinylated arginine vasopressin separated from unreacted reagents and other substances was measured as shown schematically in Fig. 9.6.

Indirectly biotinylated arginine vasopressin was allowed to react with 2,4-dinitrophenyl-fluorescein disulfide-bovine serum albumin-rabbit anti-arginine vasopressin IgG conjugate. The complex formed was trapped on affinity-purified (anti-2,4-dinitrophenyl group) IgG-coated polystyrene beads and, after washing, allowed to react with avidin-β-D-galactosidase conjugate. The polystyrene beads were washed, and the complex consisting of the three components was eluted with excess ϵN-2,4-dinitrophenyl-L-lysine and transferred to anti-fluorescein IgG-coated polystyrene beads. After washing, the complex was released from the polystyrene beads by reduction with 2-mercaptoethylamine and transferred to affinity-purified (anti-rabbit IgG) IgG-coated polystyrene beads. β-D-galactosidase activity bound to these polystyrene beads was assayed by fluorometry.

The detection limit of arginine vasopressin was 1.1 fg (1 amol)/assay (Table 9.1), which was 450-fold lower than that

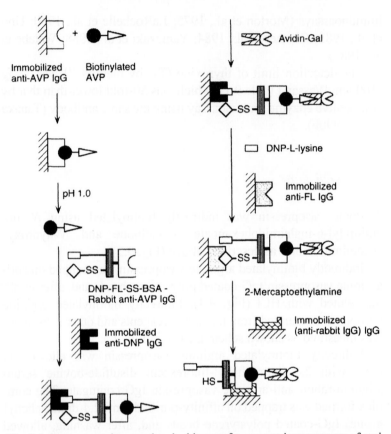

Fig. 9.6. Hetero-two-site complex double transfer enzyme immunoassay of arginine vasopressin (AVP) (method IV) (Hashida et al., 1991d). DNP, 2,4-dinitro-
phenyl group; FL, fluorescein; SS, disulfide bond; BSA, bovine serum albumin;
Gal, β-D-galactosidase.

by competitive enzyme immunoassay using the same antiserum
(Hashida et al., 1991d) and 60- to 400-fold lower than those by
competitive radioimmunoassays (Morton et al., 1975; LaRochelle
et al., 1980; Uno et al., 1982; Glänzer et al., 1984; Yamazaki et al.,
1988; Watabe et al., 1987).

The cross-reactions with arginine vasopressin-related peptides (Fig. 9.2) were as follows. The bound β-D-galactosidase activities in the presence of oxytocin (10 ng/assay), [Asu^{1,6}, Arg^8]-vasotocin (1 ng/assay), and [Arg^8]-vasotocin (antidiuretic hormone in vertebrates other than mammals) (1 ng/assay) were not significantly higher than those in the absence of these peptides (nonspecifically bound β-D-galactosidase activity) and were significantly lower than that in the presence of 1.1 fg (1 amol, the detection limit)/assay of arginine vasopressin. The cross-reaction with [Lys^8]-vasopressin (antidiuretic hormone in pig and hippopotamus) was 72% on a molar basis. These results indicated that the anti-arginine vasopressin IgG used recognized the ring structure of arginine vasopressin containing Phe^3 (Fig. 9.2).

9.4. Measurement of haptens in plasma and urine

The maximal volumes of body fluid samples such as plasma that can be used in the methods described above is limited to 5–10 μL, when samples are subjected directly to biotinylation. This is due to the fact that the recovery of haptens added to plasma samples decreases as the volume of plasma samples used increases to more than 5 μL (Fig. 9.7) (Hashida et al., 1991d). The reason for this is that the concentration of reagents used for biotinylation is approximately 5 mmol/L in the reaction mixtures, whereas amino groups are present at higher concentrations in plasma (approximately 60 mmol/L). Thus, the sensitivity of the methods described above is limited in terms of grams per unit volume of plasma. However, 5 μL of samples is sufficient for the measurement of some peptides such as angiotensin I in plasma and arginine vasopressin in urine as described below.

By method II for angiotensin I using 5 μL plasma, the recoveries of the peptide were 84–119% when the peptide at two different levels (260 and 780 ng/L) was added to three plasma samples containing 173–206 ng/L of the peptide; the within-assay variation

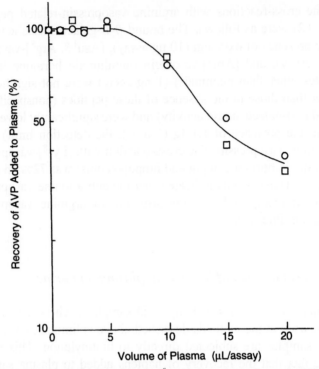

Fig. 9.7. Recovery of arginine vasopressin added to plasma by method IV. Various volumes of plasma were subjected to indirect biotinylation with and without addition of arginine vasopressin and subsequently to method IV without the second transfer (Hashida et al., 1991d). β-D-galactosidase activity bound to anti-fluorescein IgG-coated polystyrene beads was assayed. The concentration of arginine vasopressin in plasma used was 1.0 ng/L, and the amounts of arginine vasopressin added were 0.3 (circles) and 1.0 (squares) pg/assay.

coefficients at 9 different peptide levels over the range of 173–1032 ng/L was 5.9–9.9% ($n = 5$); and the assay range of the peptide was 2.6–2600 ng/L (Table 9.1) (Tanaka et al., 1989). This is sufficiently sensitive for measurement of angiotensin I in plasma of healthy subjects (154 ± 38 (SD) ng/L; range, 97–207 ng/L; $n = 7$) (Tanaka et al., 1989) and 25- to 100-fold lower than those by competitive radioimmunoassay (Fyhrquist et al., 1976) and competitive enzyme immunoassay (Scharpé et al., 1987; Aikawa et al., 1979).

By method III for arginine vasopressin using 5 μL volumes of urine, the recoveries of the peptide were 86 ± 7.6 (SD)% (range, 77–101%; n = 18), when the peptide was added at two different levels (20 and 80 ng/L) to 9 urine samples containing 6.6–64 ng/L of the peptide; the within-assay variation coefficients at 14 different peptide levels over the range of 6.6–117 ng/L was 3.0–13% (n = 5); and the assay range of the peptide was 2–2000 ng/L (Tanaka et al., 1990a). The urinary levels of arginine vasopressin in nine healthy subjects aged 22–35 years with ad libitum water intake and normal activity were 34 ± 20 (SD) ng/L (range, 6.6–64 ng/L), or 25 ± 12 (SD) ng/g creatinine (range, 8.9–44 ng/g creatinine). Therefore, the lowest level of urinary arginine vasopressin in healthy subjects with ad libitum water intake and normal activity can be measured using only 5 μL urine.

In many cases, however, the sensitivity to peptides in body fluids has to be improved in terms of grams per unit volume of samples by increasing the sample volume for tests. One method for this purpose is to extract peptides from plasma using anti-peptide IgG-coated solid phases (Tanaka et al., 1989). When angiotensin I was extracted from 50 μL of plasma using anti-angiotensin I IgG-coated polystyrene beads, the recoveries of the peptide (78 ng/L) added to four plasma samples (50 μL) containing 97–156 ng/L, were 83–120%; the within-assay variation coefficients at 8 different peptide levels over the range of 97–248 ng/L was 4.9–14%, and the assay range of angiotensin I in plasma was 0.8–260 ng/L (Table 9.1), which was 80- to 330-fold lower than those by competitive radioimmunoassay (Fyhrquist et al., 1976) and competitive enzyme immunoassay (Scharpé et al., 1987; Aikawa et al., 1979).

However, plasma arginine vasopressin has to be measured after extraction using, for example, an octadecyl silica column (SEP-PAK C_{18} cartridge, Millipore Corp., Waters Associates, Milford, MA) (Glänzer et al., 1984), because plasma proteins are associated with immunoreactivity detected by anti-arginine vasopressin antibodies (Robertson et al., 1970). This difficulty has been overcome by removing proteins from plasma samples using molecular sieves (Hashida et al., 1991c). Plasma was slightly diluted and filtered by centrifugation in a microconcentrator with a polysaccharide membrane (Centricon 30, Amicon Division W.R. Grace & Co., Beverly, MA) to separate peptides from plasma proteins. When plasma was diluted 1.3-fold, the concentrations of amino groups in the plasma filtrates of healthy subjects aged 28–37 years at 9:00 a.m. before breakfast ($n = 4$) and approximately 4 h after breakfast ($n = 8$) were both 1.7–2.1 mmol/L. When the plasma was diluted 2-fold, the concentrations of both were 1.0–1.3 mmol/L. This indicates that 100 μL of plasma filtrates corresponding to 75 μL of plasma can be used with satisfactory recovery of haptens added to plasma.

By method II for α-atrial natriuretic peptide [1–28] using 100 μL of plasma filtrates corresponding to 75 μL of plasma, the recoveries of the peptide [1–28] (30 ng/L) added to four plasma samples containing 3.6–30 ng/L of the peptide were 80–104%; the within- and between-assay variation coefficients at three different peptide levels over the range of 3.6–196 ng/L were 4.4–7.0% ($n = 10$) and 2.4–11% ($n = 10$), respectively; and the assay range of the peptide [1–28] in plasma was 0.8–1200 ng/L (Table 9.1) (Hashida et al., 1991e). Thus, peptide levels in plasma of healthy subjects can be measured without the concentration processes required for competitive radioimmunoassay (Raine et al., 1986; Hasegawa et al., 1986). The concentrations of the peptide in plasma samples of 10 healthy subjects aged 23–41 years with ad libitum water intake and normal activity approximately 4 h after breakfast were 15 ± 3.2 (SD) ng/L (range, 9.8–22 ng/L), which were lower than those (30 ± 11 ng/L; range, 15–50 ng/L) determined by a two-site enzyme immunoassay (Watanabe et al., 1989). This might have been due to the presence of peptide [6–28] and/or peptide [7–28] in plasma, which were as reactive as peptide [1–28] in conventional two-site enzyme immunoassay, but less reactive than peptide [1–28] in method II.

By method III for arginine vasopressin using 100 μL of plasma filtrate corresponding to 75 μL of plasma, the recoveries of the peptide (8 ng/L) added to four plasma samples containing 0.37–0.96 ng/L of the peptide were 77–88%; the within- and between-assay variation coefficients at 3–4 different levels over the range of 0.57–42 ng/L were 5.6–9.4% ($n = 10$) and 6.3–8.9% ($n = 10$), respectively; and the assay range of the peptide in plasma was 0.14–140 ng/L (Table 9.1) (Hashida et al., 1991c). By method III, the concentrations of arginine vasopressin in the plasma of eight healthy subjects aged 25–41 years with ad libitum water intake and normal activity approximately 4 h after breakfast were 0.72 ± 0.22 (SD) ng/L (range, 0.42–1.04 ng/L). These values were lower than those reported previously (1.2–5.2 ng/L), which were determined by competitive immunoassays only after extraction and concentration using 1–5 mL of plasma (Robertson et al., 1973; Morton et al., 1975; Hammer, 1978; LaRochelle et al., 1980; Glänzer et al., 1984; Uno et al., 1982).

By method IV for arginine vasopressin using 100 μL volumes of plasma filtrates corresponding to 75 μL of plasma, the recoveries of the peptide (0.22–2.2 ng/L) added to five plasma samples containing 0.057–0.81 ng/L of peptide were 81–96%; the within- and between-assay variation coefficients at three different peptide levels over the range of 0.071–9.7 ng/L were 6.1–8.4% ($n = 10$) and 5.4–17% ($n = 10$), respectively, and the assay range of the peptide in plasma was 14–44,000 pg/L (Table 9.1) (Hashida et al., 1991d). The concentrations of the peptide in plasma of 16 healthy subjects aged 24–42 years with ad libitum water intake and normal activity approximately 4 h after breakfast were 0.94 ± 0.48 (SD) ng/L (range, 0.35–1.94 ng/L). These values were similar to those reported previously (0.42–2.6 ng/L), which were determined by competitive immunoassays after extraction and concentration using 1–5 mL of plasma (LaRochelle et al., 1980; Glänzer et al., 1984; Yamazaki et al., 1988; Watabe et al., 1987; Uno et al., 1982).

9.5. Other methods

An alternative noncompetitive enzyme immunoassay has been described for haptens with primary amino groups such as substance P, thyroxine and endothelin (Boutten and Mamas, 1994).

Monoclonal antibodies to haptens immobilized on microplates were allowed to react with haptens. Trapped haptens were treated with homobifunctional crosslinking reagents including glutaraldehyde and disuccinimidyl suberate to couple them to monoclonal antibodies through amino groups. After successive treatments with $NaBH_4$ and HCl, immobilized haptens were allowed to react with monoclonal anti-hapten antibodies labeled with acetylcholine esterase.

The detection limit of thyroxine was similar to that by method III described above, although method IV with transfer must be more sensitive. However, the detection limit of substance P with a molecular weight of 1347 Da was 6 pg/mL, while the detection limits of arginine vasopressin with a molecular weight of 1084 Da by methods III and IV were 0.14 and 0.014 pg/mL, respectively (Table 9.1). The detection limit of endothelin with a molecular weight of 2432 was 20 pg/mL, while the detection limit of α-atrial natriuretic peptide with a molecular weight of 2800 by method II was 0.8 pg/mL.

Thus, biotinylation methods appear to be more sensitive than glutaraldehyde methods, although both methods remain to be compared more carefully.

CHAPTER 10

Properties of the reagents for enzyme-labeling

10.1. Solubility

The enzyme-labeling reagents, glutaraldehyde and periodate are dissolved in buffers. However, other reagents, such as the maleimide, thiol and pyridyldisulfide derivatives listed in Table 10.1 and Fig. 10.1 are not soluble in buffers at sufficiently high concentrations for enzyme-labeling, although sulfosuccin-imidyl derivatives are more soluble in buffers than the corresponding succinimidyl derivatives. Derivatives containing a benzene or cyclohexane ring are less soluble in buffers than other compounds. *N*,*N*'-*p*-phenylenedimaleimide is less soluble than *N*,*N*'-*o*-phenylenedimaleimide. This is the reason that the latter has been used for enzyme-labeling more frequently than the former. These derivatives may be dissolved at concentrations of 50–100 mmol/L, for example, in *N*,*N*-dimethylformamide and then added to buffers containing antigens, antibodies and enzymes so as to obtain the concentrations required for enzyme-labeling. Under this condition, most of the reagents for enzyme-labeling listed Table 10.1 and Fig. 10.1 remain soluble during conjugation reactions. However, some of them including *N*-succinimidyl-4-(*N*-maleimidomethyl)cyclohexane-1-carboxylate containing a cyclohexane ring, *N*-succinimidyl-*m*-maleimidobenzoate and *N*-succinimidyl-4-(*p*-maleimidophenyl)butyrate both containing a benzene ring are soluble only at concentrations below 1.5 mmol/L and precipitate at concentrations above 3.7 mmol/L in 0.1

TABLE 10.1

Stabilities of maleimide groups in various maleimide derivatives

Maleimide derivative	Maleimide groups remaining after incubation at 30°C at pH 7.0 for			
	0.5 h (%)	1 h (%)	3 h (%)	6 h (%)
N-succinimidylmaleimdoacetate	99	95	90	83
N-succinimidyl-4-maleimidobutyrate	96	95	86	79
N-succinimidyl-6-maleimidohexanoate	98	99	92	88
N-succinimidyl-4-(N-maleimidomethyl) cyclohexane-1-carboxylate	96	97	94	90
N-sulfosuccinimidyl-4-(N-maleimido-methyl)cyclohexane-1-carbocylate	102	100	98	100
N-succinimidyl-m-maleimidobenzoate	62	43	15	7
N-succinimidyl-4-(p-maleimidophenyl) butyrate	78	65	32	13
N-sulfosuccinimidyl-m-maleimido-benzoate	87	79	40	17
N-sulfosuccinimidyl-4-(p-maleimido-phenyl)butyrate	77	71	39	25
N,N'-o-phenylenedimaleimide	–	75	29	8
N,N'-oxydimethylenedimaleimide	–	82	48	–

Each maleimide derivative (0.7 mmol/L) was incubated in 0.1 mol/L sodium phosphate buffer, pH 7.0, at 30°C (Ishikawa et al., 1988).

mol/L sodium phosphate buffer, pH 7.0, containing, 10% N,N'-dimethylformamide at 30°C (Hashida et al., 1984).

10.2. Stability and reactivity

Reagents are in general less reactive under the conditions (pH, temperature, etc.) to keep them stable. Therefore, both the stability and reactivity of reagents for enzyme-labeling should be kept

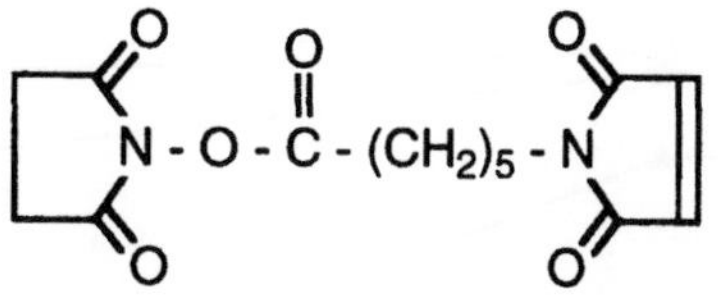

N-Succinimidyl-6-maleimidohexanoate

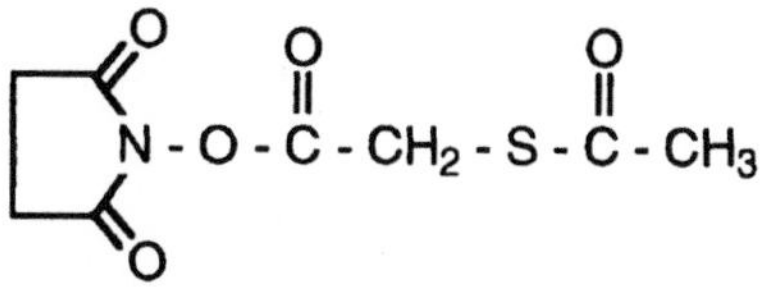

N-Succinimidyl-S-acetylthio(mercapto)acetate

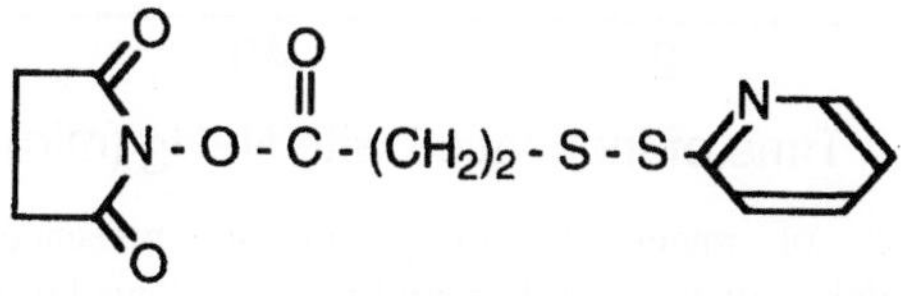

N-Succinimidyl-3-(2'-pyridyldithio)propionate

Fig. 10.1. Structures of frequently used crosslinking reagents.

in mind, and due caution is required in choosing conditions for enzyme-labeling.

Maleimide groups readily react with thiol groups at almost all pH values, and are stable at acidic pH values, although they are labile at alkaline pH values (Ishikawa et al., 1981). Even

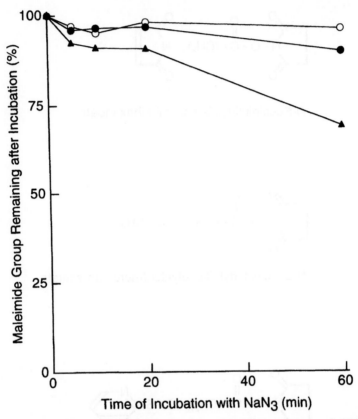

Fig. 10.2. Stabilities of maleimide groups in the presence of NaN$_3$. N-succinimidyl-6-maleimidohexanoate (3 mmol/L) was allowed to react with 10 mmol/L glycine in 0.1 mol/L sodium phosphate buffer, pH 7.0, at 30°C for 30 min and then incubated in the absence (open circles) and presence of 0.3 g/L (closed circles) or 1.0 g/L (closed triangles) NaN$_3$ at 30°C for up to 60 min. NaN$_3$ is used as an antiseptic at concentrations of 0.5–1.0 g/L.

at neutral pH, the maleimide groups of some maleimide deriva-tives, in which these groups are directly attached to a benzene ring, are not very stable (Table 10.1) (Hashida et al., 1984). They include N-succinimidyl-m-maleimidobenzoate, N-succinimidyl-4-

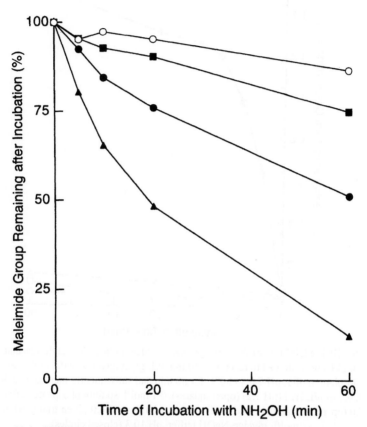

Fig. 10.3. Stabilities of maleimide groups in the presence of hydroxylamine. *N*-succinimidyl-6-maleimidohexanoate (3 mmol/L) was allowed to react with 10 mmol/L glycine in 0.1 mol/L sodium phosphate buffer, pH 7.0, at 30°C for 30 min and then incubated in the absence (open circles) and presence of 10 mmol/L (closed squares), 30 mmol/L (closed circles) or 100 mmol/L (closed triangles) hydroxylamine at 30°C for up to 60 min. Hydroxylamine is used at a concentration of 100 mmol/L to release thiol groups from *S*-acetylthiol derivatives.

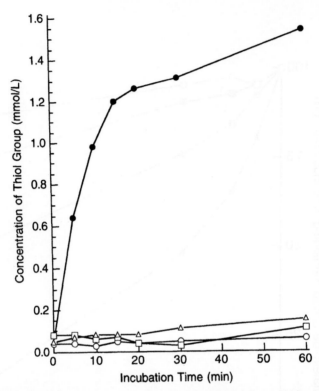

Fig. 10.4. Stabilities of S-acetyl groups. N-succinimidyl-S-acetylthioacetate (2 mmol/L) was allowed to react with 10 mmol/L glycylglycine in 0.1 mol/L sodium phosphate buffer, pH 7.0, at 30°C for 30 min and subsequently incubated at 30°C in 0.1 mol/L HCl (pH 1.2) (open squares), 0.1 mol/L sodium phosphate buffer, pH 7.0 (open circles), 0.1 mol/L sodium borate buffer, pH 9.0 (open triangles) or 0.1 mol/L glycine-NaOH buffer, pH 10.3 (closed circles).

(p-maleimidophenyl)butyrate, their N-sulfosuccinimidyl deriva-tives and N,N'-o-phenylenedimaleimide (Ishikawa et al., 1988).

In addition, maleimide groups are labile in the presence of NaN$_3$ at the concentrations (0.5–1.0 g/L) used as an antiseptic (Fig. 10.2) and in the presence of hydroxylamine at the concentrations below that used to release thiol groups from S-acetyl thiol derivatives (0.1

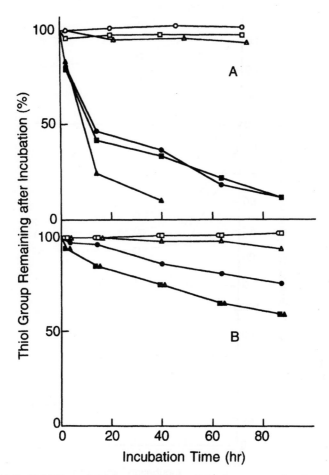

Fig. 10.5. Stabilities of thiol groups in the Fab′ fragment and reduced IgG. Reduced IgG (A), and Fab′ (B), were incubated at 4°C in 0.1 mol/L sodium phosphate buffer, pH 6.0 (circles), 6.5 (squares) and 7.0 (triangles) in the absence (closed symbols) and presence (open symbols) of 1 mmol/L EDTA (Ishikawa et al., 1981).

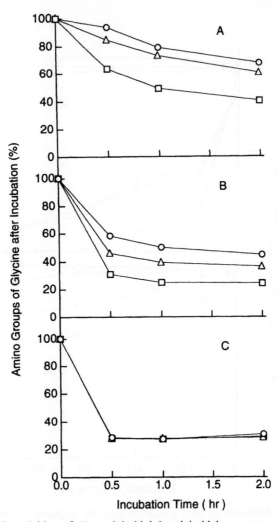

Fig. 10.6. Reactivities of *N*-succinimidyl-6-maleimidohexanoate with glycine at different pH values. *N*-succinimidyl-6-maleimidohexanoate was incubated with glycine at the same concentrations in 0.1 mol/L sodium phosphate buffer, pH 6.0 (A), 7.0 (B) and 8.0 (C) at 30°C. The concentrations of *N*-succinimidyl-6-maleimidohexanoate and glycine used were 1 (circles), 2 (triangles) and 5 (squares) mmol/L.

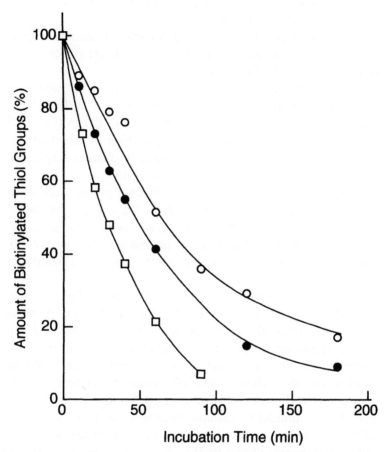

Fig. 10.7. Stability of *N*-hydroxysuccinimidobiotin at pH 7 and 8. *N*-hydroxysuccinimidobiotin (10 mmol/L) was incubated in 0.1 mol/L sodium phosphate buffer, pH 7.0 (open symbols) or 8.0 (closed symbols) at 30°C for up to 180 min. Aliquots (50 µL) of this solution after incubation was incubated with 50 µL of 4 mmol/L 2-mercaptoethanol (open and closed circles), or 2-mercaptoethylamine (open squares) in 0.1 mol/L sodium phosphate buffer, pH 7.0. After incubation, the amount of thiol groups was determined.

mol/L) (Fig. 10.3). Therefore, maleimide derivatives are stored and allowed to react with thiol groups at pH values below 7 in the absence of NaN$_3$ and hydroxylamine.

The S-acetyl group of N-succinimidyl-S-acetylthio(mercapto)-acetate (Fig. 10.1) is stable at acidic and alkaline pH values up to 9, but is labile at pH 10.3 (Fig. 10.4).

Thiol groups are slightly more stable at lower pH values, although not very stable at any pH value, and are fairly stable at acidic and alkaline pH values in the presence of EDTA (Fig. 10.5) (Ishikawa et al., 1983b). Therefore, the reaction of maleimide and thiol groups is performed at weakly acidic pH values in the presence of EDTA to keep both groups stable and reactive.

The reaction rate of maleimide with thiol groups depends on their concentrations and the temperature. The reaction between 50 nmol/mL of maleimide groups introduced into horseradish peroxidase and 50 nmol/mL of thiol groups present in rabbit Fab′ is almost complete within 5–10 h at 4°C and within 1 h at 30°C (Yoshitake et al., 1982).

Hydroxysuccinimide esters are more reactive (Fig. 10.6) but more labile at alkaline pH values (Fig. 10.7) and, therefore, used at a neutral pH value for reaction with amino and thiol groups. The reactivity of hydroxysuccinimide esters greatly varies depending on the thiol and amino compounds used and depending on the volume ratio of buffers to organic solvents such as N,N′-dimethylformamide used for dissolving these esters. N-succinimidyl-6-maleimidohexanoate is more reactive in solutions containing more than 30% of both buffers and N,N′-dimethylformamide (Table 10.2).

Reagents for enzyme-labeling including maleimide derivatives and hydroxysuccinimide esters are stable, for example, in N,N-dimethylformamide in the absence of water at −20°C for months. Therefore, these reagents are dissolved and stored, for example, in N,N-dimethylformamide and, when needed, are added to appropriate buffers containing the enzymes, antigens and antibodies to be conjugated.

TABLE 10.2

Reactivities of N-succinimidyl-6-maleimidohexanoate with glycine in buffers containing N,N'-dimethylformamide in different proportions

Proportion in the reaction mixture of		Amino groups after incubation
N,N'-dimethylformamide (%)	buffer (%)	(%)
95	5	69
90	10	47
75	25	28
50	50	19
30	70	23
10	90	34

N-succinimidyl-6-maleimidohexanoate (5 mmol/L) was incubated with 5 mmol/L glycine in 0.1 mol/L sodium phosphate buffer, pH 7.0, containing N,N'-dimethylformamide in the indicated proportions at 30°C for 30 min.

10.3. Purity

The purity of enzyme-labeling reagents is important for obtaining favorable results. Among commercially available preparations of the enzyme-labeling reagents listed in Table 10.1 and Fig. 10.1, some are of low purity (Hashida et al., 1984). It is recommended to test commercially available preparations for purity before use.

CHAPTER 11

Enzyme-labeling of antibodies

11.1. Introduction

Various methods have been developed for enzyme-labeling of antibodies using a number of different reagents (Tijssen, 1985). These methods may be divided into two groups: one-step methods and other methods (two- and three-step methods).

In one-step methods, a mixture of enzymes and antibodies is incubated with crosslinking reagents, and then the conjugate is purified. In a typical one-step method, glutaraldehyde is used as a bifunctional crosslinking reagent (Avrameas, 1969). Glutaraldehyde readily reacts with amino groups of enzymes and antibodies under mild conditions (at neutral pH and room temperature), which cause no loss of enzymatic or antigen-binding activities, and the crosslinks formed are stable. However, the reactivities of enzymes and antibodies with glutaraldehyde are different, resulting in the formation of not only heteropolymers but also homopolymers by random coupling. Polymers in which antibodies are not fully reactive may not be eliminated by conventional purification processes and cause high nonspecific signals and low precision, while homopolymers are of no use at all for specific signals. Thus, although they are simple, one-step methods are of little use for ultrasensitive enzyme immunoassays.

Since the first attempt at enzyme-labeling, by two- and three-step methods, many reagents have been used. However, most of the reagents tested have serious disadvantages, and only a few crosslinking reagents including glutaraldehyde, periodate and derivatives of maleimide and pyridyldisulfide are in current use.

Glutaraldehyde readily reacts with amino groups of proteins such as enzymes and antibodies under mild conditions to form complex crosslinks which are stable without reduction (Avrameas, 1969; Korn et al., 1972; Hardy et al., 1976a, b; Whipple and Ruta, 1974).

Oxidation of carbohydrate moieties attached to enzyme molecules by periodate generates aldehyde groups that react with amino groups of antibodies providing stable crosslinks after reduction (Fig. 11.1) (Nakane and Kawaoi, 1974).

Maleimide groups readily react with thiol groups to form stable crosslinks (Fig. 11.1) (Ishikawa et al., 1983b). Maleimide groups are introduced into one of the proteins, either the enzyme or the antibody, and thiol groups are introduced into the other protein. Thiol groups present in the native forms of enzymes such as β-D-galactosidase from *E. coli* and thiol groups generated in the hinge portion of antibody molecules by mild reduction are used to obtain useful conjugates. Pyridyldisulfide groups may be substituted for maleimide groups (Fig. 11.1), although the conjugation efficiency is lower (Carlsson et al., 1978; King et al., 1978).

Antibodies and enzymes can be indirectly and noncovalently crosslinked based on the strong affinity between biotin and avidin

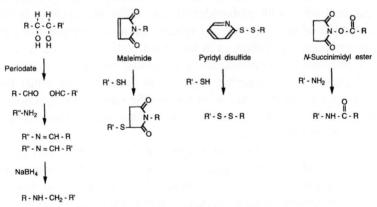

Fig. 11.1. Chemical reactions widely used for enzyme-labeling.

or streptavidin (Guesdon et al., 1979). A feature of this method is amplification of signals achieved by introduction of many biotin residues into antibody molecules and subsequent binding of avidin or streptavidin molecules linked to enzyme molecules. However, nonspecific binding is also amplified.

The two- and three-step methods for enzyme-labeling of antibodies using the reagents described above may be divided into two groups: hinge and nonhinge methods. The hinge method has a number of advantages over the nonhinge method including the absence of polymerization, low nonspecific binding of Fab′-enzyme conjugates, full retention of the antigen binding activity of Fab′ and reproducible production with high yields of monomeric Fab′-horseradish peroxidase conjugates (Ishikawa et al., 1983b). Details of these methods are described below.

11.2. Hinge method

In the hinge method, the hinge portion of antibody molecules is selectively conjugated to enzyme molecules (Fig. 4.2) (Ishikawa et al., 1983b). This is achieved using thiol groups generated in the hinge of antibody molecules by mild reduction.

Thiol groups are generated almost exclusively in the hinge portion either simply by mild reduction of IgG molecules with 2-mercaptoethylamine or by pepsin digestion of IgG molecules to $F(ab')_2$ and subsequent mild reduction of $F(ab')_2$ to Fab′ with 2-mercaptoethylamine. Fab′ can be prepared from rabbit and capybara IgG and monoclonal mouse IgG_1, IgG_{2a} and IgG_3 with high efficiency and also from sheep, goat and guinea pig IgG, although with lower efficiency.

For the reaction with thiol groups in the hinge of antibody molecules, maleimide groups are introduced into enzyme molecules. β-D-galactosidase from E. coli containing approximately 20 thiol groups in its native form is treated with excess amounts of the dimaleimide derivatives such as N,N'-o-phenylenedimaleimide and

N,N'-oxydimethylenedimaleimide listed in Table 10.1 (Fig. 4.2). There is no loss of β-D-galactosidase activity on treatment with these dimaleimide derivatives. Other enzymes containing amino groups but no thiol groups are treated with the N-succinimidyl-maleimidocarboxylates listed in Table 10.1 (Fig. 4.2). The number of maleimide groups introduced into horseradish peroxidase is limited (one to two per molecule) by the limited number of amino groups (2–3 per molecule), while the number of maleimide groups introduced into other enzyme molecules containing many amino groups depends on the reaction conditions chosen. On treatment with N-succinimidyl-maleimidocarboxylates, there is no loss of horseradish peroxidase activity. However, the activities of alkaline phosphatase from calf intestine and glucose-6-phosphate dehydrogenase from *Leuconostoc mesenteroides* lost are 40–50 and 50–70%, respectively. The highest conjugation efficiency is obtained with N-succinimidyl-6-maleimidohexanoate (Fig. 10.1) (Hashida et al., 1984).

Alternatively, maleimide groups may be introduced into the hinge portion of Fab' (Kato et al., 1976) or mildly reduced IgG (Kato et al., 1975a) by reaction with excess dimaleimide derivatives such as N,N'-o-phenylenedimaleimide and N,N'-oxydimethylenedimaleimide (Table 10.1) and then allowed to react with thiol groups introduced into enzyme molecules or present in the native form of β-D-galactosidase from *E. coli*.

The molar ratio of Fab' to horseradish peroxidase containing maleimide groups in the reaction mixture for conjugation is approximately one, since the conjugates formed are almost exclusively monomeric (Fig. 11.2) (Yoshitake et al., 1982). In contrast, the molar ratio of Fab' to other enzymes containing maleimide groups for conjugation must be 3–10 to convert all the enzyme molecules to conjugates, since unconjugated molecules of enzymes such as β-D-galactosidase from *E. coli* and alkaline phosphatase from calf intestine with molecular weights of 540 and 100 kDa, respectively, are not separated by gel filtration from enzyme conjugates with Fab' having a molecular weight of 46 kDa (Ishikawa et al., 1988).

The conjugation reaction is faster at higher temperatures and at higher concentrations of maleimide and thiol groups. When peroxidase containing approximately one maleimide group per molecule and rabbit Fab′ containing one thiol group per molecule are incubated at concentrations of 50 nmol/mL (2 and 2.3 mg/mL of protein, respectively), the conjugation is almost complete within 5–10 h at 4°C and within 1 h at 30°C (Yoshitake et al., 1982).

The hinge method has the following advantages (Ishikawa et al., 1983b).

First, there is no polymerization, since thiol groups generated in IgG and Fab′ on mild reduction are limited in both number and location in antibody molecules (Table 11.1) (Ishikawa, 1987). In addition, horseradish peroxidase has only a limited number (2–3 per molecule) of amino groups, allowing the introduction of only a limited number of maleimide groups (one to two per molecule). As a result, Fab′-horseradish peroxidase conjugates prepared by the hinge methods are almost exclusively monomeric and can be easily separated by gel filtration from unconjugated Fab′ and peroxidase, which have similar molecular weights (Fig. 11.2A). Fab′ conjugates with other enzymes including β-D-galactosidase from *E. coli* and alkaline phosphatase from calf intestine, which have much larger molecular weights than that of Fab′, are not monomeric but contain more than one molecules of Fab′ per enzyme molecule, since more than one maleimide group introduced per enzyme molecule reacts with excess Fab′ on a molar basis to convent all the enzyme molecules to conjugates.

Second, the antigen-binding activities of Fab′ and IgG are fully retained in enzyme-labeled conjugates, since the hinge portion of Fab′, which is remote from the antigen-binding site of antibody molecules, is selectively conjugated to enzyme molecules, avoiding possible steric hindrance of the antigen-binding reaction and giving high specific signals (Fig. 4.3) (Imagawa et al., 1982b).

Third, the Fab′-enzyme conjugates prepared by the hinge methods show low nonspecific bindings, since enzyme molecules cover the hinge portion of Fab′ molecules, which possibly causes high

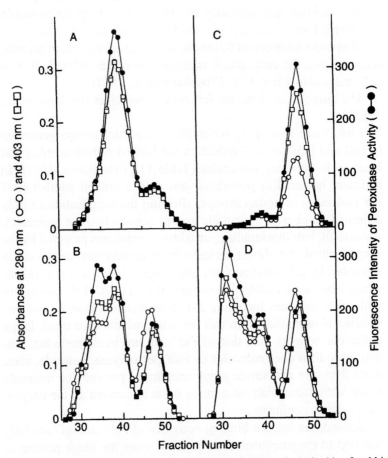

Fig. 11.2. Elution profiles from a column of Ultrogel AcA 44 of rabbit Fab′-horseradish peroxidase conjugates (Ishikawa, 1996): (A) hinge method using N-succinimidyl-6-maleimidohexanoate; (B, C and D) nonhinge methods using N-succinimidyl-4-(N-maleimidomethyl)cyclohexane-1-carboxylate (B), glutaraldehyde (C) and periodate (D).

TABLE 11.1

Characteristics of antibody-enzyme conjugates prepared by various methods

Enzyme-labeling method	Conjugate	Polymeri-zation of enzyme	Molar ratio (Fab' or IgG : enzyme)	Recovery in conjugate Fab' or IgG (%)	Enzyme (%)
Hinge method with					
maleimide	Fab'-HRP	No	1 : 1	75–85	75–85
pyridyl disulfide	Fab'-HRP	No	1 : 1	55	55
maleimide	Fab'-Gal	No	1–3 : 1	70–80	100
maleimide	Fab'-ALP	No	1–3 : 1	78	100
Non-hinge method with					
glutaraldehyde	Fab'-HRP	No	1 : 1	25	5
	Fab'-GAL	Yes	polymers	–	–
	Fab'-ALP	Yes	polymers	–	–
periodate	Fab'-HRP	Yes and No	polymers and monomer	55 20	55 20
Maleimide method (pyridyl disulfide method)	IgG-HRP	No	1 : 1–3	100	45
	IgG-GAL	No	1–3 : 1	40	100
	IgG-ALP	No	1 : 1–3	100	55

HRP: horseradish peroxidase. GAL: β-D-galactosidase from *E. coli*. ALP: alkaline phosphatase from calf intestine (Ishikawa, 1987; Ishikawa et al., 1988).

nonspecific bindings due to hydrophobicity (Fig. 4.3) (Imagawa et al., 1982b).

Fourth, Fab'-enzyme conjugates are obtained in high yields, provided that expected numbers of thiol and maleimide groups are present in Fab' and enzyme molecules, respectively (Table 11.1 and Fig. 11.2) (Ishikawa et al., 1988).

Pyridyldisulfide derivatives can be substituted for maleimide derivatives in the hinge methods. Pyridyl disulfide groups in place of maleimide groups are introduced into enzyme molecules using N-succinimidyl-3-(2-pyridyldithio)propionate (Fig. 10.1) and allowed to react with thiol groups in the hinge of Fab' (Fig. 11.3) (Imagawa et al., 1982a). Monomeric Fab'-horseradish peroxidase conjugates are formed, which have the same properties as those

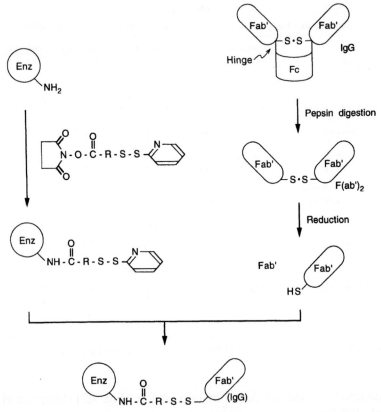

Fig. 11.3. Hinge method using pyridyl disulfide derivatives. Enz: enzyme.
—S·S—: disulfide bond.

prepared by the hinge method using maleimide derivatives. No polymerization takes place. The antigen-binding activity of Fab′ is fully retained after conjugation. The Fab′-enzyme conjugates prepared with the pyridyldisulfide derivative show as low nonspecific bindings as those with maleimide derivatives. However, the pyridyl disulfide method shows less efficient conjugation than the maleimide method.

In contrast to its efficiency for enzyme-labeling of Fab′, the con-jugation efficiency of the hinge method for IgG with enzymes is rather low, and unconjugated IgG is not easily eliminated from IgG conjugate preparations with enzymes other than β-D-galactosidase from *E. coli* by gel filtration. In addition, the antigen-binding activ-ities of IgG-enzyme conjugates prepared by the hinge and nonhinge methods are similar, since IgG molecules are larger than Fab′ molecules and may be conjugated to enzymes without covering the antigen-binding sites by enzyme molecules in the nonhinge method. Thus, there may be no advantage in the hinge method for enzyme-labeling of IgG.

11.3. Nonhinge method

In the nonhinge method, reactive groups present in, generated in or introduced into enzyme molecules are allowed to react with the corresponding reactive groups present in, generated in or intro-duced into antibody or antibody fragment molecules. The critical difference between the hinge and nonhinge methods is that reac-tive groups other than thiol groups in the hinge of antibody and related fragment molecules (amino groups in most cases) are used randomly used for enzyme-labeling in the nonhinge method, while thiol groups generated in the hinge of antibody and related fragment molecules are selectively used for conjugation in the hinge methods.

The glutaraldehyde method is a nonhinge method. In the two-step method with glutaraldehyde, which is simple and reproducible, horseradish peroxidase is treated with glutaraldehyde to introduce aldehyde groups and, after removal of free glutaraldehyde, allowed to react with antibodies to form monomeric conjugates with stable crosslinks, since the enzyme has only a small number of amino groups (Avrameas and Ternynck, 1971). All forms of antibodies, such as IgG, F(ab′)$_2$, Fab and Fab′, treated with N-ethylmaleimide or monoiodoacetate to block thiol groups in the hinge, can be con-jugated. A disadvantage of this method is that only a small fraction

(5%) of the enzyme used is recovered in antibody conjugates (Table 11.1 and Fig. 11.2C) (Imagawa et al., 1982b). Other enzymes including β-D-galactosidase from *E. coli*, alkaline phosphatase from calf intestine and antibodies containing many amino groups are polymerized with glutaraldehyde. There must be very serious loss of antigen-binding activity when antibodies are polymerized with glutaraldehyde and subsequently coated with enzyme molecules by conjugation.

The periodate method is another nonhinge method. In the two-step method with periodate, the carbohydrate moieties of horseradish peroxidase are oxidized with periodate to generate aldehyde groups and, after elimination of small molecules, allowed to react with antibodies, followed by reduction with borohydride (Wilson and Nakane, 1978). All forms of antibodies, including IgG and its fragments, can be conjugated as in the glutaraldehyde method described above. The recoveries of both the enzyme and antibodies in the conjugates are high in contrast to those by the glutaraldehyde method, although the conjugate preparation is a mixture of monomeric and polymeric conjugates (Table 11.1 and Fig. 11.2D) (Ishikawa, 1987). Increase in the yield is achieved by increase in the degree of periodate oxidation, but is associated with increase in the formation of polymerized conjugates, and antibody activity is not fully retained (Imagawa et al., 1982b).

The nonhinge method is also possible using derivatives of maleimide and pyridyldisulfide (Ishikawa et al., 1983b). For example, the thiol groups introduced into antibody molecules using *N*-succinimidyl-*S*-acetylthio(mercapto)acetate or *N*-succinimidyl-3-(2′-pyridyldithio)propionate (Fig. 10.1) are allowed to react with the maleimide groups introduced into enzyme molecules using *N*-succinimidyl-maleimidocarboxylates or dimaleimides. Alternatively, the maleimide groups introduced into antibody molecules are allowed to react with the thiol groups introduced into enzyme molecules. All forms of antibodies including IgG and its fragments can be conjugated as in the glutaraldehyde and periodate methods. Pyridyldisulfide derivatives can be substituted for maleimide derivatives (Ishikawa et al., 1983b).

The nonhinge methods have some disadvantages compared with the hinge methods described above (Ishikawa et al., 1983b).

First, some polymerization may take place, even if the number of reactive groups present in, generated in or introduced into both proteins is carefully controlled (Fig. 11.2B). In the periodate method, stronger oxidation of horseradish peroxidase with periodate increases the number of aldehyde groups generated, resulting in the formation of polymeric antibody-peroxidase conjugates, since antibodies and related fragments have many amino groups (Fig. 11.2D) (Ishikawa et al, 1988).

Second, the antigen-binding activities of Fab- and Fab'-enzyme conjugates prepared by the nonhinge method are partially impaired, giving low specific signals, since enzyme molecules may be bound to portions close to, or even the center of the antigen-binding site of the fragments due to random use of amino groups (Fig. 4.3) (Imagawa et al., 1982b).

Third, Fab'- and Fab-horseradish peroxidase conjugates prepared by the nonhinge methods show high nonspecific bindings, since enzyme molecules only partially cover the hinge portion of the fragment molecules, which is possibly hydrophobic (Fig. 4.3) (Imagawa et al., 1982b).

11.4. Monomeric antibody-enzyme conjugates

The enzyme-labeling methods described above provide monomeric conjugates with horseradish peroxidase but not with other enzymes (Table 11.1). For preparation of monomeric conjugates with other enzymes, two different methods have been developed.

In one method, affinity-purified rabbit (anti-human IgG) Fab' was allowed to react with a molar excess of β-D-galactosidase from E. coli, into which maleimide groups had been introduced, so that only one molecule of the Fab' was conjugated with each enzyme molecule, and the monomeric Fab'-β-D-galactosidase conjugate formed was separated from unconjugated β-D-galactosidase by affinity chromatography using anti-rabbit IgG antibodies (Inoue et al., 1985b). The monomeric conjugate was dissociated from anti-rabbit IgG antibodies with 4 mol/L urea, since β-D-galactosidase from *E. coli* is stable in the presence of 4 mol/L urea.

In another method, F(ab')$_2$ or IgG was converted to monomeric 2,4-dinitrophenyl-Fab'-β-D-galactosidase conjugate, and unconjugated β-D-galactosidase was removed by affinity chromatography using (anti-2,4-dinitrophenyl group) antibodies (Imagawa et al., 1984a). F(ab')$_2$ or IgG was 2,4-dinitrophenylated and converted to 2,4-dinitrophenyl-Fab'. The 2,4-dinitrophenyl-Fab' was allowed to react with a molar excess of β-D-galactosidase into which maleimide groups had been introduced, so that only one molecule of 2,4-dinitrophenyl-Fab' was conjugated to each β-D-galactosidase molecule. The monomeric 2,4-dinitrophenyl-Fab'-β-D-galactosidase conjugate formed was separated from unconjugated β-D-galactosidase by affinity chromatography using (anti-2,4-dinitrophenyl group) antibodies. Dissociation of the monomeric conjugate from (anti-2,4-dinitrophenyl) antibodies was performed with excess ϵN-2,4-dinitrophenyl-L-lysine.

11.5. Affinity-purified antibody-enzyme conjugates

Affinity-purified antibody-enzyme conjugates may be prepared by affinity-purification after enzyme-labeling, since horseradish peroxidase, for example, is fairly stable at acidic pH values used for affinity-purification (Fig. 11.4) (Inoue et al., 1985a; Ruan et al., 1985). However, affinity-purification of antibodies before enzyme-labeling is recommended for the following reasons. First, some enzymes, such as β-D-galactosidase from *E. coli*, are not stable under the conditions used for affinity-purification, such as an acidic pH and high concentration of urea (Fig. 11.5). Second, the presence of antigens released from antigen-columns in affinity-purified antibody preparations causes high backgrounds in two-site immunoassays for antigens, and it is easier to eliminate them by gel filtration before enzyme-labeling (Hashida et al., 1996c). For example, affinity-purified $F(ab')_2$ or Fab' is easily separated from the immune complexes of affinity-purified $F(ab')_2$ or Fab' and antigens released from antigen-columns by gel filtration using Ultrogel AcA 44 (Biosepra, Villeneuve la Garenne, France). This separation becomes easier when antigens are covalently conjugated to proteins with molecular weights of more than that of $F(ab')_2$ or Fab' before immobilization on columns (Kasai et al., 1990; Hashida et al., 1996c).

11.6. Microscale preparation of antibody-enzyme conjugates

Three methods are available for conjugation of small quantities of antibodies to enzymes.

In the first method, small quantities of antibodies are mixed with appropriate quantities (e.g., 1 mg) of nonspecific immunoglobulins from different species of animals as carriers, conjugated to enzymes and separated from the carrier conjugates using antibodies to the carrier antibodies (Inoue et al., 1984). This method is useful only for monomeric conjugates.

In a second method, small quantities of antibodies are mixed with appropriate quantities of nonspecific immunoglobulins as carriers, conjugated to enzymes and separated from the carrier conjugates by affinity-purification using antigens (Inoue et al., 1985a; Ruan et al., 1985).

In a third method, small quantities of antibodies are 2,4-dinitrophenylated, mixed with appropriate quantities of nonspecific immunoglobulins as carriers, conjugated to enzymes and separated from the carrier conjugates by affinity chromatography using (anti-2,4-dinitrophenyl group) antibodies (Ruan et al., 1984a).

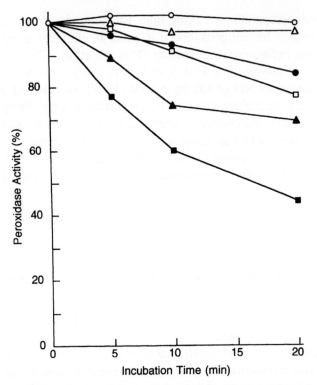

Fig. 11.4. Stability of horseradish peroxidase at acidic pH values. The enzyme was dissolved in 50 mmol/L glycine-HCl buffer (open symbols) or the same buffer containing 0.1 mol/L NaCl (closed symbols). Squares, triangles and circles indicate results at pH 2.5, 2.7 and 2.9, respectively.

11.7. Characterization and evaluation of antibody-enzyme conjugates

11.7.1. Molecular size

Irrespective of whether maleimide or pyridyl disulfide derivatives are used, the rabbit Fab′-horseradish peroxidase conjugates prepared by the hinge methods are largely monomeric as evident from their elution profiles on gel filtration, although a mouse Fab′ (IgG$_1$)-

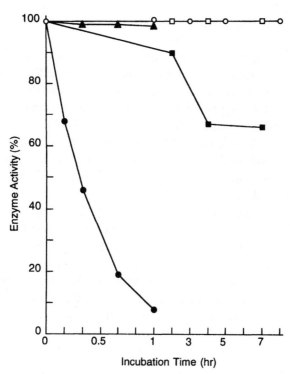

Fig. 11.5. Stability of enzymes in the presence of urea. Squares, circles and tri-angles indicate results with horseradish peroxidase, β-D-galactosidase from *E. coli* and alkaline phosphatase from calf intestine, respectively. Open and closed symbols indicate the presence of 4 and 6 mol/L urea, respectively.

horseradish peroxidase conjugate preparation contains conjugates of slightly larger molecular weights (Fig. 11.2 and Table 11.1) (Yoshitake et al., 1982). This is because thiol groups in the hinge of Fab′ are limited both in number and location and the number of maleimide groups introduced per horseradish peroxidase mole-cule is very small (1–2 per molecule) due to the limited number of amino groups (2–3 per molecule). The two-step glutaralde-hyde method also provides a monomeric Fab′ (or Fab)-horseradish peroxidase conjugate, whereas polymers are formed besides the monomeric conjugate in the periodate method (Fig. 11.2 and Table 11.1) (Ishikawa et al., 1983b).

The conjugates of Fab′ and other enzymes such as β-D-galactosidase from *E. coli* and alkaline phosphatase from calf intestine are heterogeneous. In the Fab′ conjugates with these enzymes prepared by the hinge methods, enzyme molecules are not polymerized but associated with different numbers of Fab′ molecules, while in the glutaraldehyde method these enzymes are polymerized (Figs. 11.6, 11.7 and Table 11.1) (Ishikawa et al., 1983b). Monomeric conjugates with these enzymes are obtained only by other methods as described above.

The conjugates of IgG and enzymes prepared by the nonhinge methods with derivatives of maleimide or pyridyldisulfide are also heterogeneous (Figs. 11.6–11.8 and Table 11.1) (Ishikawa et al., 1983b). IgG molecules are not polymerized but associated with different numbers of peroxidase or alkaline phosphatase molecules. In IgG-β-D-galactosidase conjugates, β-D-galactosidase molecules are not polymerized but associated with different numbers of IgG molecules (Table 11.1).

11.7.2. Purity

The monomeric Fab′-horseradish peroxidase conjugates prepared by the hinge methods are well separated from unconjugated peroxidase and Fab′ by gel filtration on a column of Ultrogel AcA 44 (Biosepra, Villeneuve la Garenne, France), provided that the column used is sufficiently long (Fig. 11.2) (Yoshitake et al., 1982). The purity of Fab′-peroxidase conjugate preparations was deduced in two different ways (Ishikawa et al., 1983b). (1) Peroxidase activity in the conjugate preparations obtained by the hinge methods was almost completely (98–99%) adsorbed to a column of (anti-IgG) IgG-Sepharose 4B (Amersham Pharmacia Biotech, Uppsala, Sweden), indicating that there was little unconjugated peroxidase in the conjugate preparations. (2) When the fluorescein-labeled

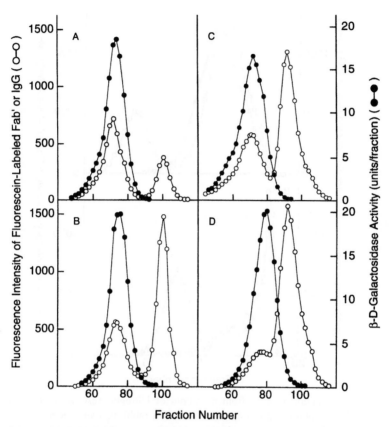

Fig. 11.6. Elution profiles from a column of Sepharose 6B of the rabbit Fab′- and rabbit IgG-β-D-galactosidase conjugates prepared in two different ways by the hinge method using N,N'-o-phenylenedimaleimide (Ruan et al., 1984b; Ishikawa et al., 1988). First, the maleimide groups introduced into β-D-galactosidase molecules from *E. coli* by treatment with excess N,N'-o-phenylenedimaleimide were allowed to react with the thiol groups generated in the hinge of Fab′ (A), or the reduced IgG (C). Second, the thiol groups in the native form of β-D-galactosidase were allowed to react with the maleimide groups introduced into the hinge of Fab′ (B), or the reduced IgG (D) by treatment with excess N,N'-o-phenylenedimaleimide.

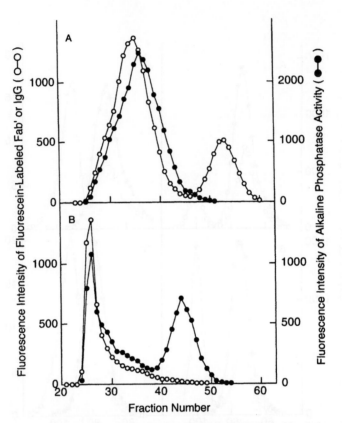

Fig. 11.7. Elution profiles from a column of Ultrogel AcA 34 of the rabbit Fab'-alkaline phosphatase conjugate (A) and the rabbit IgG-alkaline phosphatase conjugate (B) prepared by the hinge and nonhinge methods, respectively, using N-succinimidyl-6-maleimidohexanoate (Ishikawa et al., 1988).

Fab'-peroxidase preparations obtained by the hinge methods were applied to a column of concanavalin A-Sepharose 4B (Amersham Pharmacia Biotech, Uppsala, Sweden), the adsorption of fluorescence intensity was 90–95%, indicating that little unconjugated $F(ab')_2$ was present. Conjugates of high purity could readily be

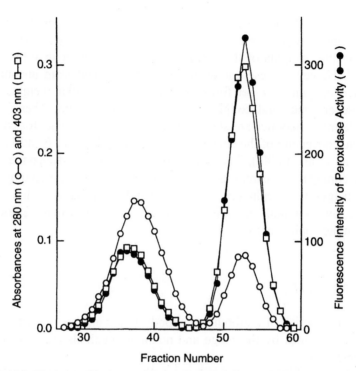

Fig. 11.8. Elution profile from a column of Ultrogel AcA 34 of the mouse monoclonal IgG$_1$-horseradish peroxidase conjugate prepared by the nonhinge method
using N-succinimidyl-4-(N-maleimidomethyl)cyclohexane-1-carboxylate. The
number of peroxidase molecules conjugated per IgG molecule was 1.0–2.7.

obtained by elution from the column with 2-methyl-D-mannoside
(Ishikawa et al., 1983b).

The purity of Fab'-peroxidase conjugates prepared by the glutaraldehyde and periodate methods tend to be lower (Imagawa et al.,
1982b). In the glutaraldehyde method, separation of the conjugates
from unconjugated peroxidase is often not complete, since much
peroxidase remains unconjugated.

The Fab' conjugates with β-D-galactosidase and alkaline phosphatase prepared by the hinge methods are well separated from

unconjugated Fab' by gel filtration using sufficiently long columns of Sepharose 6B and Ultrogel AcA 34, respectively, since the molecular weights of these enzymes are much larger than that of Fab'. However, these conjugates are not separated from unconjugated enzymes by gel filtration, since the molecular weights of these enzymes and conjugates are not very different. Therefore, maleimide-enzymes are allowed to react with excess Fab' for complete conversion of the enzymes to conjugates (Figs. 11.6 and 11.7) (Ruan et al., 1984b). The proportion of unconjugated enzymes in the conjugate preparations can be examined by use of a column of (anti-IgG) IgG-Sepharose 4B (Amersham Pharmacia Biotech, Uppsala, Sweden) and comparison of the enzyme activity in the effluent with the applied activity.

11.7.3. Yield

The recoveries of antibodies, antibody fragments and enzymes in the conjugates by the hinge and nonhinge methods are shown in Table 11.1.

In the hinge method for labeling Fab' with horseradish peroxidase, the recoveries of both the enzyme and Fab' in the conjugates are very high (75–85%) with N-succinimidyl-4-(N-maleimidomethyl)-cyclohexane-1-carboxylate (Imagawa et al., 1982b) and N-succinimidyl-6-maleimidohexanoate (Hashida et al., 1984) (Fig. 11.2), but lower (55%) with N-succinimidyl-3-(2-dithiopyridyl)propionate (Imagawa et al., 1982a). The recovery of horseradish peroxidase in the conjugates is very low in the glutaraldehyde method and is fairly high in the periodate method, although accompanied by polymeric conjugates (Fig. 11.2) (Imagawa et al., 1982b).

In the hinge method, in which thiol groups in the hinge of Fab' are allowed to react with the maleimide groups introduced into molecules of β-D-galactosidase from E. coli and alkaline phosphatase from calf intestine, the recoveries of the enzymes in the conjugates are almost complete, and the recoveries of Fab′ are 70–80% (Figs. 11.6 and 11.7) (Ruan et al., 1984b). When the maleimide groups introduced into Fab′ molecules by reaction with excess $N,N′$-o-phenylenedimaleimide were allowed to react with the thiol groups in the native form of β-D-galactosidase from $E.$ $coli$, the recovery of Fab′ in the conjugate was lower (38%) (Figs. 11.6 and 11.9) (Ruan et al., 1984b). When the thiol groups in the hinge of reduced IgG or the maleimide groups introduced into the hinge of reduced IgG by reaction with excess $N,N′$-o-phenylenedimaleimide were used for conjugation, the recovery of IgG in β-D-galactosidase conjugate were lower (40 or 24%) than that of Fab′ (Figs. 11.6 and 11.9) (Ruan et al., 1984b).

11.7.4. Stability

The activities of horseradish peroxidase and β-D-galactosidase from $E.$ $coli$ in the conjugates prepared by the hinge methods using maleimide derivatives are stable for at least four years when stored under the conditions described in Chapter 13. Alkaline phosphatase from calf intestine may be similarly stable.

The antigen-binding activity of Fab′ in the conjugates prepared by the hinge methods using maleimide derivatives appears to be stable for years under the conditions described in Chapter 13, although the stability may vary depending on the antibodies. No significant loss of antigen-binding activity was observed for 3–4 years in horseradish peroxidase conjugates with rabbit anti-human growth hormone Fab′, goat anti-human α-fetoprotein Fab′, rabbit anti-human chorionic gonadotropin Fab′ and rabbit anti-human ferritin Fab′ or in β-D-galactosidase conjugates with rabbit anti-human ferritin Fab′, goat anti-human IgE Fab′ and goat anti-human α-fetoprotein Fab′.

The crosslinks formed by the hinge methods using maleimide derivatives are also stable for years under the conditions described in Chapter 13. This was confirmed as follows. After

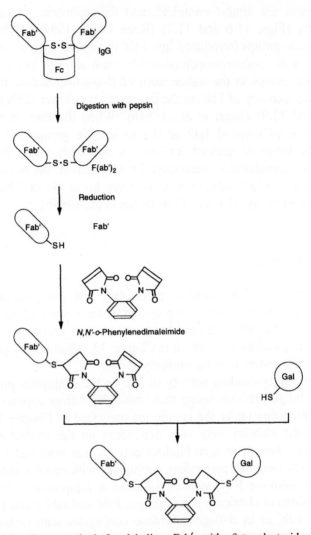

Fig. 11.9. Hinge method for labeling Fab′ with β-D-galactosidase using N,N′-o-phenylenedimaleimide. Maleimide groups were introduced into Fab′ molecules by treatment with excess N,N′-o-phenylenedimaleimide and then allowed to react with thiol groups in the native form of β-D-galactosidase from E. coli.

TABLE 11.2

Stability of Fab'-horseradish peroxidase conjugate

Day of storage	Peroxidase activity (%)		Adsorption to human IgG-Sepharose 4B (%)		
	Concentration of Fab'-peroxidase conjugate (μg/mL)				
	1	10	1	10	50
0	100	100	90	90	90
7	90	112	85	87	89
30	68	111	82	86	88
90	27	107	77	85	85
180	1.8	103	73	79	81

Anti-human IgG Fab'-horseradish peroxidase conjugate prepared by the hinge method using a maleimide derivative was stored at 4°C in 10 mmol/L sodium phosphate buffer, pH 7.0, containing 0.1 mol/L NaCl, 1 g/L bovine serum albumin and 50 mg/L merthiolate.

3–4 year storage under the conditions described in Chapter 13, the Fab'-peroxidase conjugate and the fluorescein-labeled Fab'-β-D-galactosidase conjugate prepared by the hinge methods using maleimide derivatives were subjected to gel filtration on columns of Ultrogel AcA 44 (Biosepra, Villeneuve la Garenne, France) and Sepharose 6B (Amersham Pharmacia Biotech, Uppsala, Sweden), respectively. Little activity corresponding to free peroxidase and little fluorescence intensity corresponding to free fluorescein-labeled Fab' were detected.

However, Fab'-enzyme conjugates are not very stable at low concentrations. When anti-human IgG Fab'-horseradish peroxidase conjugate was stored at 4°C at a concentration of 1 μg/mL, the enzyme activity decreased 30–70% within 30–90 days, although the antigen-binding activity decreased much more slowly (Table 11.2). Thus, Fab'-peroxidase conjugates should be stored at concentrations of over 10 μg/mL.

11.7.5. Specific and nonspecific bindings of antibody-enzyme conjugates

Fab′-enzyme conjugates prepared by the hinge methods are more useful than IgG-enzyme conjugates for improving the sensitivity of noncompetitive solid phase enzyme immunoassays (Fig. 4.3A) (Ishikawa et al., 1983b). Fab′-enzyme conjugates prepared by the hinge methods show not only much lower nonspecific bindings than IgG-enzyme conjugates but also as high specific bindings as IgG-enzyme conjugates, since the antigen-binding activity of Fab′ is fully retained in the conjugates because of selective conjugation of the hinge portion, which is remote from the antigen-binding site. However, it is difficult to prepare $F(ab')_2$ from IgG_{2b} of mouse by pepsin digestion. In some cases, the antigen-binding activity may be partially or totally lost by pepsin digestion and/or by reduction with 2-mercaptoethylamine (Hashida et al., 1985).

Fab′-enzyme conjugates prepared by hinge methods are more useful for improving the sensitivity of noncompetitive solid phase enzyme immunoassays than Fab′- and Fab-enzyme conjugates prepared by nonhinge methods (Fig. 4.3B, C and Table 11.3) (Ishikawa et al., 1983b). The antigen-binding activity of Fab′ is fully retained in conjugates prepared by hinge methods as described above, while those of Fab′ and Fab are partially lost in conjugates prepared by nonhinge methods, in which amino groups including those close to or even in the center of the antigen-binding site are randomly used for conjugation. In addition, the Fab′-enzyme conjugates prepared by hinge methods show lower nonspecific bindings than the Fab′- and Fab-enzyme conjugates prepared by nonhinge methods, probably because the hinge portion, which may be hydrophobic, causing high nonspecific binding, is constantly covered by enzyme molecules in hinge methods but not in nonhinge methods. In consistency with this, Fab′-peroxidase conjugates prepared by hinge methods are more useful in immunohistochemical stainings of antigens then those prepared by nonhinge methods (Imagawa et al., 1982a; Ishikawa et al., 1983c).

TABLE 11.3

Specific and nonspecific bindings of anti-human chorionic gonadotropin (hCG) Fab'-horseradish peroxidase conjugates prepared by various methods in two-site enzyme immunoassay of hCG

Conjugation method	Binding of anti-hCG Fab'-peroxidase conjugate		Ratio S/N
	Nonspecific (N) (%)	Specific (S) (%)	
Hinge method			
maleimide	0.0040	0.40	100
pyridyl disulfide	0.0040	0.38	95
Nonhinge method			
maleimide	0.021	0.14	6.7
pyridyl disulfide	0.016	0.19	12
glutaraldehyde	0.034	0.11	3.2
periodate monomeric	0.031	0.18	5.8
polymeric	0.060	0.22	3.7

The peroxidase activities nonspecifically and specifically bound were examined in two-site enzyme immunoassay of hCG, in which individual polystyrene beads coated with rabbit anti-hCG IgG were incubated in the absence and presence of hCG (40 mU/assay) at 37°C for 4 h and then with rabbit anti-hCG Fab'-horseradish peroxidase conjugates (200 ng/assay) prepared by various methods at 37°C for 6 h. Bound peroxidase activities are expressed as percentages of the peroxidase activities used per assay.

11.7.6. Comparison of the hinge method and the biotin-avidin method

In the biotin-avidin method, antibodies are connected with enzymes through links between biotin residues introduced into antibody molecules and avidin labeled with enzymes. Therefore, there is no need to conjugate antibodies to enzymes covalently. The enzyme activity bound to antibodies through the biotin-avidin links increases with the increase in the number of biotin residues introduced into antibody molecules, enhancing the specific signals. However, the nonspecific binding of biotinylated antibodies to solid phases also increases with the increase in the number of biotin residues introduced, and avidin-enzyme conjugates are bound to biotinylated antibodies nonspecifically adsorbed on the solid phases, enhancing the nonspecific signals.

CHAPTER 12

Preparation and affinity-purification of IgG fragments

Reproducible methods are described below. However, unexpected results may be observed in some cases. Favorable results may be obtained by changing conditions, such as the concentration of reagents, pH, time, temperature etc.

12.1. Preparations of F(ab')₂ and Fab'

12.1.1. Pepsin digestion of IgG to F(ab')₂

1. Prepare 3–5 mg of IgG in 0.5 mL. $E_{280} = 1.5 \text{ g}^{-1} \text{L cm}^{-1}$ for rabbit IgG (Palmer and Nisonoff, 1964) and $1.4 \text{ g}^{-1} \text{L cm}^{-1}$ for mouse IgG (Ey et al., 1978). The molecular weight of IgG is 150,000 (Dorrington and Tanford, 1970; Gorini et al., 1969).
2. Dialyze the IgG solution against 0.1 mol/L sodium acetate buffer containing 0.1 mol/L NaCl at 4°C. Use acetate buffer of pH 4.5 for IgG from most species of animals such as rabbit, goat, sheep, guinea pig and capybara and monoclonal mouse IgG$_{2a}$ and IgG$_3$ (Lamoyi and Nisonoff, 1983) but of pH 4.2 for monoclonal mouse IgG$_1$ and of pH 4.7–4.9 for monoclonal mouse IgG$_{2b}$.
3. Add 0.06–0.2 mg of pepsin from porcine gastric mucosa to the dialyzed solution.
4. Incubate the mixture at 37°C for 6–24 h.

249

5. Adjust the digest to pH 7 with 2 mol/L Tris-HCl buffer, pH 8.0.
6. Subject the neutralized solution to gel filtration using a column (1.5 × 45 cm) of Ultrogel AcA 44 (Biosepra, Villeneuve la Garenne, France) in 0.1 mol/L sodium phosphate buffer, pH 7.0 (Fig. 12.1). Adjust the flow rate to 0.5–0.8 mL/min. Collect fractions of 1.0 mL.
7. Concentrate the pooled fractions to 0.45 mL in a microconcentrator (Centricon-30, Amicon Division W. R. Grace & Co., Beverly, MA) by centrifugation at 2000 × g at 4°C for 30 min.
8. Calculate the amount of F(ab')$_2$ from the extinction coefficient at 280 nm and the molecular weight. $E_{280} = 1.48$ g^{-1} L cm^{-1} for rabbit F(ab')$_2$ (Mandy and Nisonoff, 1963) and 1.4 g^{-1} L cm^{-1} for mouse F(ab')$_2$ (Ey et al., 1978). The molecular weights of rabbit and mouse F(ab')$_2$ are 92,000 (Jaquet and Cebra, 1965; Utsumi and Karush, 1965) and 95,000–110,000 (Gorini et al., 1969; Svasti and Milstein, 1972; Lamoyi and Nisonoff, 1983), respectively.

12.1.2. Reduction of F(ab')$_2$ to Fab'

1. Prepare 2–5 mg of F(ab')$_2$ in 0.45 mL of 0.1 mol/L sodium phosphate buffer, pH 6.0, containing 5 mmol/L EDTA.
2. Add 0.05 mL of 0.1 mol/L 2-mercaptoethylamine to the solution.
3. Incubate the mixture at 37°C for 1.5 h.
4. Subject the incubated mixture to gel filtration using a column (1.5 × 45 cm) of Ultrogel AcA 44 (Biosepra, Villeneuve la Garenne, France) in 0.1 mol/L sodium phosphate buffer, pH 6.0, containing 5 mmol/L EDTA. Adjust the flow rate to 0.5–0.8 mL/min. Collect fractions of 1.0 mL.
This process confirms the complete split of F(ab')$_2$ to Fab' and separates Fab' from other proteins including F(ab')$_2$ that is not split by reduction. If this step is unnecessary, subject the incubated mixture to gel filtration using a column (1.5 × 45 cm)

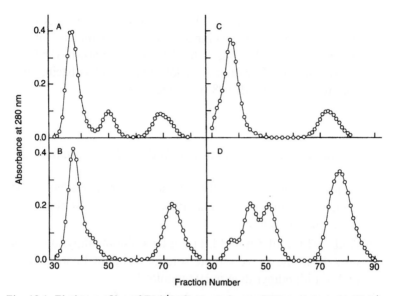

Fig. 12.1. Elution profiles of F(ab')$_2$ from a column of Ultrogel AcA 44. F(ab')$_2$ was prepared by pepsin digestion of rabbit IgG (A) and mouse IgG$_1$ (B), IgG$_{2a}$ (C) and IgG$_{2b}$ (D) (Ishikawa et al., 1988).

of Sephadex G-25 (Amersham Pharmacia Biotech, Uppsala, Sweden) in the same buffer. Alternatively, rapid gel filtration is possible using a centrifuged column (Penefsky, 1979). Wash a column (1.0 × 6.4 cm, 5 mL) of Sephadex G-50 fine (Amersham Pharmacia Biotech, Uppsala, Sweden) with the same buffer and centrifuge it in a test tube at 100 × g for 2 min. Apply the reaction mixture to the column, and centrifuge it in the same way.

5. Concentrate the pooled fractions in a microconcentrator (Centricon-30) by centrifugation at 2000 × g at 4°C for 30 min. There is no need for concentration when a centrifuged column is used.

6. Measure the content of thiol groups in Fab' as described below, and calculate the average number of thiol groups generated in Fab'. E$_{280}$ = 1.48 g^{-1} L cm^{-1} for rabbit Fab' (Mandy and

Nisonoff, 1963) and 1.4 $g^{-1} L cm^{-1}$ for mouse Fab' (Ey et al., 1978). The molecular weights of rabbit and mouse Fab' are 46,000 (Jaquet and Cebra, 1965; Utsumi and Karush, 1965) and 47,000–58,000 (Gorini et al., 1969; Svasti and Milstein, 1972; Lamoyi and Nisonoff, 1983), respectively.

12.1.3. Measurement of thiol groups in the Fab' preparation

1. Prepare 0.5 mL of 0.1 mol/L sodium phosphate buffer, pH 6.0, containing Fab' with an absorbance at 280 nm of above 0.32 (0.23 mg/mL, 5 nmol/mL).
2. Add 0.02 mL of 5 mmol/L (1.1 g/L) 4,4'-dithiodipyridine (mol wt 220) to the above sample solution. The final concentration of 4,4'-dithiodipyridine is 192 nmol/mL.
3. Incubate the mixture at room temperature for 5 min.
4. Measure the absorbance of the reaction mixture at 324 nm.
5. Calculate the average number of thiol groups per Fab' molecule. The molar extinction coefficient of pyridine-4-thione at 324 nm is 19,800 $mol^{-1} L cm^{-1}$ (0.0198 $nmol^{-1} mL cm^{-1}$) (Grassetti and Murray, 1967). The average number of thiol groups per Fab' molecule is approximately 1 in rabbit Fab' and 1–3 in Fab's from other species.

12.1.4. Blocking thiol groups of Fab'

1. Incubate $F(ab')_2$ with 10 mmol/L 2-mercaptoethylamine as described above.
2. Add 0.1 mL of 0.1 mol/L N-ethylmaleimide to 0.5 mL of the mixture. Sodium monoiodoacetate may be substituted for N-ethylmaleimide.
3. Incubate the mixture at 30°C for 60 min.

4. Subject the incubated mixture to gel filtration using a column (1.0 × 45 cm) of Ultrogel AcA 44 (Biosepra, Villeneuve la Garenne, France) in 0.15 mol/L NaCl.

12.2. Preparations of affinity-purified IgG, F(ab')$_2$ and Fab'

12.2.1. Affinity purification of IgG

Antibody IgG is affinity-purified by elution from, for example, a column of antigen-Sepharose 4B (Amersham Pharmacia Biotech, Uppsala, Sweden) under conditions to dissociate antigen-antibody complexes, such as low pH values (Ishikawa et al., 1980; Imagawa et al., 1981; Ruan et al., 1984a, 1985; Hashida et al., 1996c) and high concentrations of urea (Inoue et al., 1985a) and inorganic salts such as KSCN, KI and MgCl$_2$ (Hashida and Ishikawa, 1990). Low pH values are widely used, since the eluates containing affinity-purified IgG can be readily neutralized by addition of buffers of higher pH values, whereas removal of urea or inorganic salts at high concentrations by methods such as dialysis and gel filtration is time-consuming.

For use of affinity-purified IgG in ultrasensitive immunoassays of antigens, it is essential to remove the small amounts of the antigens released from antigen-columns during affinity-purification and present in the preparation of affinity-purified IgG, since their presence causes high nonspecific signals (Ruan et al., 1985; Kasai et al., 1990; Hashida and Ishikawa, 1990; Hashida et al., 1996c). The immune complexes of affinity-purified IgG and antigens released from the column may be removed by gel filtration (Fig. 12.2).

However, antigen-free affinity-purified F(ab')$_2$ and Fab' can be prepared more easily by gel filtration either before or after enzyme-labeling as described below (Ruan et al., 1985; Kasai et al., 1990; Hashida and Ishikawa, 1990; Hashida et al., 1996c).

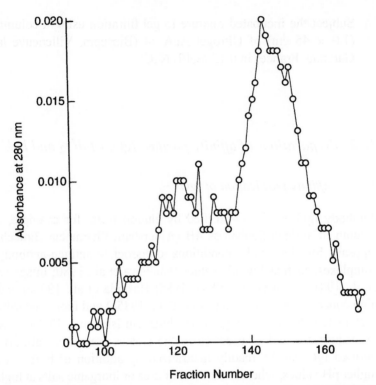

Fig. 12.2. Elution profile of affinity-purified 2,4-dinitrophenyl-biotinyl-rabbit anti-human ferritin IgG from a column of Ultrogel AcA 34. 2,4-dinitrophenyl-biotinyl-rabbit anti-human ferritin IgG was affinity-purified by elution from a column of human ferritin-Sepharose 4B with 3 mol/L potassium thiocyanate and subjected to gel filtration on a column (1.5 × 60 cm) of Ultrogel AcA 34. Fraction volumes were 0.5 mL.

12.2.2. Affinity purification of F(ab′)₂

1. Couple 10 mg of antigens to 1 g (3.5 mL in wet volume) of CNBr-activated Sepharose 4B following the instructions of the manufacturer (Amersham Pharmacia Biotech, Uppsala, Sweden). Conjugations of antigens to some proteins such as bovine serum albumin and nonspecific IgG and coupling the

conjugated proteins to CNBr-activated Sepharose 4B facilitate elimination of antigens released from the antigen-Sepharose 4B on gel filtration (Kasai et al., 1990; Hashida et al., 1996c).

2. Apply 5–20 mg of antibody $F(ab')_2$ in 2 mL of 50 mmol/L sodium phosphate buffer, pH 7.0, to a column (5 × 14 mm; 0.275 mL) of antigen-Sepharose 4B at a flow rate of 1 mL/h. The amount of antibody $F(ab')_2$ that can be applied depends on the content of specific antibody $F(ab')_2$. Minimal volumes of antigen-Sepharose 4B should be used to reduce the amount of antigens released from the Sepharose 4B.

3. Wash the column with 20 mL of the same buffer.

4. Elute the specific antibody $F(ab')_2$ from the column at low pH values or with higher concentrations of inorganic salts or urea. Specific antibodies may be eluted with either 0.1 mol/L KCl containing 0.008 mol/L HCl, pH 2.3–2.5 (Ishikawa et al., 1980), 0.1 mol/L glycine-HCl buffer, pH 2.5, containing 0–1.0 mol/L NaCl (Imagawa et al., 1981), 4 mol/L urea (Inoue et al., 1985a) or 3 mol/L KSCN (Hashida and Ishikawa, 1990).

5. Neutralize the eluate with 0.5 mol/L Tris-HCl buffer, pH 8.0, or 0.2 mol/L sodium phosphate buffer, pH 8.0, or remove the urea or KSCN by dialysis or gel filtration.

6. Either before or after reduction with 2-mercaptoethylamine, subject the affinity-purified antibody $F(ab')_2$ in 0.5 mL of 50 mmol/L sodium phosphate buffer, pH 7.0, to gel filtration using a column (1.0 × 60 cm) of Ultrogel AcA 44 (Biosepra, Villeneuve la Garenne, France) to eliminate the released antigens from the column (Figs. 12.3 and 12.4) (Kasai et al., 1990; Hashida and Ishikawa, 1990; Hashida et al., 1996c). Adjust the flow rate to 0.3–0.5 mL/min. Collect fractions of 1.0 mL. It is also possible to eliminate the complexes of antigens released from antigen-columns and affinity-purified Fab'-peroxidase conjugates by gel filtration (Fig. 12.5) (Ruan et al., 1985).

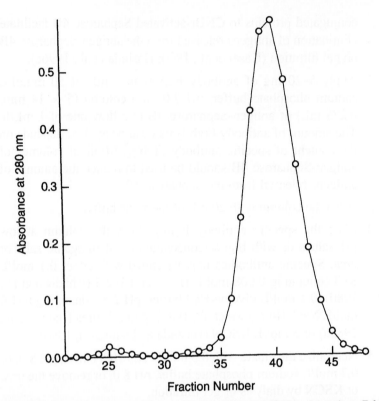

Fig. 12.3. Elution profile of affinity-purified rabbit anti-HIV-1 p24 antigen Fab′ from a column of Ultrogel AcA 44. Rabbit anti-HIV-1 p24 antigen F(ab′)₂ was affinity-purified by elution from a column of recombinant HIV-1 p24 antigen (rp24)-nonspecific rabbit IgG-Sepharose 4B, reduced to Fab′ with 2-mercaptoethylamine and subjected to gel filtration on a column (1.0 × 45 cm) of Ultrogel AcA 44 to eliminate the anti-p24 Fab′ complex with rp24-nonspecific rabbit IgG conjugate. Fraction volumes were 0.5 mL.

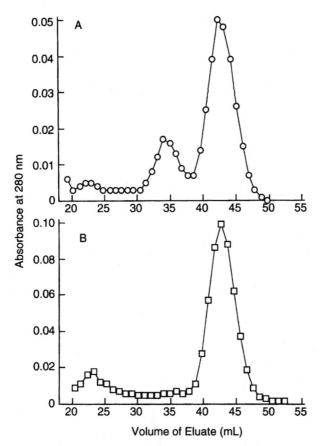

Fig. 12.4. Elution profiles of affinity-purified rabbit anti-hGH Fab′ from a column of Ultrogel AcA 44. Rabbit anti-hGH F(ab′)$_2$ was affinity-purified by elution from a column of hGH-biotinyl-nonspecific rabbit IgG-Sepharose 4B with 0.2 mol/L glycine-HCl buffer, pH 2.5, reduced to Fab′ with 2-mercaptoethylamine and subjected to gel filtration on a column (1.5 × 45 cm) of Ultrogel AcA 44 to eliminate the complex of anti-hGH Fab′ with hGH-biotinyl-nonspecific rabbit IgG conjugate (A). Alternatively, affinity-purified rabbit anti-hGH F(ab′)$_2$ was passed through a column of avidin-Sepharose 4B to eliminate the complex of anti-hGH Fab′ with hGH-biotinyl-nonspecific rabbit IgG conjugate, reduced to Fab′ with 2-mercaptoethylamine and subjected to gel filtration on a column (1.5 × 45 cm) of Ultrogel AcA 44 (B).

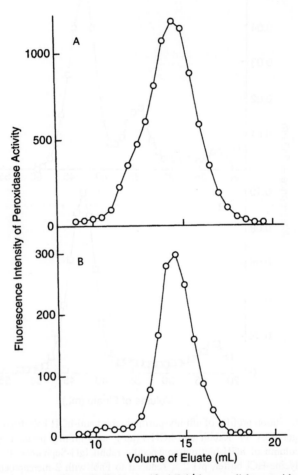

Fig. 12.5. Elution profiles of affinity-purified Fab′-horseradish peroxidase conjugates from a column of Ultrogel AcA 44. Antibody F(ab′)$_2$ was affinity-purified, reduced and conjugated to peroxidase by the hinge method described in Chapters 11 and 13 of this volume (Ruan et al., 1985). A: anti-insulin Fab′-peroxidase conjugate. B: anti-human chorionic gonadotropin Fab′-peroxidase conjugate.

12.2.3. Direct affinity-purifications of F(ab')₂ and Fab' from antiserum

Antiserum may be digested directly with pepsin to obtain affinity-purified $F(ab')_2$ (Inoue et al., 1985b).

1. Prepare a mixture of 2 mL of rabbit antiserum and 2 mL of 0.1 mol/L sodium acetate buffer, pH 4.5, containing 0.1 mol/L NaCl.
2. Dialyze the mixture against the same buffer.
3. Dissolve 2 mg of pepsin in the dialyzed mixture.
4. Incubate the dialyzed mixture at 37°C overnight.
5. Purify the antibody $F(ab')_2$ by affinity chromatography as described above either before or after reduction with 2-mercaptoethylamine.

CHAPTER 13

Protocol for enzyme-labeling of antibodies

13.1. Introduction

The hinge and nonhinge methods using glutaraldehyde, periodate and derivatives of maleimide and pyridyldisulfide described in Chapter 11 are reproducible, provided that appropriate numbers of reactive groups are introduced into the protein molecules to be conjugated and allowed to react after complete elimination of free reactive groups.

However, unexpected results may be observed in some cases. Favorable results may be obtained by changing conditions, such as the concentration of reagents, pH, time, temperature, etc.

13.2. Labeling of Fab' with peroxidase by the hinge method using maleimide derivatives

13.2.1. Preparation of 6-maleimidohexanoyl-horseradish peroxidase

1. Prepare 3 mg (75 nmol) of horseradish peroxidase (HRP) [E_{403} = 2.275 $g^{-1} L cm^{-1}$ and mol wt = 40,000 (Keilin and Hartree, 1951)] in 0.45 mL of 0.1 mol/L sodium phosphate buffer, pH 7.0.
2. Prepare 20–30 mmol/L N-succinimidyl-6-maleimidohexanoate (SMH) (mol wt 308) (Dojindo Laboratories, Kumamoto, Japan) in N,N-dimethylformamide.

3. Add 0.05 mL of 20–30 mmol/L SMH to the HRP solution.

4. Incubate the mixture at 30°C for 30 min.

5. Centrifuge the mixture briefly to remove precipitates, if any.

6. Subject the incubated mixture to gel filtration using a column (1.0 × 45 cm) of Sephadex G-25 (Amersham Pharmacia Biotech, Uppsala, Sweden) in 0.1 mol/L sodium phosphate buffer, pH 6.0. Adjust the flow rate to 0.6–0.8 mL/min. Collect fractions of 0.5–1.0 mL. A more rapid gel filtration procedure is available using a centrifuged column (Penefsky, 1979). Wash a column (1.0 × 6.4 cm, 5 mL) of Sephadex G-50 fine (Amersham Pharmacia Biotech, Uppsala, Sweden) with the same buffer and centrifuge it in a test tube at 100 × g for 2 min. Apply the reaction mixture to a centrifuged column, and centrifuge it in the same way.

7. Concentrate the pooled fractions in a microconcentrator (Centricon-30, Amicon Division W. R. Grace & Co.) by centrifugation at 2000 × g at 4°C. Do not use NaN_3 as preservative, since it inactivates peroxidase and accelerates the decomposition of maleimide groups (Fig. 10.2). Concentration is not required when the centrifuged column is used.

8. Measure the content of maleimide groups in peroxidase as described below, and calculate the average number of maleimide groups introduced per peroxidase molecule.

13.2.2. Measurement of maleimide groups

1. Prepare 0.45 mL of 0.1 mol/L sodium phosphate buffer, pH 6.0, containing 6-maleimidohexanoyl-peroxidase with an absorbance at 403 nm of above 1.0 (0.44 mg/mL, 11 nmol/mL). Use 0.45 mL of the same buffer as a control.

2. Prepare 50 mmol/L EDTA, pH 6.0, containing 0.5 mmol/L 2-mercaptoethylamine-HCl (mol wt 113.6).

3. Add 0.05 mL of the 2-mercaptoethylamine-EDTA to 0.45 mL of the above sample. The final concentration of 2-mercaptoethylamine is 50 nmol/mL.
4. Incubate the reaction mixture at 30°C for 20 min.
5. Add 0.02 mL of 5 mmol/L 4,4'-dithiodipyridine (mol wt 220.3) (1.1 g/L). The final concentration of 4,4'-dithiodipyridine is 192 nmol/mL.
6. Incubate the reaction mixture at 30°C for 5 min.
7. Measure the absorbance at 324 nm. The extinction coefficient at 324 nm of pyridine-4-thione is 19,800 $mol^{-1} L cm^{-1}$ (0.0198 $nmol^{-1} mL cm^{-1}$) (Grassetti and Murray, 1967). The absorbance at 324 nm of the control in the absence of maleimide groups is approximately 1. About 1–2 maleimide groups are introduced per peroxidase molecule, and the enzyme activity is fully retained.

13.2.3. Conjugation of Fab' with 6-maleimidohexanoyl-peroxidase

1. Incubate 1.8 mg (45 nmol) of 6-maleimidohexanoyl-peroxidase with 2.0 mg (43 nmol) of Fab' in 1 mL of 0.1 mol/L sodium phosphate buffer, pH 6.0, containing 2.5 mmol/L EDTA at 4°C for 20 h or at 30°C for 1 h. The final concentrations of 6-maleimidohexanoyl-peroxidase and Fab' in the reaction mixture for conjugation should be 0.01–0.05 mmol/L.
2. Incubate the reaction mixture with 5 μL of 100 mmol/L 2-mercaptoethylamine at 30°C for 10 min and 10 μL of 100 mmol/L N-ethylmaleimide at 30°C for 10 min.
3. Subject the incubated mixture to gel filtration using a column (1.5 × 45–100 cm) of Ultrogel AcA 44 (Biosepra, Villeneuve la Garenne, France) in 0.1 mol/L sodium phosphate buffer, pH 6.5. Adjust the flow rate to 0.5 mL/min. Collect fractions of 1.0 mL.
4. Measure the absorbances at 280 and 403 nm of each fraction.
5. Measure the peroxidase activity of each fraction (Fig. 11.2A).

6. Add 1/98 volume each of 2–5 g/L thimerosal and 100 g/L bovine serum albumin to each fraction containing Fab′.
7. Store the conjugate at 4°C. Do not use NaN$_3$ as a preservative, since it inactivates peroxidase.

13.3. Labeling of Fab′ with β-D-galactosidase by the hinge method using maleimide derivatives

13.3.1. Introduction of maleimide groups into β-D-galactosidase

1. Prepare 2.5 mg (4.6 nmol) of β-D-galactosidase [E_{280} = 2.09 g^{-1} L cm^{-1} and mol wt = 540,000 (Craven et al., 1965)] in 0.5 mL of 0.1 mol/L sodium phosphate buffer, pH 6.0.
2. Add 0.005 mL of 200 mmol/L N,N′-o-phenylenedimaleimide (mol wt 268) in N,N-dimethylformamide to the above solution. N,N′-oxydimethylenedimaleimide may be substituted for N,N′-o-phenylenedimaleimide (Table 10.1).
3. Incubate the reaction mixture at 30°C for 20 min.
4. Subject the incubated mixture to gel filtration by centrifugation using a column (1.0 × 6.4 cm, 5 mL) of Sephadex G-50 fine (Amersham Pharmacia Biotech, Uppsala, Sweden) in 0.1 mol/L sodium phosphate buffer, pH 6.0.
5. Measure the content of maleimide groups in β-D-galactosidase as described for 6-maleimidohexanoyl-peroxidase, and calculate the average number of maleimide groups introduced per β-D-galactosidase molecule, which is approximately 15. Loss of β-D-galactosidase activity by this treatment is approximately 10%.

13.3.2. Conjugation of Fab′ with maleimide-β-D-galactosidase

1. Incubate 2 mg (3.7 nmol) of the maleimide-β-D-galactosidase with 0.51–0.85 mg (11–18 nmol) of Fab′ in 2 mL of 0.1

mol/L sodium phosphate buffer, pH 6.0, containing 2.5 mmol/L EDTA at 4°C for 15–24 h. Addition of a small amount of fluorescein-labeled nonspecific Fab' (2.5%) helps monitoring the conjugation efficiency of Fab'.

2. Subject the incubated mixture to gel filtration using a column (1.6 × 65 cm) of Sepharose 6B (Amersham Pharmacia Biotech, Uppsala, Sweden) in 10 mmol/L sodium phosphate buffer, pH 6.5, containing 0.1 mol/L NaCl, 1 mmol/L MgCl$_2$, 1 g/L NaN$_3$ and 1 g/L bovine serum albumin (buffer A). Adjust the flow rate to 0.3 mL/min. Collect fractions of 1.0 mL.

3. Measure the fluorescence intensity of fluorescein-labeled Fab' of each fraction using 490 nm for excitation and 510 nm for emission analysis with a standard of 1 nmol/L fluorescein to monitor the conjugation efficiency of Fab'.

4. Measure the β-D-galactosidase activity of each fraction (Fig. 11.6A).

5. Store the conjugate in buffer A at 4°C.

13.4. Labeling of Fab' with alkaline phosphatase by the hinge method using maleimide derivatives

13.4.1. Preparation of 6-maleimidohexanoyl-alkaline phosphatase

1. Prepare 3 mg (30 nmol) of alkaline phosphatase from calf intestine [E_{280} = 0.99 g^{-1} L cm^{-1} (Morton, 1955) and mol wt = 100,000 (Engström, 1961)] (Boehringer Mannheim GmbH, Mannheim, Germany) in 0.5 mL.

2. Dialyze the enzyme solution against 50 mmol/L sodium borate buffer, pH 7.6, containing 1 mmol/L MgCl$_2$ and 0.1 mmol/L ZnCl$_2$.

3. Incubate the dialyzed enzyme solution (3 mg/0.69 mL) with 0.01 mL of 140 mmol/L N-succinimidyl-6-maleimidohexanoate (mol wt 308.3) in N,N-dimethylformamide at 30°C for 0.5 h.

4. Subject the incubated mixture to gel filtration by centrifugation using a column (1.1 × 5.3 cm, 5 mL) of Sephadex G-50 fine (Amersham Pharmacia Biotech, Uppsala, Sweden) in 0.1 mol/L Tris-HCl buffer, pH 7.0, containing 1 mmol/L $MgCl_2$ and 0.1 mmol/L $ZnCl_2$ (buffer T).

5. Measure the content of maleimide groups as described for 6-maleimidohexanoyl-peroxidase, and calculate the average number of maleimide groups introduced per enzyme molecule, which is approximately 7. Loss of enzyme activity by introduction of maleimide groups is 32%.

13.4.2. Conjugation of Fab' with maleimide-alkaline phosphatase

1. Incubate 1 mg (10 nmol) of the maleimide-alkaline phosphatase in 0.25 mL of buffer T with 2.3 mg (50 nmol) of Fab' plus 0.03 mg of fluorescein-labeled Fab' in 0.25 mL of 0.1 mol/L sodium phosphate buffer, pH 6.0, containing 5 mmol/L EDTA at 4°C for 20 h. Addition of a small amount of fluorescein-labeled nonspecific Fab' (2.5%) helps monitoring the conjugation efficiency of Fab'.

2. Incubate the mixture with 2.5 μL of 100 mmol/L 2-mercaptoethylamine at 30°C for 10 min and with 10 μL of 100 mmol/L N-ethylmaleimide at 30°C for 10 min.

3. Subject the incubated mixture to gel filtration using a column (1.5 × 45 cm) of Ultrogel AcA 34 (Biosepra, Villeneuve la Garenne, France) in 10 mmol/L Tris-HCl buffer, pH 6.8, containing 0.1 mol/L NaCl, 1 mmol/L $MgCl_2$, 0.1 mmol/L $ZnCl_2$, and 0.5 g/L NaN_3. Adjust the flow rate to 0.4–0.6 mL/min. Collect fractions of 1.0 mL.

4. Measure the fluorescence intensity of fluorescein-labeled Fab' of each fraction using 490 nm for excitation and 510 nm for emission analysis with a standard of 1 nmol/L fluorescein to monitor the conjugation efficiency of Fab'.

5. Measure the alkaline phosphatase activity of each fraction (Fig. 11.7A).
6. Add 1/99 volume of 100 g/L bovine serum albumin to each fraction.
7. Store the conjugate at 4°C.

13.5. Labeling of Fab' with glucose-6-phosphate dehydrogenase by the hinge method using maleimide derivatives

13.5.1. Introduction of maleimide groups into glucose-6-phosphate dehydrogenase

1. Prepare 0.5 mg (4.9 nmol) of glucose-6-phosphate dehydrogenase from *Leuconostoc mesenteroides* [E_{280} = 1.15 g^{-1} L cm^{-1} and mol wt = 103,700 (Olive and Levy, 1971)] in 0.5 mL.
2. Dialyze the above enzyme solution against 0.1 mol/L sodium phosphate buffer, pH 7.0.
3. Prepare 0.76 mg (2500 nmol) of glucose-6-phosphate disodium salt (mol wt 304.2) in 0.005 mL of deionized water and 0.66 mg (1000 nmol) of NAD$^+$ (mol wt 663.4) in 0.005 mL of deionized water.
4. Prepare 40–100 mmol/L N-succinimidyl-4-(N-maleimido-methyl)cyclohexane-1-carboxylate (mol wt 334.3) in N,N-di-methylformamide.
5. Incubate the above enzyme solution (0.5 mg/0.5 mL) with 0.005 mL of the glucose-6-phosphate solution and 0.005 mL of the NAD$^+$ solution at 30°C for 5 min.
6. Add 0.02 mL of maleimide reagent solution to the mixture.
7. Incubate the mixture at 30°C for 30 min.
8. Remove small molecules by gel filtration using 0.1 mol/L sodium phosphate buffer, pH 6.0.
9. Measure the content of maleimide groups as described for 6-maleimidohexanoyl-peroxidase, and calculate the average

number of maleimide groups introduced per enzyme molecule, which is approximately 5. Loss of enzyme activity by introduction of maleimide groups is 50–70%.

13.5.2. Conjugation of Fab' with maleimide-glucose-6-phosphate dehydrogenase

1. Incubate 0.5 mg (4.8 nmol) of maleimide-glucose-6-phosphate dehydrogenase in 0.6 mL of 0.1 mol/L sodium phosphate buffer, pH 6.0, with 2.2 mg (48 nmol) of Fab' plus 0.06 mg of fluorescein-labeled nonspecific Fab' in 1 mL of 0.1 mol/L sodium phosphate buffer, pH 6.0, containing 5 mmol/L EDTA at 4°C for 20 h.
2. Incubate the mixture with 5 μL of 100 mmol/L 2-mercaptoethylamine at 30°C for 10 min and 10 μL of 100 mmol/L N-ethylmaleimide at 30°C for 10 min.
3. Subject the incubated mixture to gel filtration using a column (1.5 × 45 cm) of Ultrogel AcA 34 (Biosepra, Villeneuve la Garenne, France) in 0.1 mol/L sodium phosphate buffer, pH 6.5. Adjust the flow rate to 0.4–0.6 mL/min.
4. Measure the glucose-6-phosphate dehydrogenase activity of each fraction.
5. Add 1/98 volumes of 100 g/L bovine serum albumin and 100 g/L NaN$_3$ to each fraction.
6. Store the conjugate at 4°C.

13.6. Labeling of IgG with β-D-galactosidase by the hinge method using maleimide derivatives

13.6.1. Reduction of IgG

1. Prepare 2–5 mg of IgG in 0.45 mL of 0.1 mol/L sodium phosphate buffer, pH 6.0, containing 5 mmol/L EDTA.

2. Incubate the above IgG solution (0.45 mL) with 0.05 mL of 0.1 mol/L 2-mercaptoethylamine at 37°C for 1.5 h.

3. Remove small molecules by gel filtration using 0.1 mol/L sodium phosphate buffer, pH 6.0, containing 5 mmol/L EDTA.

4. Calculate the amount of reduced IgG from the extinction coefficient at 280 nm and the molecular weight. $E_{280} = 1.5$ $g^{-1} L cm^{-1}$ for rabbit IgG (Palmer and Nisonoff, 1964) and $1.4 g^{-1} L cm^{-1}$ for mouse IgG (Ey et al., 1978). The molecular weight of IgG is 150,000 (Dorrington and Tanford, 1970; Gorini et al., 1969).

13.6.2. Introduction of maleimide groups into β-D-galactosidase

1. Introduce maleimide groups into β-D-galactosidase molecules as described for labeling of Fab' with β-D-galactosidase by the hinge method using maleimide derivatives.

13.6.3. Conjugation of reduced IgG with maleimide-β-D-galactosidase

1. Incubate 2 mg (3.7 nmol) of maleimide-β-D-galactosidase with 1.8 mg (12 nmol) of reduced IgG in 2 mL of 0.1 mol/L sodium phosphate buffer, pH 6.0, containing 2.5 mmol/L EDTA at 4°C for 15–24 h. Addition of a small amount of fluorescein-labeled nonspecific IgG (2.5%) helps in monitoring the conjugation efficiency of IgG.

2. Subject the incubated mixture to gel filtration using a column (1.6 × 65 cm) of Sepharose 6B (Amersham Pharmacia Biotech, Uppsala, Sweden) in 10 mmol/L sodium phosphate buffer, pH 6.5, containing 0.1 mol/L NaCl, 1 mmol/L $MgCl_2$, 1 g/L NaN_3 and 1 g/L bovine serum albumin (buffer A). Adjust the flow rate to 0.3 mL/min. Collect fractions of 1.0 mL.

3. Measure the fluorescence intensity of fluorescein-labeled IgG of each fraction using 490 nm for excitation and 510 nm for emission analysis with a standard of 1 nmol/L fluorescein to monitor the conjugation efficiency of IgG.
4. Measure the β-D-galactosidase activity of each fraction (Fig. 11.6C).
5. Store the conjugate in buffer A at 4°C.

13.7. Labeling of Fab' with peroxidase by the hinge method using pyridyl disulfide derivatives

13.7.1. Introduction of pyridyl disulfide groups into peroxidase

1. Prepare 4 mg (100 nmol) of horseradish peroxidase (HRP) [E_{403} = 2.275 g^{-1} L cm^{-1} and mol wt = 40,000 (Keilin and Hartree, 1951)] in 0.6 mL of 0.1 mol/L sodium phosphate buffer, pH 7.5.
2. Prepare 40 mmol/L N-succinimidyl-3-(2-pyridyldithio)propionate (SPDP) (mol wt 312.5) in ethanol.
3. Incubate the HRP solution (0.6 mL) with 0.12 mL of the SPDP solution at 25°C for 30 min.
4. Remove small molecules by gel filtration using 0.1 mol/L sodium phosphate buffer, pH 6.0.

13.7.2. Measurement of pyridyl disulfide groups

1. Prepare 0.5 mL of 0.1 mol/L sodium phosphate buffer, pH 6.0, containing pyridyldisulfide-peroxidase with an absorbance at 403 nm of above 2.0 (0.88 mg/mL, 22 nmol/mL).
2. Incubate the sample solution with 0.02 mL of 100 mmol/L (15.4 mg/mL) dithiothreitol (mol wt 154.3) at 30°C for 20 min. The final concentration of dithiothreitol is 3850 nmol/mL.
3. Measure the absorbance at 343 nm.
4. Calculate the average number of pyridyl disulfide groups introduced per peroxidase molecule, which is approximately 2.5.

The extinction coefficient at 343 nm of pyridine-2-thione is 8080 $mol^{-1}\, L\, cm^{-1}$ (0.00808 $nmol^{-1}\, mL\, cm^{-1}$) (Stuchbury et al., 1975).

13.7.3. Conjugation of Fab' with pyridyldisulfide-peroxidase

1. Incubate 1.8 mg (45 nmol) of pyridyl disulfide-peroxidase with 2 mg (43 nmol) of Fab' in 0.44 mL of 0.1 mol/L sodium phosphate buffer, pH 6.0, containing 2.5 mmol/L EDTA at 30°C for 2.5 h. The final concentrations of the pyridyl disulfide-peroxidase and Fab' should be 100 nmol/mL or more.
2. Subject the incubated mixture to gel filtration using a column (1.5 × 45–100 cm) of Ultrogel AcA 44 (Biosepra, Villeneuve la Garenne, France) in 0.1 mol/L sodium phosphate buffer, pH 6.5. Adjust the flow rate to 0.5–0.8 mL/min. Collect fractions of 1.0 mL.
3. Measure the absorbances at 280 and 403 nm of each fraction.
4. Measure the peroxidase activity of each fraction.
5. Add 1/98 volume each of 2–5 g/L thimerosal and 100 g/L bovine serum albumin to each fraction.
6. Store the conjugate at 4°C. Do not use NaN_3 as a preservative, since it inactivates peroxidase.

13.8. Nonhinge method

13.8.1. Conjugation of Fab' with glutaraldehyde-treated peroxidase

1. Prepare 10 mg of horseradish peroxidase (HRP) in 0.19 mL of 0.1 mol/L sodium phosphate buffer, pH 6.8.
2. Incubate the HRP solution (0.19 mL) with 0.01 mL of 250 g/L glutaraldehyde at room temperature for 18 h.
3. Subject the incubated mixture to gel filtration using a column (1 × 45 cm) of Ultrogel AcA 44 (Biosepra, Villeneuve la Garenne,

France) in 0.15 mol/L NaCl to remove excess glutaraldehyde and dimer and/or polymers of HRP.

4. Incubate 4.8 mg (120 nmol) of the glutaraldehyde-treated HRP in 0.5 mL of 0.15 mol/L NaCl with 1.2 mg (25 nmol) of SH-blocked Fab′ (Chapter 12) in 0.5 mL of 0.15 mol/L NaCl, and 0.1 mL of 1 mol/L sodium carbonate buffer, pH 9.5, at 4°C for 24 h.

5. Incubate the above reaction mixture with 0.05 mL of 0.2 mol/L L-lysine-HCl in 0.25 mol/L sodium phosphate buffer, pH 8.0, at 4°C for 2 h.

6. Subject the reaction mixture to a column (1.5 × 45 cm) of Ultrogel AcA 44 (Biosepra, Villeneuve la Garenne, France) (Fig. 11.2C).

7. Store the conjugate as described for the hinge method.

13.8.2. Conjugation of Fab′ with periodate-oxidized peroxidase

1. Prepare 2 mg of horseradish peroxidase (HRP) in 0.5 mL of deionized water.

2. Incubate the HRP solution with 0.1 mL of 0.1 mol/L $NaIO_4$ at room temperature for 10 min.

3. Add 0.05 mL of ethylene glycol to the mixture.

4. Incubate the above mixture at room temperature for 5 min.

5. Remove small molecules by gel filtration using 1 mmol/L sodium acetate buffer, pH 4.4.

6. Incubate 1.6 mg (40 nmol) of oxidized HRP in 0.4 mL of 1 mmol/L sodium acetate buffer, pH 4.4, with 1.8 mg (40 nmol) of SH-blocked Fab′ (Chapter 12) in 0.4 mL of 0.15 mol/L NaCl, and 0.02 mL of 1 mol/L sodium carbonate buffer, pH 9.5, at 25°C for 2 h.

7. Add 0.04 mL of 4 g/L sodium borohydride to the mixture.

8. Incubate the mixture at 4°C for 2 h.

9. Subject the incubated mixture to gel filtration using a column (1.5 × 45 cm) of Ultrogel AcA 44 (Biosepra, Villeneuve la Garenne, France) (Fig. 11.2D).
10. Store the conjugate as described for the hinge method.

13.8.3. Preparation of mercaptoacetyl-IgG and F(ab')₂

1. Prepare 2 mg (13 nmol) of rabbit IgG in 0.48 mL of 0.1 mol/L sodium phosphate buffer, pH 7.0. $E_{280} = 1.5\ g^{-1}\ L\ cm^{-1}$ (Palmer and Nisonoff, 1964). The molecular weight of IgG is 150,000 (Dorrington and Tanford, 1970).
2. Prepare 5 mmol/L N-succinimidyl-S-acetylmercaptoacetate (SATA) (mol wt 231) (Pierce, Rockford, IL) in N,N-dimethylformamide (1.155 mg/mL).
3. Incubate 0.48 mL of the IgG solution with 0.02 mL of 5 mmol/L SATA at 30°C for 30 min.
4. Add 0.03 mL of 0.1 mol/L EDTA, pH 7.0, 0.05 mL of 1 mol/L Tris-HCl buffer, pH 7.0, and 0.015 mL of 4 mol/L hydroxylamine, pH 7.0, to the mixture.
5. Incubate the mixture at 30°C for 5 min.
6. Remove small molecules by gel filtration using 0.1 mol/L sodium phosphate buffer, pH 6.0, containing 5 mmol/L EDTA.
7. Measure the content of thiol groups as described for Fab'. The average number of thiol groups introduced per IgG molecule is approximately 2. Thiol groups are introduced into F(ab')₂ in the same way.

13.8.4. Conjugation of mercaptoacetyl-IgG and F(ab')₂ with 6-maleimidohexanoyl-peroxidase

1. Incubate 6-maleimidohexanoyl-peroxidase (3 mg, 75 nmol) (see the hinge method for labeling Fab') with mercaptoacetyl-IgG (2.3 mg, 15 nmol) or F(ab')₂ (1.4 mg, 15 nmol) in 0.5 mL

of 0.1 mol/L sodium phosphate buffer, pH 6.0, containing 2–3 mmol/L EDTA at 4°C for 20 h.

2. Subject the incubated mixture to gel filtration using a column (1.5 × 45 cm) of Ultrogel AcA 34 (Biosepra, Villeneuve la Garenne, France) in 0.1 mol/L sodium phosphate buffer, pH 6.5. Adjust the flow rate to 0.4–0.6 mL/min. Collect fractions of 1.0 mL.

3. Measure the absorbances at 280 and 403 nm of each fraction.

4. Measure the peroxidase activity of each fraction (Fig. 11.8).

5. Add 1/98 volume each of 2–5 g/L thimerosal and 100 g/L bovine serum albumin to each fraction.

6. Store the conjugate at 4°C. Do not use NaN_3 as a preservative, since it inactivates peroxidase.

13.8.5. Conjugations of mercaptoacetyl-IgG and F(ab')$_2$ with 6-maleimidohexanoyl-alkaline phosphatase

1. Incubate 6-maleimidohexanoyl-alkaline phosphatase (2.5 mg, 25 nmol) in 0.25 mL of 0.1 mol/L Tris-HCl buffer, pH 7.0, containing 1 mmol/L $MgCl_2$ and 0.1 mmol/L $ZnCl_2$ (buffer T) with mercaptoacetyl-IgG (2.3 mg, 15 nmol) plus fluorescein-labeled IgG (0.058 mg) or mercaptoacetyl F(ab')$_2$ (2.8 mg, 30 nmol) plus fluorescein-labeled F(ab')$_2$ (0.035 mg) in 0.25 mL of 0.1 mol/L sodium phosphate buffer, pH 6.0, containing 5 mmol/L EDTA at 4°C for 20 h.

2. Subject the incubated mixture to gel filtration using a column (1.5 × 45 cm) of Ultrogel AcA 34 (Biosepra, Villeneuve la Garenne, France) in 10 mmol/L Tris-HCl buffer, pH 6.8, containing 0.1 mol/L NaCl, 1 mmol/L $MgCl_2$, 0.1 mol/L $ZnCl_2$, and 0.5 g/L NaN_3. Adjust the flow rate to 0.4–0.6 mL/min. Collect fractions of 1.0 mL.

3. Measure the fluorescence intensity of fluorescein-labeled IgG or F(ab')$_2$ of each fraction using 490 nm for excitation and 510 nm for emission analysis with a standard of 1 nmol/L

fluorescein to monitor the conjugation efficiency of IgG or F(ab')$_2$.

4. Measure the alkaline phosphatase activity of each fraction (Fig. 11.7).
5. Add 1/99 volume of 100 g/L bovine serum albumin to each fraction.
6. Store the conjugate at 4°C.

CHAPTER 14

Protocol for labeling avidin with 2,4-dinitrophenyl groups and β-D-galactosidase

Reproducible methods are described below. However, unexpected results may be observed in some cases. Favorable results may be obtained by changing conditions, such as the concentration of reagents, pH, time, temperature etc.

14.1. Labeling of avidin with 2,4-dinitrophenyl groups

14.1.1. Preparation of mercaptoacetyl-avidin

1. Prepare 4.0 mg (59 nmol) of avidin [E_{280} = 1.54 g^{-1} L cm^{-1} and mol wt = 68,000 (Green, 1975)] (Vector Laboratories Inc., Burlingame, CA) in 0.42 mL of 0.1 mol/L sodium phosphate buffer, pH 7.0.
2. Incubate the avidin solution (0.42 mL) with 0.022 mL of 10 mmol/L N-succinimidyl-S-acetylmercaptoacetate (Boehringer Mannheim GmbH, Mannheim, Germany) in N,N-dimethylformamide at 30°C for 30 min.
3. Incubate the mixture with 0.02 mL of 0.1 mol/L EDTA, pH 7.0, 0.06 mL of 1 mol/L Tris-HCl buffer, pH 7.0, and 0.015 mL of 4 mol/L hydroxylamine, pH 7.0, at 30°C for 5 min.

Hydroxylamine should be added 10 min before addition of αN-maleimidohexanoyl-ϵN-2,4-dinitrophenyl-L-lysine.

14.1.2. Preparation of αN-6-maleimidohexanoyl-ϵN-2,4-dinitrophenyl-L-lysine

1. Incubate 0.14 mL of 10 mmol/L ϵN-2,4-dinitrophenyl-L-lysine-HCl·H_2O (mol wt 367) in 0.1 mol/L sodium phosphate buffer, pH 7.0, with 0.06 mL of 10 mmol/L N-succinimidyl-6-maleimidohexanoate (mol wt 308.3) in N,N-dimethylformamide at 30°C for 30 min.

14.1.3. Conjugation of αN-6-maleimidohexanoyl-ϵN-2,4-dinitrophenyl-L-lysine with mercaptoacetyl-avidin

1. Incubate the mercaptoacetyl-avidin solution (4.0 mg, 59 nmol/0.54 mL) with the αN-6-maleimidohexanoyl-ϵN-2,4-dinitrophenyl-L-lysine solution (600 nmol/0.2 mL) at 30°C for 30 min.
2. Subject the incubated mixture to gel filtration by centrifugation using a column (1.1 × 5.3 cm, 5 mL) of Sephadex G-50 fine (Amersham Pharmacia Biotech) in 0.1 mol/L sodium phosphate buffer, pH 7.0.
3. Measure the content of 2,4-dinitrophenyl groups [$E_{360} = 17,400$ $mol^{-1} L cm^{-1}$ and $E_{360}/E_{280} = 1/0.32$ (Eisen et al., 1954)], in avidin, and calculate the average number of 2,4-dinitrophenyl groups introduced per avidin molecule, which is approximately 3.
4. Add 1/100 volume of 10% NaN_3 to each fraction.
5. Store 2,4-dinitrophenyl-avidin at 4°C.

14.2. Labeling of avidin with 2,4-dinitrophenyl-bovine serum albumin

14.2.1. Preparation of mercaptoacetyl-2,4-dinitrophenyl-bovine serum albumin

1. Prepare 2,4-dinitrophenyl bovine serum albumin (Fig. 8.1) (3.3 mg, 50 nmol) in 1.0 mL of 0.1 mol/L sodium phosphate buffer, pH 7.0.
2. Incubate the solution (1.0 mL) with 8 μL of 50 mmol/L N-succinimidyl-S-acetylmercaptoacetate (Boehringer Mannheim GmbH, Mannheim, Germany) in N,N-dimethylformamide at 30°C for 30 min.
3. Incubate the mixture with 0.06 mL of 0.1 mol/L EDTA, pH 7.0, 0.12 mL of 1 mol/L Tris-HCl buffer, pH 7.0, and 0.14 mL of 1 mol/L hydroxylamine, pH 7.0, at 30°C for 5 min.
4. Subject the incubated mixture to gel filtration by centrifugation using a column (1.1 × 7.5 cm, 7 mL) of Sephadex G-50 fine (Amersham Pharmacia Biotech) in 0.1 mol/L sodium phosphate buffer, pH 6.0 containing 5 mmol/L EDTA.
5. Measure the content of thiol groups in 2,4-dinitrophenyl-bovine serum albumin as described for that in Fab' (Chapter 12), and calculate the average number of thiol groups introduced per albumin molecule, which is approximately one.

14.2.2. Preparation of 6-maleimidohexanoyl-avidin

1. Prepare 3.2 mg (47 nmol) of avidin [E_{280} = 1.54 g^{-1} L cm^{-1} and mol wt = 68,000 (Green, 1975)] in 0.97 mL of 0.1 mol/L sodium phosphate buffer, pH 7.0.
2. Incubate the avidin solution (0.97 mL) with 30 μL of 5 mmol/L N-succinimidyl-6-maleimidohexanoate (mol wt 308) (Dojindo Laboratories, Kumamoto, Japan) in N,N-dimethylformamide at 30°C for 30 min.

3. Subject the incubated mixture to gel filtration by centrifugation using a column (1.1 × 7.5 cm, 7 mL) of Sephadex G-50 fine (Amersham Pharmacia Biotech) in 0.1 mol/L sodium phosphate buffer, pH 6.0 containing 5 mmol/L EDTA.

4. Measure the content of maleimide groups in avidin as described for that in 6-maleimidohexanoyl-peroxidase (Chapter 13), and calculate the average number of maleimide groups introduced per avidin molecule, which is approximately 2.

14.2.3. Conjugation of 6-maleimidohexanoyl-avidin with mercaptoacetyl-2,4-dinitrophenyl-bovine serum albumin

1. Incubate mercaptoacetyl-2,4-dinitrophenyl-bovine serum albumin (2.5 mg, 38 nmol) in 0.6 mL of 0.1 mol/L sodium phosphate buffer, pH 6.0, containing 5 mmol/L EDTA with 6-maleimidohexanoyl-avidin (2.6 mg, 38 nmol) in 0.4 mL of 0.1 mol/L sodium phosphate buffer, pH 6.0, containing 5 mmol/L EDTA at 4°C for 20 h.

2. Incubate the mixture with 0.005 mL of 100 mmol/L 2-mercaptoethylamine in 0.1 mol/L sodium phosphate buffer, pH 6.0, containing 5 mmol/L EDTA at 30°C for 10 min and 0.01 mL of 100 mmol/L N-ethylmaleimide at 30°C for 10 min.

3. Subject the incubated mixture to gel filtration using a column (1.5 × 45 cm) of Ultrogel AcA 44 (Biosepra, Villeneuve la Garenne, France) in 0.1 mol/L sodium phosphate buffer, pH 7.0.

4. Calculate the amount of 2,4-dinitrophenyl-bovine serum albumin-avidin conjugate from the absorbances at 280 nm and 360 nm (Fig. 14.1).

5. Add 1/100 volume of 10% NaN_3 to each fraction.

6. Store the conjugate at 4°C.

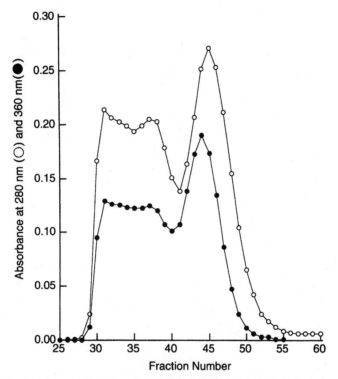

Fig. 14.1. Elution profile of 2,4-dinitrophenyl-bovine serum albumin-avidin conjugate from a column of Ultrogel AcA 44. The column size was 1.5 × 45 cm, and the fraction volume was 1.0 mL.

14.3. Labeling of avidin with β-D-galactosidase

1. Prepare 2.7 mg (5 nmol) of β-D-galactosidase [E_{280} = 2.09 $g^{-1} L cm^{-1}$ and mol wt = 54,000 (Craven et al., 1965)] in 1.2 mL of 0.1 mol/L sodium phosphate buffer, pH 6.0 containing 5 mmol/L EDTA.

2. Incubate the enzyme solution with 0.5 mg (7.4 nmol) of 6-maleimidohexanoyl-avidin in 1.3 mL of 0.1 mol/L sodium phosphate buffer, pH 6.0, containing 5 mmol/L EDTA at 4°C for 20 h.

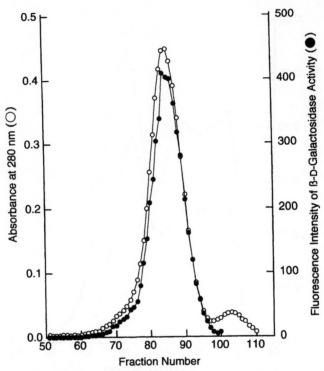

Fig. 14.2. Elution profile of avidin-β-D-galactosidase conjugate from a column of Sepharose 6B. The column size was 1.6 × 65 cm, and fraction volumes were 1.0 mL.

3. Incubate the mixture with 0.02 mL of 100 mmol/L 2-mercaptoethylamine in 0.1 mol/L sodium phosphate buffer, pH 6.0, containing 5 mmol/L EDTA at 30°C for 10 min.

4. Subject the incubated mixture to gel filtration using a column (1.6 × 65 cm) of Sepharose 6B (Amersham Pharmacia Biotech) in 10 mmol/L sodium phosphate buffer, pH 6.5, containing 0.1 mol/L NaCl, 0.1% bovine serum albumin, 1 mmol/L MgCl$_2$ and 0.1% NaN$_3$ (Fig. 14.2).

5. Calculate the amount of the conjugate from the β-D-galactosidase activity.

CHAPTER 15

Enzyme-labeling of antigens

Antigens may be conjugated with enzymes in the same way as IgG and related fragments are conjugated with enzymes by non-hinge methods (Chapters 11 and 13). In the two-step method with glutaraldehyde, which is simple and reproducible, horseradish peroxidase is treated with glutaraldehyde to introduce aldehyde groups and, after removal of free glutaraldehyde, allowed to react with antigens to induce formation of monomeric conjugates with stable crosslinks, since the enzyme has only a small number of amino groups (2–3 per molecule) (Avrameas and Ternynck, 1971). In the two-step method with periodate, the carbohydrate moieties of horseradish peroxidase are first oxidized with periodate to generate aldehyde groups. Then after elimination of small molecules, they are allowed to react with antigens and reduced with borohydride (Wilson and Nakane, 1978). In the two-step maleimide method, thiol groups are introduced into either antigens or enzymes and allowed to react with maleimide groups introduced into the other protein.

In general, however, the antigen-enzyme conjugates prepared by these methods are heterogeneous. Antigen molecules are not polymerized but become associated with different numbers of enzyme molecules. Alternatively, enzyme molecules are not polymerized but become associated with different numbers of antigen molecules. Monomeric antigen-enzyme conjugates can only be prepared by complex methods as described in Chapter 11. Moreover, except in certain cases, it is difficult to conjugate enzyme molecules with specified sites of antigen molecules. Thus, the binding of mono-clonal antibodies to antigen-enzyme conjugates may be prevented by steric hindrance.

In Chapter 16, the two-step maleimide method is described. Thiol groups are introduced into antigen molecules and are allowed to react with the maleimide groups introduced into enzyme mole-cules. Thiol groups are introduced into antigen molecules because they can be determined more easily than maleimide groups and be-cause in most cases antigens are less readily available than enzymes. The two-step maleimide method is highly reproducible, provided that appropriate numbers of thiol and maleimide groups are intro-duced into antigen and enzyme molecules, respectively, and that free thiol and maleimide groups are eliminated completely before conjugation.

Even under appropriately controlled conditions, however, poly-merization may take place. This was the case in the conjuga-tion of recombinant HIV-1 reverse transcriptase (rRT) with β-D-galactosidase from *E. coli* (Hashinaka et al., 1994b), whereas no polymerization was observed in the conjugations of recombinant HIV-1 p24 and p17 antigens with β-D-galactosidase from *E. coli* (Hashida et al., 1994a).

For reduction of polymerization, three two-step maleimide methods (methods I, II and III) have been tested for the conjugation of rRT with β-D-galactosidase from *E. coli* (Fig. 15.1) (Hashinaka et al., 1994b).

In method I, maleimide groups were introduced into β-D-galactosidase molecules by treatment with excess N,N'-*o*-phenylenedimaleimide and allowed to react with the thiol groups introduced into rRT molecules using N-succinimidyl-S-acetylmercaptoacetate. An average of 17–18 maleimide groups were introduced per β-D-galactosidase molecule. The specific ac-tivity of β-D-galactosidase was 28% lower than the original activity after the introduction of maleimide groups, and 40% lower after the conjugation. The conjugate was largely polymerized (Fig. 15.2A).

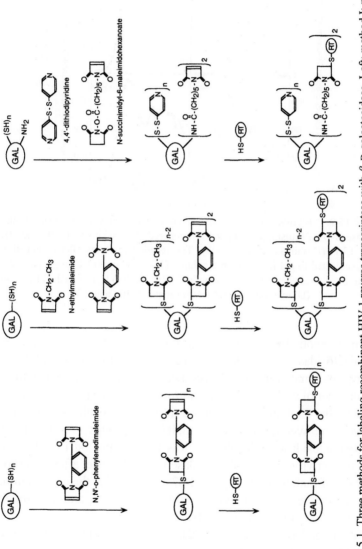

Fig. 15.1. Three methods for labeling recombinant HIV-1 reverse transcriptase with β-D-galactosidase. Left: method I; middle: method II; right: method III. GAL: β-D-galactosidase.

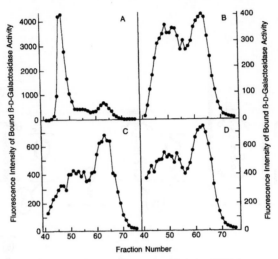

Fig. 15.2. Elution profiles of recombinant HIV-1 reverse trans-criptase-β-D-galactosidase conjugates prepared by methods I, II and III (Fig. 15.1) (Hashinaka et al., 1994b). The reaction mixtures after conjugation were subjected to gel filtration on a column (1.5 × 60 cm) of Ultrogel AcA 22. Fraction volumes were 1.0 mL. (A) method I; (B) method II; (C) method IIIa; and (D) method IIIb. See text for methods IIIa and IIIb.

In method II, maleimide groups were introduced into β-D-galactosidase molecules by treatment with excess N,N'-o-phenylenedimaleimide in the presence of N-ethylmaleimide to limit the number of maleimide groups introduced and were allowed to re-act with the thiol groups introduced into rRT molecules as described above. The average number of maleimide groups introduced per β-D-galactosidase molecule was less than in method I (3–4). The specific activity of β-D-galactosidase was 62% lower after the intro-duction of maleimide groups and 67% lower after the conjugation. The conjugate was still significantly polymerized, although much less than in method I (Fig. 15.2B).

In method III, β-D-galactosidase was treated first with excess 4,4′-dithiodipyridine to block thiol groups completely. Then it was treated with N-succinimidyl-6-maleimidohexanoate to introduce maleimide groups and allowed to react with the thiol groups introduced into rRT molecules as described above. An average of one to two maleimide groups were introduced per β-D-galactosidase molecule. The conjugate was divided into two parts: one part was subjected to gel filtration without any treatment (method IIIa) and the other was first treated with excess 2-mercaptoethylamine to remove thiopyridine from β-D-galactosidase molecules and then subjected to gel filtration (method IIIb). In methods IIIa and b, the specific activity of β-D-galactosidase was lowered 17 and 8%, respectively, by conjugation. The conjugates were less polymerized than in method II (Figs. 15.2C, D).

The conjugates prepared by the three different methods were tested by immune complex transfer enzyme immunoassay V of antibody IgG to HIV-1 RT using urine samples from HIV-1 seropositive and seronegative subjects. The highest positive signal [fluorescence intensity of β-D-galactosidase activity bound to the second solid phase in the presence of urine from an HIV-1 seropositive subject (see Chapters 5–8)] was obtained with polymerized conjugates prepared by method I, and the lowest positive signal with those prepared by method II. However, the highest negative signal was observed with the polymerized conjugates prepared by method I and the second highest negative signal was observed with the conjugates obtained by method IIIb. As a result, the highest ratio of positive to negative signals was obtained with the conjugates obtained by method IIIa, and the lowest ratios with the conjugates obtained by methods I and IIIb.

Thus, method IIIa provided the highest yield of conjugates with the least polymerization, the least loss of specific enzyme activity and the lowest nonspecific binding. In methods I, II and IIIb, the yields of useful conjugates were low due to extensive polymerization, significant loss of specific enzyme activity and/or high nonspecific binding.

Method IIIa may be useful for labeling some other antigens with β-D-galactosidase from *E. coli*.

CHAPTER 16

Protocol for enzyme-labeling of antigens

Reproducible methods are described below. However, unexpected results may be observed in some cases. Favorable results may be obtained by changing conditions, such as the concentration of reagents, pH, time, temperature etc.

16.1. Labeling of recombinant HIV-1 reverse transcriptase (rRT) with 2,4-dinitrophenyl groups

16.1.1. Preparation of mercaptoacetyl-bovine serum albumin

1. Prepare 5 mg (75 nmol) of bovine serum albumin [E_{280} = 0.63 g^{-1} L cm^{-1} (Webster, 1970) and mol wt = 66,200 (Peters, 1975)] in 0.45 mL of 0.1 mol/L sodium phosphate buffer, pH 7.0.

2. Incubate the above solution with 50 μL of 20 mmol/L N-succinimidyl-S-acetylmercaptoacetate (mol wt 231) in N,N-dimethylformamide at 30°C for 30 min.

3. Incubate the reaction mixture with 20 μL of 1 mol/L Tris-HCl buffer, pH 7.0, 30 μL of 0.1 mol/L EDTA, pH 7.0, and 60 μL of 1 mol/L hydroxylamine, pH 7.0, at 30°C for 5 min. Hydroxylamine should be added 10 min before αN-6-maleimidohexanoyl-ϵN-2,4-dinitrophenyl-L-lysine.

289

16.1.2. Preparation of α N-6-maleimidohexanoyl-ε N-2,4-dinitrophenyl-L-lysine

1. Incubate 0.35 mL of 15 mmol/L ε N-2,4-dinitrophenyl-L-lysine-HCl. H_2O (mol wt 367) in 0.1 mol/L sodium phosphate buffer, pH 7.0, with 0.15 mL of 15 mmol/L N-succinimidyl-6-maleimidohexanoate (mol wt 308.3) in N,N-dimethylformamide at 30°C for 30 min.

16.1.3. Conjugation of 6-maleimidohexanoyl-ε N-2,4-dinitrophenyl-L-lysine with mercaptoacetyl-bovine serum albumin

1. Incubate the mercaptoacetyl-bovine serum albumin solution (5 mg, 75 nmol/0.61 mL) with 0.5 mL of α N-6-maleimidohexanoyl-ε N-2,4-dinitrophenyl-L-lysine solution at 30°C for 30 min.
2. Subject the incubated mixture to gel filtration by centrifugation using a column (1.1 × 6.3 cm, 6 mL) of Sephadex G-50 fine (Amersham Pharmacia Biotech, Uppsala, Sweden) in 0.1 mol/L sodium phosphate buffer, pH 7.0.
3. Measure the content of 2,4-dinitrophenyl groups [E_{360} = 17,400 $mol^{-1} L cm^{-1}$ and E_{360}/E_{280} = 1/0.32 (Eisen et al., 1954)] in bovine serum albumin and calculate the average number of 2,4-dinitrophenyl groups introduced per albumin molecule, which is approximately 5.
4. Store the fractions containing 2,4-dinitrophenyl-bovine serum albumin at −20°C.

16.1.4. Preparation of 6-maleimidohexanoyl-2,4-dinitrophenyl-bovine serum albumin

1. Incubate 2,4-dinitrophenyl-bovine serum albumin (3.7 mg, 56 nmol) in 1.0 mL of 0.1 mol/L sodium phosphate buffer,

pH 7.0, with 30 μL of 16.5 mmol/L N-succinimidyl-6-maleimidohexanoate in N,N-dimethylformamide at 30°C for 30 min.

2. Subject the incubated mixture to gel filtration by centrifugation using a column (1.1 × 6.3 cm, 6 mL) of Sephadex G-50 fine (Amersham Pharmacia Biotech, Uppsala, Sweden) in 0.1 mol/L sodium phosphate buffer, pH 6.0.

3. Calculate the average number of maleimide groups introduced per albumin molecule, which is approximately 6.

16.1.5. Preparation of mercaptoacetyl-rRT

1. Prepare rRT (1.0 mg, 16 nmol) in 0.5 mL of 0.1 mol/L sodium phosphate buffer, pH 7.0, containing 0.01% Triton X-100.

2. Incubate the rRT solution with 0.025 mL of 5–10 mmol/L N-succinimidyl-S-acetylmercaptoacetate in N,N-dimethylformamide at 30°C for 30 min.

3. Incubate the mixture with 0.05 mL of 0.1 mol/L EDTA, pH 7.0, 0.05 mL of 1 mol/L Tris-HCl buffer, pH 7.0, and 0.06 mL of 1 mol/L hydroxylamine, pH 7.0, at 30°C for 15 min.

4. Subject the incubated mixture to gel filtration using a column (1.0 × 30 cm) of Sephadex G-25 (Amersham Pharmacia Biotech, Uppsala, Sweden) in 0.1 mol/L sodium phosphate buffer, pH 6.0, containing 5 mmol/L EDTA and 0.01% Triton X-100.

5. Calculate the average number of thiol groups introduced per rRT molecule, which is 2–3. Determine the amount of rRT by estimation of amino groups using fluorescamine (Udenfriend et al., 1972) and bovine serum albumin [$E_{280} = 0.63$ g^{-1} L cm^{-1} (Webster, 1970) and mol wt = 66,200 (Peters, 1975)] as a standard.

16.1.6. Conjugation of mercaptoacetyl-rRT to 6-maleimidohexanoyl-2,4-dinitrophenyl-bovine serum albumin

1. Incubate mercaptoacetyl-rRT (0.14 mg, 2.2 nmol) in 0.1 mL of 0.1 mol/L sodium phosphate buffer, pH 6.0, containing 5 mmol/L EDTA and 0.01% Triton X-100 with 6-maleimidohexanoyl-2,4-dinitrophenyl-bovine serum albumin (0.15 mg, 2.2 nmol) in 10 μL of 0.1 mol/L sodium phosphate buffer, pH 6.0, at 30°C for 60 min.

2. Incubate the reaction mixture with 10 μL of 10 mmol/L 2-mercaptoethylamine in 0.1 mol/L sodium phosphate buffer, pH 6.0, containing 5 mmol/L EDTA at 30°C for 15 min and subsequently with 20 μL of 10 mmol/L N-ethylmaleimide in the same buffer at 30°C for 15 min.

3. Subject the incubated mixture to gel filtration using a column (1.5 × 45 cm) of Ultrogel AcA 34 (Biosepra, Villeneuve la Garenne, France) in 10 mmol/L sodium phosphate buffer, pH 7.0, containing 0.1 mol/L NaCl and 0.01% Triton X-100.

4. Calculate the average number of rRT molecules conjugated per 2,4-dinitrophenyl-bovine serum albumin molecule, which is approximately 2, from the concentration of 2,4-dinitrophenyl-bovine serum albumin and the total protein concentration determined by estimation of amino groups as described above.

5. Calculate the amount of 2,4-dinitrophenyl-bovine serum albumin-rRT conjugate as described for 2,4-dinitrophenyl-bovine serum albumin.

6. Store the conjugate in the presence of 1.0 g/L NaN$_3$ at 4°C.

16.2. Labeling of recombinant HIV-1 p17 antigen (rp17) with 2,4-dinitrophenyl groups

16.2.1. Preparation of mercaptoacetyl-rp17

1. Prepare rp17 (0.76 mg, 45 nmol) in 0.48 mL of 0.1 mol/L sodium phosphate buffer, pH 7.0.
2. Incubate the rp17 solution with 20 μL of 5 mmol/L N-succinimidyl-S-acetylmercaptoacetate in N,N-dimethyl-formamide at 30°C for 30 min.
3. Incubate the reaction mixture with 30 μL of 0.1 mol/L EDTA, pH 7.0, 60 μL of 1 mol/L Tris-HCl buffer, pH 7.0, and 70 μL of 1 mol/L hydroxylamine, pH 7.0, at 30°C for 15 min.
4. Subject the incubated mixture to gel filtration using a column (1.0 × 45 cm) of Sephadex G-25 (Amersham Pharmacia Biotech, Uppsala, Sweden) in 0.1 mol/L sodium phosphate buffer, pH 6.0, containing 5 mmol/L EDTA and 0.35 mol/L urea. Determine the concentration of rp17 with a commercial protein assay kit using bovine serum albumin as a standard, and taking its molecular weight as 17,000.
5. Calculate the average number of thiol groups introduced per rp17 molecule, which is 1–2.

16.2.2. Conjugation of mercaptoacetyl-rp17 with 6-maleimidohexanoyl-2,4-dinitrophenyl-bovine serum albumin

1. Incubate mercaptoacetyl-rp17 (0.51 mg, 30 nmol) in 0.3 mL of 0.1 mol/L sodium phosphate buffer, pH 6.0, containing 5 mmol/L EDTA and 0.35 mol/L urea with 6-maleimidohexanoyl-2,4-dinitrophenyl-bovine serum albumin (0.5 mg, 7.5 nmol) in 90 μL of 0.1 mol/L sodium phosphate buffer, pH 6.0, at 4°C for 20 h.
2. Incubate the mixture with 10 μL of 0.1 mol/L 2-mercaptoethylamine in 0.1 mol/L sodium phosphate buffer,

pH 6.0, containing 5 mmol/L EDTA at 30°C for 15 min and subsequently with 20 μL of 0.1 mol/L N-ethylmaleimide in the same buffer at 30°C for 15 min.

3. Subject the incubated mixture to gel filtration using a column (1.5 × 45 cm) of Ultrogel AcA 44 (Biosepra, Villeneuve la Garenne, France) in 10 mmol/L sodium phosphate buffer, pH 7.0, containing 0.1 mol/L NaCl (Fig. 16.1A).

4. Calculate the average number of rp17 molecules conjugated per albumin molecule, which is approximately 3, from the concentration of 2,4-dinitrophenyl-bovine serum albumin and the total protein concentration determined with a commercial protein assay kit as described above.

5. Calculate the amount of the conjugate as described for 2,4-dinitrophenyl-bovine serum albumin.

6. Store the conjugate in the presence of 1.0 g/L NaN$_3$ at 4°C.

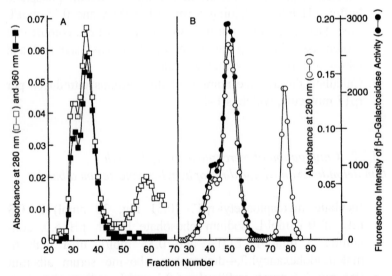

Fig. 16.1. Elution profiles of 2,4-dinitrophenyl-bovine serum albumin-recombinant HIV-1 p17 conjugate (A), and recombinant HIV-1 p17-β-D-galactosidase conjugate (B), from columns of Ultrogel AcA 44 and AcA 22, respectively.

16.3. Labeling of recombinant HIV-1 p24 antigen (rp24) with 2,4-dinitrophenyl groups

16.3.1. Preparation of mercaptoacetyl-rp24

1. Prepare rp24 (1.6 mg, 67 nmol) in 0.48 mL of 0.1 mol/L sodium phosphate buffer, pH 7.0.
2. Incubate the rp24 solution with 20 μL of 5 mmol/L N-succinimidyl-S-acetylmercaptoacetate in N,N-dimethylformamide at 30°C for 30 min.
3. Incubate the above mixture with 30 μL of 0.1 mol/L EDTA, pH 7.0, 60 μL of 1 mol/L Tris-HCl buffer, pH 7.0, and 70 μL of 1 mol/L hydroxylamine, pH 7.0, at 30°C for 15 min.
4. Subject the incubated mixture to gel filtration by centrifugation using a column (1.1 × 5.3 cm, 5 mL) of Sephadex G-50 fine (Amersham Pharmacia Biotech, Uppsala, Sweden) in 0.1 mol/L sodium phosphate buffer, pH 6.0, containing 5 mmol/L EDTA.
5. Determine the concentration of rp24 with a commercial protein assay kit using bovine serum albumin as a standard, and taking its molecular weight as 24,000.
6. Calculate the average number of thiol groups introduced per rp24 molecule, which is approximately 1.

16.3.2. Conjugation of mercaptoacetyl-rp24 with 6-maleimidohexanoyl-2,4-dinitrophenyl-bovine serum albumin

1. Incubate mercaptoacetyl-rp24 (0.46 mg, 19 nmol) in 0.25 mL of 0.1 mol/L sodium phosphate buffer, pH 6.0, containing 5 mmol/L EDTA with 6-maleimidohexanoyl-2,4-dinitrophenyl-bovine serum albumin (0.32 mg, 4.8 nmol) in 70 μL of 0.1 mol/L sodium phosphate buffer, pH 6.0, at 4°C for 20 h.
2. Incubate the mixture with 10 μL of 0.1 mol/L 2-mercaptoethylamine in 0.1 mol/L sodium phosphate buffer, pH 6.0, containing 5 mmol/L EDTA at 30°C for 15 min and

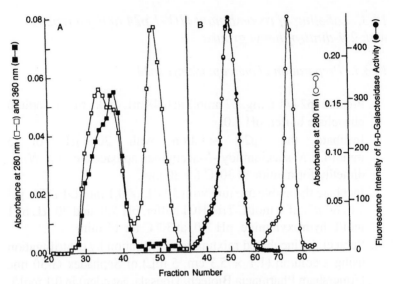

Fig. 16.2. Elution profiles of 2,4-dinitrophenyl-bovine serum albumin-recombinant HIV-1 p24 conjugate (A), and recombinant HIV-1 p24-β-D-galactosidase conjugate (B), from columns of Ultrogel AcA 44 and AcA 22, respectively (Hashida et al., 1994a).

then with 20 μL of 0.1 mol/L N-ethylmaleimide in the same buffer at 30°C for 15 min.

3. Subject the incubated mixture to gel filtration using a column (1.5 × 45 cm) of Ultrogel AcA 44 (Biosepra, Villeneuve la Garenne, France) in 10 mmol/L sodium phosphate buffer, pH 7.0, containing 0.1 mol/L NaCl (Fig. 16.2A).

4. Calculate the average number of rp24 molecules conjugated per albumin molecule, which is 2–3, from the concentration of 2,4-dinitrophenyl-bovine serum albumin and the total protein concentration determined with a commercial protein assay kit as described above.

5. Calculate the amount of the conjugate as described for 2,4-dinitrophenyl-bovine serum albumin.

6. Store the conjugate in the presence of 1.0 g/L NaN$_3$ at 4°C.

16.4. Labeling of recombinant HIV-1 reverse transcriptase (rRT) with β-D-galactosidase: method I

16.4.1. Preparation of maleimide-β-D-galactosidase I

1. Incubate β-D-galactosidase from *E. coli* (lyophilized for enzyme immunoassay, Boehringer Mannheim GmbH, Mannheim, Germany) (2.6 mg, 4.8 nmol) in 450 μL of 0.1 mol/L sodium phosphate buffer, pH 6.0, with 50 μL of 30 mmol/L N,N'-*o*-phenylenedimaleimide in N,N-dimethylformamide at 30°C for 20 min.
2. Mix the incubated mixture with 100 μL of 0.1 mol/L sodium phosphate buffer, pH 6.0, and subject the mixture to gel filtration by centrifugation using a column (1.1 × 5.3 cm, 5 mL) of Sephadex G-50 fine (Amersham Pharmacia Biotech, Uppsala, Sweden) in 0.1 mol/L sodium phosphate buffer, pH 6.0.
3. Calculate the average number of maleimide groups introduced per β-D-galactosidase molecule, which is 17–18.

16.4.2. Conjugation of mercaptoacetyl-rRT with maleimide-β-D-galactosidase I

1. Incubate mercaptoacetyl-rRT (0.40 mg, 6.3 nmol) in 0.5 mL of 0.1 mol/L sodium phosphate buffer, pH 6.0, containing 5 mmol/L EDTA and 0.01% Triton X-100 with maleimide-β-D-galactosidase I (1.1 mg, 2.1 nmol) in 0.5 mL of 0.1 mol/L sodium phosphate buffer, pH 6.0, at 4°C for 20 h.
2. Incubate the reaction mixture with 10 μL of 0.1 mol/L 2-mercaptoethylamine in 0.1 mol/L sodium phosphate buffer, pH 6.0, containing 5 mmol/L EDTA at 30°C for 15 min and then with 20 μL of 0.1 mol/L N-ethylmaleimide in the same buffer at 30°C for 15 min.
3. Subject the incubated mixture to gel filtration using a column (1.5 × 60 cm) of Ultrogel AcA 22 (Biosepra, Villeneuve la

Garenne, France) in 10 mmol/L sodium phosphate buffer, pH 7.0, containing 0.1 g/L bovine serum albumin, 0.1 mol/L NaCl, 1.0 mmol/L $MgCl_2$, 1.0 g/L NaN_3 and 0.01% Triton X-100 (Fig. 15.2A).

4. Store the fractions containing the conjugate at 4°C.
5. Calculate the average number of rRT molecules conjugated per β-D-galactosidase molecule, which is 3.0, from the decrease in the number of maleimide groups.
6. Calculate the amount of conjugate from the β-D-galactosidase activity.

16.5. Labeling of recombinant HIV-1 reverse transcriptase (rRT) with β-D-galactosidase: method II

16.5.1. Preparation of maleimide-β-D-galactosidase II

1. Incubate β-D-galactosidase from *E. coli* (2.6 mg, 4.8 nmol) in 463 μL of 0.1 mol/L sodium phosphate buffer, pH 6.0, with a mixture of 18.3 μL of 60 mmol/L N,N'-o-phenylenedimaleimide in N,N-dimethylformamide and 68.8 μL of 240 mmol/L N-ethylmaleimide in N,N-dimethylformamide at 30°C for 20 min.
2. Mix the reaction mixture with 50 μL of 0.1 mol/L sodium phosphate buffer, pH 6.0, and subject the mixture to gel filtration as described in method I.
3. Calculate the average number of maleimide groups introduced per β-D-galactosidase molecule, which is 3–4.

16.5.2. Conjugation of mercaptoacetyl-rRT with maleimide-β-D-galactosidase II

1. Incubate mercaptoacetyl-rRT (0.40 mg, 6.3 nmol) in 0.5 mL of 0.1 mol/L sodium phosphate buffer, pH 6.0, containing 5

mmol/L EDTA and 0.01% Triton X-100 with maleimide-β-D-galactosidase II (0.70 mg, 1.3 nmol) in 0.5 mL of 0.1 mol/L sodium phosphate buffer, pH 6.0, at 4°C for 20 h.

2. Incubate the reaction mixture with 10 μL of 0.1 mol/L 2-mercaptoethylamine in 0.1 mol/L sodium phosphate buffer, pH 6.0, containing 5 mmol/L EDTA at 30°C for 15 min and subsequently with 20 μL of 0.1 mol/L N-ethylmaleimide in the same buffer at 30°C for 15 min.

3. Subject the reaction mixture to gel filtration as described in method I (Fig. 15.2B).

4. Store fractions containing the conjugate at 4°C. The average number of rRT molecules conjugated per β-D-galactosidase molecule is approximately 3, as calculated from decrease in the number of maleimide groups. The amount of conjugate is calculated from the β-D-galactosidase activity.

16.6. Labeling of recombinant HIV-1 reverse transcriptase (rRT) with β-D-galactosidase: method III

16.6.1. Preparation of maleimide-β-D-galactosidase III

1. Incubate β-D-galactosidase from E. coli (2.5 mg, 4.6 nmol) in 190 μL of 0.1 mol/L sodium phosphate buffer, pH 7.0, with 10 μL of 40 mmol/L 4,4'-dithiodipyridine in N,N-dimethylformamide at 30°C for 15 min.

2. Subject the incubated mixture to gel filtration by centrifugation using a column (1.1 × 2.6 cm, 2.5 mL) of Sephadex G-50 fine (Amersham Pharmacia Biotech, Uppsala, Sweden) in 0.1 mol/L sodium phosphate buffer, pH 7.0.

3. Incubate the filtrate (200 μL) with 10.5 μL of 2.0 mmol/L N-succinimidyl-6-maleimidohexanoate in N,N-dimethylformamide at 30°C for 15 min.

4. Mix the reaction mixture with 50 μL of 0.1 mol/L sodium phosphate buffer, pH 6.0, and subject the mixture to gel fil-

tration by centrifugation using a column (1.1 × 2.6 cm, 2.5 mL) of Sephadex G-50 fine (Amersham Pharmacia Biotech, Uppsala, Sweden) in 0.1 mol/L sodium phosphate buffer, pH 6.0. The average number of maleimide groups introduced per β-D-galactosidase molecule is 1–2.

16.6.2. Conjugation of mercaptoacetyl-rRT with maleimide-β-D-galactosidase III

1. Incubate mercaptoacetyl-rRT (0.44 mg, 7.0 nmol) in 0.3 mL of 0.1 mol/L sodium phosphate buffer, pH 6.0, containing 5 mmol/L EDTA and 0.01% Triton X-100 with maleimide-β-D-galactosidase III (0.94 mg, 1.8 nmol) in 0.2 mL of 0.1 mol/L sodium phosphate buffer, pH 6.0, and 0.38 mL of 0.1 mol/L sodium phosphate buffer, pH 6.0, at 4°C for 20 h.

2. Incubate the reaction mixture with 20 μL of 22 mmol/L N-ethylmaleimide in 0.1 mol/L sodium phosphate buffer, pH 6.0, at 30°C for 5 min.

3. Subject half portion (450 μL) of the incubation mixture to gel filtration as described in method I (method IIIa) (Fig. 15.2C).

4. Incubate the rest (450 μL) with 10 μL of 50 mmol/L 2-mercaptoethylamine in 0.1 mol/L sodium phosphate buffer, pH 6.0, containing 5 mmol/L EDTA at 30°C for 5 min.

5. Subject the reaction mixture to gel filtration as described in method I (method IIIb) (Fig. 15.2D).

6. Store fractions containing the conjugate at 4°C.

7. Calculate the average number of rRT molecules conjugated per β-D-galactosidase molecule, which is 1–2, from the decrease in the number of maleimide groups.

8. Calculate the amount of conjugate from the β-D-galactosidase activity.

16.7. Labeling of recombinant HIV-1 p17 (rp17) with β-D-galactosidase

1. Incubate mercaptoacetyl-rp17 (0.1 mg, 6.0 nmol) in 0.5 mL of 0.1 mol/L sodium phosphate buffer, pH 6.0, containing 5 mmol/L EDTA and 0.35 mol/L urea with maleimide-β-D-galactosidase I (1.1 mg, 2.0 nmol) in 0.5 mL of 0.1 mol/L sodium phosphate buffer, pH 6.0, containing 5 mmol/L EDTA, at 4°C for 20 h.
2. Incubate the reaction mixture with 10 μL of 0.1 mol/L 2-mercaptoethylamine in 0.1 mol/L sodium phosphate buffer, pH 6.0, containing 5 mmol/L EDTA at 30°C for 15 min and then with 20 μL of 10 mmol/L N-ethylmaleimide in 0.1 mol/L sodium phosphate buffer, pH 6.0, containing 5 mmol/L EDTA at 30°C for 15 min.
3. Subject the incubated mixture to gel filtration using a column (1.5 × 45 cm) of Ultrogel AcA 22 (Biosepra, Villeneuve la Garenne, France) in 10 mmol/L sodium phosphate buffer, pH 7.0, containing 0.1 g/L bovine serum albumin, 0.1 mol/L NaCl, 1.0 mmol/L $MgCl_2$ and 1.0 g/L NaN_3 (Fig. 16.1B).
4. Store fractions containing the conjugate at 4°C.
5. Calculate the average number of rp17 molecules conjugated per β-D-galactosidase molecule, which is 2–3, from decrease in the number of maleimide groups.
6. Calculate the amount of the conjugate from the β-D-galactosidase activity.

16.8. Labeling of recombinant HIV-1 p24 (rp24) with β-D-galactosidase

1. Incubate mercaptoacetyl-rp24 (0.19 mg, 8.0 nmol) in 0.5 mL of 0.1 mol/L sodium phosphate buffer, pH 6.0, containing 5 mmol/L EDTA with maleimide-β-D-galactosidase I (1.1 mg, 2.0 nmol) in 0.5 mL of the same buffer at 4°C for 20 h.

2. Incubate the mixture with 10 μL of 0.1 mol/L 2-mercaptoethylamine in 0.1 mol/L sodium phosphate buffer, pH 6.0, containing 5 mmol/L EDTA at 30°C for 15 min and then with 20 μL of 0.1 mol/L N-ethylmaleimide in the same buffer at 30°C for 15 min.

3. Subject the incubated mixture to gel filtration using a column (1.5 × 45 cm) of Ultrogel AcA 22 (Biosepra, Villeneuve la Garenne, France) in 10 mmol/L sodium phosphate buffer, pH 7.0, containing 0.1 g/L bovine serum albumin, 0.1 mol/L NaCl, 1.0 mmol/L MgCl$_2$ and 1.0 g/L NaN$_3$ (Fig. 16.2B).

4. Store fractions containing the conjugate at 4°C.

5. Calculate the average number of rp24 molecules conjugated per β-D-galactosidase molecule, which is approximately 2, from decrease in the number of maleimide groups.

6. Calculate the amount of the conjugate from the β-D-galactosidase activity.

CHAPTER 17

Assays of enzymes

17.1. Introduction

In general, fluorometry is more sensitive than colorimetry for assays of enzymes. The detection limits of β-D-galactosidase from *E. coli* and alkaline phosphatase from calf intestine by fluorometry using 4-methylumbelliferyl derivatives are 1000- to 5000-fold less than those by colorimetry using nitrophenyl derivatives (Ishikawa and Kato, 1978; Ishikawa et al., 1983a, b; Ishikawa, 1987). However, the detection limit of horseradish peroxidase by fluorometry using 3-(4-hydroxyphenyl)propionic acid is only 5- to 20-fold less than that by colorimetry using *o*-phenylenediamine or 3,3',5,5'-tetramethylbenzidine (Ishikawa et al., 1983a,b; Ishikawa, 1987). A colorimetric assay of alkaline phosphatase from calf intestine by enzymatic cycling (Johannsson et al., 1985) is as sensitive as or more sensitive than its fluorometric assay using 4-methylumbelliferyl-phosphate. Luminescent assays of alkaline-phosphatase from calf intestine (Bronstein et al., 1989), β-D-galactosidase from *E. coli* (Tanaka and Ishikawa, 1986; 1990) and glucose-6-phosphate dehydrogenase from *Leuconostoc mesenteroides* (Tanaka and Ishikawa, 1984) are capable of detecting zeptomole amounts of the enzymes.

Reproducible methods are described below. However, unexpected results may be observed in some cases. Favorable results may be obtained by changing conditions, such as the concentration of reagents, pH, time, temperature, etc.

17.2. Assay of peroxidase

17.2.1. Colorimetric assay of peroxidase with o-phenylenediamine

1. Dissolve 0.11 g of o-phenylenediamine (mol wt 108) (hydrogen donor) in 100 mL of 50 mmol/L sodium acetate buffer, pH 5.0, containing 0.25 g/L bovine serum albumin immediately before use.
2. Mix 0.01 mL of enzyme samples with 0.15 mL of the hydrogen donor solution.
3. Incubate the enzyme/hydrogen donor mixture with 0.05 mL of 1 g/L H_2O_2 at 30°C for 10 min.
4. Stop the enzyme reaction by addition of 0.8 mL of 0.5 mol/L H_2SO_4 containing 1 g/L Na_2SO_3.
5. Read the absorbance at 491 nm. The detection limit of horseradish peroxidase is 25 amol (1 pg) in a 10 min assay.

17.2.2. Colorimetric assay of peroxidase with 3,3',5,5'-tetramethylbenzidine

1. Dissolve 13.4 mg of 3,3',5,5'-tetramethylbenzidine (mol wt 240) (hydrogen donor) in 1 mL of N,N-dimethylformamide and then add 100 mL of 0.1 mol/L sodium acetate buffer, pH 5.5 containing 0.1 g/L Tween 20.
2. Mix 0.01 mL enzyme samples with 0.6 mL of the hydrogen donor solution.
3. Incubate the enzyme/hydrogen donor mixture with 0.2 mL of 0.1 g/L H_2O_2 at 30°C for 10–100 min.
4. Stop the enzyme reaction by addition of 0.2 mL of 2 mol/L H_2SO_4.
5. Read the absorbance at 450 nm. The detection limits of horseradish peroxidase in 10 and 100 min assays are 50 and 10 amol (2 and 0.4 pg), respectively.

17.2.3. Fluorometric assay of peroxidase with 3-(4-hydroxyphenyl)propionic acid

1. Dissolve 0.3 g of 3-(4-hydroxyphenyl)propionic acid (hydrogen donor) in 50 mL of 0.1 mol/L sodium phosphate buffer, pH 8.0. The pH is lowered to 7.
2. Prepare enzyme samples in 0.01 mL of 10 mmol/L sodium phosphate buffer, pH 7.0, containing 0.1 mol/L NaCl and 0.5 g/L bovine serum albumin.
3. Mix 0.01 mL of enzyme samples with 0.1 mL of the hydrogen donor solution.
4. Incubate the enzyme/hydrogen donor solution with 0.05 mL of 0.15 g/L H_2O_2 at 30°C for 10–100 min.
5. Stop the enzyme reaction by addition of 2.5 mL of 0.1 mol/L glycine-NaOH buffer, pH 10.3.
6. Read the fluorescence intensity using 320 nm for excitation and 405 nm for emission analysis. Use 0.2–1.0 mg/L of quinine in 0.05 mol/L H_2SO_4 as a standard. The detection limits of horseradish peroxidase in 10 and 100 min assays are 5 and 0.5 amol (200 and 20 fg), respectively.

17.3. Assay of β-D-galactosidase

17.3.1. Colorimetric assay of β-D-galactosidase with o-nitrophenyl-β-D-galactoside

1. Dissolve 150 mg (0.5 mmol) of o-nitrophenyl-β-D-galactoside (mol wt 301.3) (substrate) in 10 mL of 10 mmol/L sodium phosphate buffer, pH 7.0, containing 0.1 mol/L NaCl, 1 mmol/L $MgCl_2$, 0.05–1.0 g/L bovine serum albumin and 1 g/L NaN_3 (buffer A).
2. Prepare enzyme samples in 0.4 mL of buffer A.
3. Incubate 0.4 mL of enzyme samples with 0.1 mL of the substrate solution at 30°C for 10–100 min.

4. Stop the enzyme reaction by addition of 2 mL of 0.1 mol/L Na$_2$CO$_3$.
5. Read the absorbance at 420 nm. The detection limits of β-D-galactosidase from *E. coli* in 10 and 100 min assays are 1 and 0.1 fmol (540 and 54 pg), respectively.

17.3.2. Fluorometric assay of β-D-galactosidase with 4-methylumbelliferyl-β-D-galactoside

1. Dissolve 10 mg (0.03 mmol) of 4-methylumbelliferyl-β-D-galactoside (mol wt 338.3) (substrate) in 2.0 mL of *N,N*-dimethylformamide and mix the solution with 98 mL of deionized water.
2. Prepare enzyme samples in 0.1 mL of 10 mmol/L sodium phosphate buffer, pH 7.0, containing 0.1 mol/L NaCl, 1 mmol/L MgCl$_2$, 0.05–1.0 g/L bovine serum albumin and 1 g/L NaN$_3$.
3. Incubate 0.1 mL of enzyme samples with 0.05 mL of the substrate solution at 30°C for 10–1000 min.
4. Stop the enzyme reaction by addition of 2.5 mL of 0.1 mol/L glycine-NaOH buffer, pH 10.3.
5. Read the fluorescence intensity using 360 nm for excitation and 450 nm for emission analysis. Use 10–1000 nmol/L 4-methylumbelliferone (mol wt 176.2) in 0.1 mol/L glycine-NaOH buffer, pH 10.3, as a standard. The detection limits of β-D-galactosidase from *E. coli* in 10, 100 and 1000 min assays are 0.2, 0.02 and 0.002 amol (110, 11 and 1.1 fg), respectively.

17.4. Assay of alkaline phosphatase

17.4.1. Colorimetric assay of alkaline phosphatase with p-nitrophenylphosphate

1. Dissolve 20 mg (0.054 mmol) of *p*-nitrophenylphosphate disodium salt (mol wt 371.2) (substrate) in 10 mL of 0.1 mol/L

glycine-NaOH buffer, pH 10.3, containing 1 mmol/L $MgCl_2$, 0.1 mmol/L $ZnCl_2$, 0.5 g/L NaN_3 and 0.25 g/L egg albumin.

2. Incubate enzyme samples in 0.5 mL of the same buffer with 0.5 mL of the substrate solution at 30°C for 10 min.

3. Stop the enzyme reaction by addition of 0.5 mL of 1 mol/L NaOH.

4. Read the absorbance at 405 nm. The detection limit of alkaline phosphatase from calf intestine in a 10 min assay is 10 fmol (1 ng).

17.4.2. Colorimetric assay of alkaline phosphatase by enzymatic cycling

1. Dissolve 3.0 mg (4000 nmol) of NADP (mol wt 743.4) (substrate) in 10 mL of deionized water (substrate solution).

2. Dissolve 4 mg of alcohol dehydrogenase, 4 mg of diaphorase and 2.8 mg (5,500 nmol) of p-iodonitrotetrazolium violet (mol wt 505.7) in 10 mL of 25 mmol/L sodium phosphate buffer, pH 7.2, containing 40 g/L ethanol (cycling solution).

3. Prepare enzyme samples in 0.08 mL of 0.1 mol/L diethanolamine buffer, pH 9.5, containing 2 mmol/L $MgCl_2$, 0.2 mmol/L $ZnCl_2$, 0.2 g/L bovine serum albumin and 2 g/L NaN_3.

4. Incubate 0.08 mL of enzyme samples with 0.08 mL of the substrate solution at 30°C for 10–100 min.

5. Incubate the reaction mixture with 0.3 mL of the cycling solution at 30°C for 20 min.

6. Stop the cycling reaction by addition of 0.075 mL of 0.4 mol/L HCl.

7. Read the absorbance at 495 nm. The detection limit of alkaline phosphatase from calf intestine in a 100 min assay is 0.3 amol (30 fg).

17.4.3. Fluorometric assay of alkaline phosphatase with 4-methylumbelliferyl phosphate

1. Dissolve 2.6 mg (0.01 mmol) of 4-methylumbelliferyl phosphate (mol wt 256.2) (substrate) in 33.3 mL of 0.1 mol/L glycine-NaOH buffer, pH 9.5.
2. Prepare enzyme samples in 0.1 mL of 0.1 mol/L glycine-NaOH buffer, pH 9.5, containing 1 mmol/L $MgCl_2$, 0.1 mmol/L $ZnCl_2$, 0.5 g/L NaN_3 and 0.25 g/L egg albumin.
3. Incubate 0.1 mL of enzyme samples with 0.05 mL of the substrate solution at 30°C for 10–100 min.
4. Stop the enzyme reaction by addition of 2.5 mL of 0.5 mol/L K_2HPO_4-KOH buffer, pH 10.4, containing 10 mmol/L EDTA.
5. Read the fluorescence intensity using 360 nm for excitation and 450 nm for emission analysis. Use 100 nmol/L 4-methylumbelliferone in the same buffer as a standard. The detection limits of alkaline phosphatase from calf intestine in 10 and 100 min assays are 10 and 1.0 amol (1.0 and 0.1 pg), respectively.

17.5. Assay of glucose-6-phosphate dehydrogenase

17.5.1. Bioluminescent assay of glucose-6-phosphate dehydrogenase

1. Dissolve 10 mg (0.033 mmol) of glucose-6-phosphate disodium salt (mol wt 304.2) (substrate) and 7.3 mg (0.011 mmol) of NAD^+ (mol wt 663.4) in 10 mL of 95 mmol/L Tris-HCl buffer, pH 7.8, containing 3.5 mmol/L $MgCl_2$ (substrate solution).
2. Dissolve 2.5 mg of FMN in 5 mL of 10 mmol/L sodium phosphate buffer, pH 7.0, and adjust the concentration of FMN to 0.1 mmol/L taking its extinction coefficient at 450 nm as 1.22×10^4 mol^{-1} L cm^{-1}.
3. Dissolve 1 mg of lyophilized luciferase from *Photobacterium fischeri* in 1.0 mL of deionized water.

4. Dissolve 1 U of lyophilized NAD(P)H:FMN oxidoreductase from *P. fischeri* in 1.0 mL of 50 nmol/L sodium phosphate buffer, pH 7.0, containing 40% (v/v) glycerol, 1 mmol/L EDTA and 0.1 mmol/L dithiothreitol.

5. Dissolve 0.25 mg of myristic aldehyde in a mixture of 10 g/L bovine serum albumin (1.25 mL) and 2 g/L Triton X-100 (1.25 mL).

6. Prepare enzyme samples in a total volume of 0.005 mL of 0.1 mol/L Tris-HCl buffer, pH 7.8, containing 4 mmol/L $MgCl_2$ and 1 g/L egg albumin.

7. Incubate 0.005 mL of enzyme samples with 0.05 mL of the substrate solution at 30°C for 10–100 min.

8. Stop the enzyme reaction by incubation at 100°C for 30 sec.

9. Mix 0.355 mL of 0.1 mol/L sodium phosphate buffer, pH 6.5, 0.01 mL of the FMN solution, 0.005 mL of the luciferase solution, 0.02 mL of the NAD(P)H: FMN oxidoreductase solution and 0.01 mL of the myristic aldehyde solution in a polypropylene vial.

10. Add 0.05 mL of the heated mixture to the polypropylene vial.

11. Measure the luminescence intensity between 15 and 45 sec after addition of the heated mixture. The detection limits of glucose-6-phosphate dehydrogenase from *L. mesenteroides* in 10 and 100 min assays are 0.055 amol and 0.0055 amol, respectively.

References

Aikawa, T., Suzuki, S., Murayama, M., Hashiba, K., Kitagawa, T. and Ishikawa, E. (1979). Enzyme immunoassay of angiotensin I. Endocrinology *105*, 1–6.

Avrameas, S. (1969). Coupling of enzymes to proteins with glutaraldehyde. Use of the conjugate for the detection of antigens and antibodies. Immunochemistry *6*, 43–52.

Avrameas, S. and Ternynck, T. (1971). Peroxidase labelled antibody and Fab conjugates with enhanced intracellular penetration. Immunochemistry *8*, 1175–1179.

Berson, S.A. and Yalow, R.S. (1959). Species-specificity of human anti-beef, pork insulin serum. J. Clin. Invest. *38*, 2017–2025.

Boutton, B. and Mamas, S. (1994). Immunometric assay of low molecular weight haptens containing primary amino groups. Anal. Chem. *66*, 16–22.

Bronstein, I., Edwards, B. and Voyta, J.C. (1989). 1,2-Dioxetanes: novel chemiluminescent enzyme substrates. Applications to immunoassays. J. Biolum. Chemilum. *4*, 99–111.

Carlsson, J., Drevin, H. and Axén, R. (1978). Protein thiolation and reversible protein-protein conjugation. Biochem. J. *173*, 723–737.

Craven, G.R., Steers. Jr., E. and Anfinsen, C.B. (1965). Purification, composition, and molecular weight of the β-galactosidase of *Escherichia coli* Kl2. J. Biol. Chem. *240*, 2468–2477.

Dorrington., K.J. and Tanford, C. (1970). Molecular size and conformation of immunoglobulins. Adv. Immunol. *12*, 333–381.

Editorial (1976). ELISA: a replacement for radioimmunoassay? Lancet *ii*, 406–407.

Eisen, H.N., Carsten, M.E. and Belman, S. (1954). Studies of hypersensitivity to low molecular substrances. III. The 2,4-dinitrophenyl group as a determinant in the precipitin reaction. J. Immunol. *73*, 296–308.

Ekins, R. (1976). ELISA: a replacement for radioimmunoassays? Lancet *ii*, 569–570.

Engström, L. (1961). Studies on calf-intestinal alkaline phosphatase. I. Chromatographic purification, microheterogeneity and some other properties of the purified enzyme. Biochim. Biophys. Acta *52*, 36–48.

Engvall, E. and Perlmann, P. (1971). Enzyme-linked immunosorbent assay (ELISA). Quantitative assay of immunoglobulin G. Immunochemistry *8*, 871–874.

Ey, P.L., Prowse, S.J. and Jenkin, C.R. (1978). Isolation of pure IgG$_1$, IgG$_{2a}$ and IgG$_{2b}$ immunoglobulins from mouse serum using protein A-Sepharose. Immunochemistry *15*, 429–436.

Fyhrquist, F., Soveri, P., Puutula, L. and Stenman, U-H. (1976). Radioimmunoassay of plasma renin activity. Clin. Chem. *22*, 250–256.

Glänzer, K., Appenheimer, M., Krück, F., Vetter, W. and Vetter, H. (1984). Measurement of 8-arginine-vasopressin by radioimmunoassay: development and application to urine and plasma samples using one extraction method. Acta Endocrinol. *106*, 317–329.

Gorini, G., Medgyesi, G.A. and Doria, G. (1969). Heterogeneity of mouse myeloma γG globulins as revealed by enzymatic proteolysis. J. Immunol. *103*, 1132–1142.

Grassetti, D.R. and Murray, Jr., J.F. (1967). Determination of sulfhydryl groups with 2,2'- or 4,4'-dithiodipyridine. Arch. Biochem. Biophys. *119*, 41–49.

Green, N.M. (1975). Avidin. Adv. Protein Chem. *29*, 85–133.

Guesdon, J.-L., Ternynck, T. and Avrameas, S. (1979). The use of avidin-biotin interaction in immunoenzymatic techniques. J. Histochem. Cytochem. *27*, 1131–1139.

Hammer, M. (1978). Radioimmunoassay of 8-arginine-vasopressin (antidiuretic hormone) in human plasma. Scand. J. Clin. Lab. Invest. *38*, 707–716.

Hardy, P.M., Hughes, G.J. and Rydon, H.N. (1976a). Formation of quaternary pyridinium compounds by the action of glutaraldehyde on proteins. J. Chem. Soc. Chem. Commun. *5*, 157–158.

Hardy, P.M., Nicholls, A.C. and Rydon, H.N. (1976b). The nature of the cross-linking of proteins by glutraldehyde. Part I. Interaction of glutaraldehyde with the aminogroups of 6-aminohexanoic acid and of α-N-acetyl-lysine. J. Chem. Soc. Perkin Trans. 1. *9*, 958–962.

Hasegawa, K., Matsushita, Y., Inoue, T., Morii, H., Ishibashi, M. and Yamaji, T. (1986). Plasma levels of artial natriuretic peptide in patients with chronic renal failure. J. Clin. Endocrinol. Metab. *63*, 819–822.

Hashida, S. and Ishikawa, E. (1985). Use of normal IgG and its fragments to lower the non-specific binding of Fab'-enzyme conjugates in sandwich enzyme immunoassay. Anal. Lett. *18*, 1143–1155.

Hashida, S. and Ishikawa, E. (1990). Detection of one milliattomole of ferritin by novel and ultrasensitive enzyme immunoassay. J. Biochem. *108*, 960–964.

Hashida, S., Nakagawa, K., Imagawa, M., Inoue, S., Yoshitake, S., Ishikawa, E., Endo, Y., Ohtaki, S., Ichioka, Y. and Nakajima, K. (1983). Use of inorganic salts to minimize serum interference in a sandwich enzyme immunoassay for human growth hormone using Fab′-horseradish peroxidase conjugate. Clin. Chim. Acta *135*, 263–273.

Hashida, S., Imagawa, M., Inoue, S., Ruan, K-h. and Ishikawa, E. (1984). More useful maleimide compounds for the conjugation of Fab′ to horseradish peroxidase through thiol groups in the hinge. J. Appl. Biochem. *6*, 56–63.

Hashida, S., Imagawa, M., Ishikawa, E. and Freytag, J.W. (1985). A simple method for the conjugation of affinity-purified Fab′ to horseradish peroxidase and β-D-galactosidase from *Escherichia coli*. J. Immunoassay *6*, 111–123.

Hashida, S., Ishikawa, E., Mukoyama, M., Nakao, K. and Imura, H. (1988a). Direct measurement of α-human atrial natriuretic polypeptide in plasma by sensitive enzyme immunoassay. J. Clin. Lab. Anal. *2*, 161–167.

Hashida, S., Ishikawa, E., Nakao, K., Mukoyama, M. and Imura, H. (1988b). Enzyme immunoassay for α-human atrial natriuretic polypeptide – direct measurement of plasma level. Clin. Chim. Acta *175*, 11–18.

Hashida, S., Tanaka, K., Kohno, T. and Ishikawa, E. (1988c). Novel and ultrasensitive sandwich enzyme immunoassay (sandwich transfer enzyme immunoassay) for antigens. Anal. Lett. *21*, 1141–1154.

Hashida, S., Ishikawa, E., Mukoyama, M., Nakao, K. and Imura, H. (1991a). Highly sensitive two-site enzyme immunoassays for human atrial natriuretic polypeptides. In: Atrial and Brain Natriuretic Peptides (Matsuo, H. and Imura, H., eds.). (Proceedings of the Kyoto Symposium on ANP, 1988) Kodansha Scientific Ltd., Tokyo, pp. 97–119.

Hashida, S., Tanaka, K., Inoue, S., Hayakawa, K. and Ishikawa, E. (1991b). Time-resolved fluorometric sandwich immunoassay for human growth hormone in serum and urine. J. Clin. Lab. Anal. *5*, 38–42.

Hashida, S., Tanaka, K., Yamamoto, N., Uno, T., Yamaguchi, K. and Ishikawa, E. (1991c). Novel and sensitive noncompetitive enzyme immunoassay (hetero-two-site enzyme immunoassay) for arginine vasopressin in plasma. Anal. Lett. *24*, 1109–1123.

Hashida, S., Tanaka, K., Yamamoto, N., Uno, T., Yamaguchi, K. and Ishikawa, E. (1991d). Detection of one attomole of [Arg[8]]-vasopressin by novel noncompetitive enzyme immunoassay (hetero-two-site complex transfer enzyme immunoassay). J. Biochem. *110*, 486–492.

Hashida, S., Yamamoto, N. and Ishikawa, E. (1991e). Novel and sensitive noncompetitive enzyme immunoassay (hetero-two-site enzyme immunoassay) for α-human atrial natriuretic peptide in plasma. J. Clin. Lab. Anal. *5*, 324–330.

Hashida, S., Hirota, K., Hashinaka, K., Saitoh, A., Nakata, A., Shinagawa, H., Oka, S., Shimada, K., Mimaya, J., Matsushita, S. and Ishikawa, E. (1993). Detection of antibody IgG to HIV-1 in urine by sensitive enzyme immunoassay (immune complex transfer enzyme immunoassay) using recombinant proteins as antigens for diagnosis of HIV-1 infection. J. Clin. Lab. Anal. *7*, 353–364.

Hashida, S., Hashinaka, K., Hirota, K., Saitoh, A., Nakata, A., Shinagawa, H., Oka, S., Shimada, K., Mimaya, J., Matsushita, S. and Ishikawa, E. (1994a). Detection of antibody IgG to HIV-1 in urine by ultrasensitive enzyme immunoassay (immune complex transfer enzyme immunoassay) using recombinant p24 as antigen for diagnosis of HIV-1 infection. J. Clin. Lab. Anal. *8*, 86–95.

Hashida, S., Hirota, K., Kohno, T. and Ishikawa, E. (1994b). Anti-HTLV-I IgG in urine detected by sensitive enzyme immunoassay (immune complex transfer enzyme immunoassay) using a synthetic peptide, cys-*env* gp46(188–224), as antigen. J. Clin. Lab. Anal. *8*, 149–156.

Hashida, S., Hashinaka, K., Nishikata, I., Oka, S., Shimada, K., Saitoh, A., Takamizawa, A., Shinagawa, H. and Ishikawa, E. (1995a). Measurement of human immunodeficiency virus type 1 p24 in serum by an ultrasensitive enzyme immunoassay, the two-site immune complex transfer enzyme immunoassay. J. Clin. Microbiol. *33*, 298–303.

Hashida, S., Hashinaka, K., Nishikata, I., Oka, S., Shimada, K., Saito, A., Takamizawa, A., Shinagawa, H., Yano, S., Kojima, H., Izumi, T. and Ishikawa, E. (1995b). Immune complex transfer enzyme immunoassay that is more sensitive and specific than Western blotting for detection of antibody immunoglobulin G to human immunodeficiency virus type 1 in serum with recombinant *pol* and *gag* proteins as antigens. Clin. Diag. Lab. Immunol. *2*, 535–541.

Hashida, S., Hirota, K., Hashinaka, K., Saitoh, A., Nakata, A., Shinagawa, H., Oka, S., Shimada, K., Mimaya, J., Matsushita, S. and Ishikawa, E. (1995c). Anti-HIV-1 IgG in urine detected by sensitive enzyme immunoassay (immune complex transfer enzyme immunoassay) using recombinant proteins as antigens for diagnosis of HIV-1 infection. Clin. Chem. Enzym. Comms. *6*, 277–290.

Hashida, S., Hashinaka, K., Nishikata, I., Oka, S., Shimada, K., Saito, A., Takamizawa, A., Shinagawa, H. and Ishikawa, E. (1996a). Shortening of the window period in diagnosis of HIV-1 infection by simultaneous detection of p24 antigen and antibody IgG to p17 and reverse transcriptase in serum with ultrasensitive enzyme immunoassay. J. Virol. Methods *62*, 43–53.

Hashida, S., Hashinaka, K., Nishikata, I., Saito, A., Takamizawa, A., Shinagawa, H. and Ishikawa, E. (1996b). Earlier diagnosis of HIV-1 infection by simultaneous detection of p24 antigen and antibody IgGs to p17 and reverse transcriptase in serum with enzyme immunoassay. J. Clin. Lab. Anal. *10*, 213–219.

Hashida, S., Hashinaka, K., Nishikata, I., Saito, A., Takamizawa, A., Shinagawa, H. and Ishikawa, E. (1996c). Ultrasensitive and more specific enzyme immunoassay (immune complex transfer enzyme immunoassay) for p24 antigen of HIV-1 in serum using affinity-purified rabbit anti-p24 Fab′ and monoclonal mouse anti-p24 Fab′. J. Clin. Lab. Anal. *10*, 302–307.

Hashida, S., Hashinaka, K., Ishikawa, S. and Ishikawa, E. (1997). More reliable diagnosis of infection with human immunodeficiency virus type 1 (HIV-1) by detection of antibody IgGs to *pol* and *gag* proteins of HIV-1 and p24 antigen of HIV-1 in urine, saliva and/or serum with highly sensitive and specific enzyme immunoassay (immune complex transfer enzyme immunoassay): a review. J. Clin. Lab. Anal. *11*, 267–286.

Hashida, S., Ishikawa, S., Hashinaka, K., Nishikata, I., Oka, S., Shimada, K., Saito, A., Takamizawa, A., Shinagawa, H. and Ishikawa, E. (1998a). Optimal conditions of immune complex transfer enzyme immunoassays for antibody IgGs to HIV-1 using recombinant p17, p24, and reverse transcriptase as antigens. J. Clin. Lab. Anal. *12*, 98–107.

Hashida, S., Ishikawa, S., Hashinaka, K., Nishikata, I., Saito, A., Takamizawa, A., Shinagawa, H. and Ishikawa, E. (1998b). Optimal conditions of immune complex transfer enzyme immunoassay for p24 antigen of HIV-1. J. Clin. Lab. Anal. *12*, 115–120.

Hashida, S., Ishikawa, S., Nishikata, I., Hashinaka, K., Oka, S. and Ishikawa, E. (1998c). Immune complex transfer enzyme immunoassay for antibody IgM to HIV-1 p17 antigen. J. Clin. Lab. Anal. *12*, 329–336.

Hashinaka, K., Hashida, S., Hirota, K., Saitoh, A., Nakata, A., Shinagawa, H., Oka, S., Shimada, K. and Ishikawa, E. (1994a). Detection of anti-human immunodeficiency virus type 1 (HIV-1) immunoglobulin G in urine by an ultrasensitive enzyme immunoassay (immune complex transfer enzyme immunoassay) with recombinant reverse transcriptase as an antigen. J. Clin. Microbiol. *32*, 819–822.

Hashinaka, K., Hashida, S., Saitoh, A., Nakata, A., Shinagawa, H., Oka, S., Shimada, K. and Ishikawa, E. (1994b). Conjugation of recombinant reverse transcriptase of HIV-1 to β-D-galactosidase from *Escherichia coli* for ultrasensitive enzyme immunoassay (immune complex transfer enzyme immunoassay) of anti-HIV-1 IgG. J. Immunol. Methods *172*, 179–187.

Hirota, K., Kohno, T., Sugiyama, S. and Ishikawa, E. (1991). Simpler and more sensitive immune complex transfer enzyme immunoassay for anti-insulin IgG in serum using β-D-galactosidase as label. Clin. Chem. Enzym. Comms. *4*, 27–38.

Hirota, K., Kohno, T., Toshimori, H., Matsukura, S., Hachisu, T., Ishikawa, S. and Ishikawa, E. (1993). Detection of anti-thyroglobulin immunoglobulin G in urine by sensitive enzyme immunoassay (immune complex transfer enzyme immunoassay) as a diagnostic aid for autoimmune thyroid diseases. Anal. Lett. *26*, 17–31.

Hirota, K., Hashida, S., Hashinaka, K., Kohno, T., Saitoh, A., Shinagawa, H., Nakata, A., Oka, S., Shimada, K. and Ishikawa, E. (1994). Sensitive enzyme immunoassay (immune complex transfer enzyme immunoassay) for antibodies to reverse transcriptase (RT) of human immunodeficiency virus type 1 (HIV-1) using recombinant RT of HIV-1 as antigen. Clin. Chem. Enzym. Comms. *6*, 175–184.

Imagawa, M., Yoshitake, S., Ishikawa, E., Endo, Y., Ohtaki, S., Kano, E. and Tsunetoshi, Y. (1981). Highly sensitive sandwich enzyme immunoassay of human IgE with β-D-galactosidase from *Escherichia coli*. Clin. Chim. Acta *117*, 199–207.

Imagawa, M., Hashida, S., Ishikawa, E. and Sumiyoshi, A. (1982a). Evaluation of Fab'-horseradish peroxidase conjugates prepared using pyridyl disulfide compounds. J. Appl. Biochem. *4*, 400–410.

Imagawa, M., Yoshitake, S., Hamaguchi, Y., Ishikawa, E., Niitsu, Y., Urushizaki, I., Kanazawa, R., Tachibana, S., Nakazawa, N. and Ogawa, H. (1982b). Characteristics and evaluation of antibody-horseradish peroxidase conjugates prepared by using a maleimide compound, glutaraldehyde, and periodate. J. Appl. Biochem. *4*, 41–57.

Imagawa, M., Yoshitake, S., Hashida, S. and Ishikawa, E. (1982c). Effect of temperature on the sensitivity of sandwich enzyme immunoassay with Fab'-horseradish peroxidase conjugate. Anal. Lett. *15*, 1467–1477.

Imagawa, M., Hashida, S., Ishikawa, E., Mori, H., Nakai, C., Ichioka, Y. and Nakajima, K. (1983). A highly sensitive sandwich enzyme immunoassay for insulin in human serum developed using capybara anti-insulin Fab'-horseradish peroxidase conjugate. Anal. Lett. *16*, 1509–1523.

Imagawa, M., Hashida, S., Ishikawa, E. and Freytag, J.W. (1984a). Preparation of a monomeric 2,4-dinitrophenyl Fab'-β-D-galactosidase conjugate for immunoenzymometric assay. J. Biochem. *96*, 1727–1735.

Imagawa, M., Hashida, S., Ishikawa, E., Niitsu, Y., Urushizaki, I., Kanazawa, R., Tachibana, S., Nakazawa, N. and Ogawa, H. (1984b). Comparison of β-D-galactosidase from *Escherichia coli* and horseradish peroxidase as labels of anti-human ferritin Fab' by sandwich enzyme immunoassay technique. J. Biochem. *96*, 659–664.

Imagawa, M., Hashida, S., Ohta, Y. and Ishikawa, E. (1984c). Evaluation of β-D-galactosidase from *Escherichia coli* and horseradish peroxidase as labels by sandwich enzyme immunoassay technique. Ann. Clin. Biochem. *21*, 310–317.

Inoue, S., Imagawa, M., Hashida, S., Ruan, K. H. and Ishikawa, E. (1984). A small scale preparation of affinity-purified rabbit Fab'-horseradish peroxidase conjugate for enzyme immunoassay. Anal. Lett. *17*, 229–242.

Inoue, S., Hashida, S., Kohno, T., Tanaka, K. and Ishikawa, E. (1985a). A micro-scale method for the conjugation of affinity-purified Fab′ to β-D-galactosidase from *Escherichia coli*. J. Biochem. *98*, 1387–1394.

Inoue, S., Hashida, S., Tanaka, K., Imagawa, M. and Ishikawa, E. (1985b). Preparation of monomeric affinity-purified Fab′-β-D-galactosidase conjugate for immunoenzymometric assay. Anal. Lett. *18*, 1331–1344.

Ishikawa, E. (1987). Development and clinical application of sensitive enzyme immunoassay for macromolecular antigens—a review. Clin. Biochem. *20*, 375–385.

Ishikawa, E. (1996). Labeling of antibodies and antigens. In: Immunoassay (Diamandis, E.P., and Christopoulos, T.K., eds.). Academic Press, San Diego, pp. 191–204.

Ishikawa, E. and Kato, K. (1978). Ultrasensitive enzyme immunoassay. Scand. J Immunol. *8* (Suppl. 7), 43–55.

Ishikawa, E. and Kohno, T. (1989). Development and applications of sensitive enzyme immunoassay for antibodies: a review. J. Clin. Lab. Anal. *3*, 252–265.

Ishikawa, E., Hamaguchi, Y., Imagawa, M., Inada, M., Imura, H., Nakazawa, N. and Ogawa, H. (1980). An improved preparation of antibody-coated polystyrene beads for sandwich enzyme immunoassay. J. Immunoassay *1*, 385–398.

Ishikawa, E., Yamada, Y., Yoshitake, S. and Kawaguchi, H. (1981). A more stable maleimide, for enzyme labeling. In: Enzyme Immunoassay (Ishikawa, E., Kawai, T. and Miyai, K., eds.). Igaku-shoin, Tokyo and New York, pp. 90–105.

Ishikawa, E., Imagawa, M., Yoshitake, S., Niitsu, Y., Urushizaki, I., Inada, M., Imura, H., Kanazawa, R., Tachibana, S., Nakazawa, N. and Ogawa, H. (1982). Major factors limiting sensitivity of sandwich enzyme immunoassay for ferritin, immunoglobulin E, and thyroid-stimulating hormone. Ann. Clin. Biochem. *19*, 379–384.

Ishikawa, E., Imagawa, M. and Hashida, S. (1983a). Ultrasensitive enzyme immunoassay using fluorogenic, luminogenic, radioactive and related substrates and factors to limit the sensitivity. Dev. Immunol. *18*, 219–232.

Ishikawa, E., Imagawa, M., Hashida, S., Yoshitake, S., Hamaguchi, Y. and Ueno, T. (1983b). Enzyme-labeling of antibodies and their fragments for enzyme immunoassay and immunohistochemical staining. J. Immunoassay *4*, 209–327.

Ishikawa, E., Yoshitake, S., Imagawa, M. and Sumiyoshi, A. (1983c). Preparation of monomeric Fab′-horseradish peroxidase conjugate using thiol groups in the hinge and its evaluation in enzyme immunoassay and immunohistochemical staining. Ann. N.Y. Acad. Sci. *420*, 74–89.

Ishikawa, E., Hashida, S., Nakagawa, K. and Ohtaki, S. (1986). Human growth hormone, hGH. In: Methods of Enzymatic Analysis (Bergmeyer, H.U.,

Bergmeyer, J. and Graßl, M., eds.), Vol. IX, VCH Verlagsgesellschaft mbH, Weinheim, pp. 362–373.

Ishikawa, E., Hashida, S., Kato, Y. and Imura, H. (1987). Sensitive enzyme immunoassay of human growth hormone for clinical application: a review. J. Clin. Lab. Anal. *1*, 238–242.

Ishikawa, E., Hashida, S., Kohno, T. and Tanaka, K. (1988). Methods for enzyme-labeling of antigens, antibodies and their fragments. In: Nonisotopic Immunoassay (Ngo, T.T., ed.). Plenum, New York, pp. 27–55.

Ishikawa, E., Hashida, S., Tanaka, K. and Kohno, T. (1989a). Ultrasensitive enzyme immunoassay for antigens: technology and applications—a review. Clin. Chem. Enzym. Comms. *1*, 199–215.

Ishikawa, E., Hashida, S., Tanaka, K. and Kohno, T. (1989b). Development and applications of ultrasensitive enzyme immunoassay for antigens and antibodies. Clin. Chim. Acta *185*, 223–230.

Ishikawa, E., Hashida, S., Kohno, T. and Hirota, K. (1990a). Ultrasensitive enzyme immunoassay. Clin. Chim. Acta *194*, 51–72.

Ishikawa, E., Tanaka, K. and Hashida, S. (1990b). Novel and sensitive noncompetitive (two-site) immunoassay for haptens with emphasis on peptides. Clin. Biochem. *23*, 445–453.

Ishikawa, E., Hashida, S. and Kohno, T. (1991). Development of ultrasensitive enzyme immunoassay reviewed with emphasis on factors which limit the sensitivity. Mol. Cell. Prob. *5*, 81–95.

Ishikawa, E., Hashida, S., Kohno, T., Hirota, K., Hashinaka, K. and Ishikawa, S. (1993). Principle and applications of ultrasensitive enzyme immunoassay (immune complex transfer enzyme immunoassay) for antibodies in body fluids. J. Clin. Lab. Anal. *7*, 376–393.

Ishikawa, E., Ishikawa, S., Hashida, S. and Hashinaka, K. (1998). Potential of the immune complex transfer enzyme immunoassay for antigens and antibodies to improve the sensitivity and its limitations. J. Clin. Lab. Anal. *12*, 154–161.

Ishikawa, S. and Ishikawa, E. (1994). Novel and sensitive enzyme immunoassay for urinary antibody IgG to β-D-galactosidase from *Escherichia coli*. Anal. Lett. *27*, 337–350.

Ishikawa, S., Kohno, T., Hashida, S. and Ishikawa, E. (1992). Use of non-specific $F(ab')_2$ and inactive β-D-galactosidase to reduce the nonspecific binding of anti-ferritin Fab'-β-D-galactosidase conjugate in two-site enzyme immunoassay for ferritin. Anal. Lett. *25*, 695–706.

Ishikawa, S., Hashida, S., Hashinaka, K., Hirota, K., Saitoh, A., Takamizawa, A., Shinagawa, H., Oka, S., Shimada, K. and Ishikawa, E. (1995a). Diagnosis of HIV-1 infection with whole saliva by detection of antibody IgG to HIV-1 with ultrasensitive enzyme immunoassay using recombinant reverse transcriptase as antigen. J. Acquir. Immune Defic. Syndr. Human Retrovirol. *10*, 41–47.

Ishikawa, S., Hashida, S., Nakamoto, H., Tanaka, S., Kojima, M. and Ishikawa, E. (1995b). Further simplification of ultrasensitive enzyme immunoassay (immune complex transfer enzyme immunoassay) for anti-HTLV-I IgG using microplates and fluororeader. J. Clin. Lab. Anal. *9*, 204–211.

Ishikawa, S., Hashida, S., Nakamoto, H., Tanaka, S., Kojima, M. and Ishikawa, E. (1995c). Simpler and more sensitive immune complex transfer enzyme immunoassay for anti-HTLV-I IgG using modified polystyrene beads, microplates and fluororeader. Anal. Lett. *28*, 1611–1618.

Ishikawa, S., Hashida, S., Hashinaka, K., Hirota, K., Kojima, M., Saito, A., Takamizawa, A., Shinagawa, H., Oka, S., Shimada, K. and Ishikawa, E. (1996). Whole saliva dried on filter paper for diagnosis of HIV-1 infection by detection of antibody IgG to HIV-1 with ultrasensitive enzyme immunoassay using recombinant reverse transcriptase as antigen. J. Clin. Lab. Anal. *10*, 35–41.

Ishikawa, S., Hashida, S., Hashinaka, K., Kojima, M., Saito, A., Takamizawa, A., Shinagawa, H., Oka, S., Shimada, K. and Ishikawa, E. (1997). More sensitive immune complex transfer enzyme immunoassay for antibody IgG to p17 of HIV-1 with shorter incubation time for immunoreactions and larger volumes of serum samples. J. Clin. Lab. Anal. *11*, 244–250.

Ishikawa, S., Hashida, S., Hashinaka, K., Adachi, A., Oka, S. and Ishikawa, E. (1998a). Ultrasensitive and rapid enzyme immunoassay (thin aqueous layer immune complex transfer enzyme immunoassay) for antibody IgG to HIV-1 p17 antigen. J. Clin. Lab. Anal. *12*, 179–189.

Ishikawa, S., Hashida, S., Hashinaka, K., Adachi, A., Oka, S. and Ishikawa, E. (1998b). Rapid formation of the immune complexes on solid phase in the immune complex transfer enzyme immunoassays for HIV-1 p24 antigen and antibody IgGs to HIV-1. J. Clin. Lab. Anal. *12*, 227–237.

Ishikawa, S., Hashida, S., Hashinaka, K. and Ishikawa, E. (1998c). Rapid and ultrasensitive enzyme immunoassay (thin aqueous layer immune complex transfer enzyme immunoassay) for HIV-1 p24 antigen. J. Clin. Lab. Anal. *12*, 205–212.

Ishikawa, S., Hashinaka, K., Hashida, S., Oka, S. and Ishikawa, E. (1998d). Sensitive enzyme immunoassay of antibodies to HIV-1 p17 antigen using indirectly immobilized recombinant p17 for diagnosis of HIV-1 infection. J. Clin. Lab. Anal. *12*, 343–350.

Ishikawa, S., Hashinaka, K., Hashida, S., Oka, S. and Ishikawa, E. (1999). Use of indirectly immobilized recombinant p17 antigen for detection of antibodies to HIV-1 by enzyme immunoassay. J. Clin. Lab. Anal. *13*, 9–18.

Jaquet, H. and Cebra, J.J. (1965). Comparison of two precipitaing derivatives of rabbit antibody: fragment I dimer and the product of pepsin digestion. Biochemistry *4*, 954–963.

Johannsson, A., Stanley, C.J. and Self, C.H. (1985). A fast highly sensitive colorimetric enzyme immunoassay system demonstrating benefits of enzyme amplification in clinical chemistry. Clin. Chim. Acta *148*, 119–124.

Kasai, Y., Hashida, S., Tanaka, K., Chichibu, K., Usuki, H. and Ishikawa, E. (1990). Sensitive sandwich enzyme immunoassay for human erythropoietin. Clin. Chem. Enzym. Comms. *2*, 137–143.

Kato, K., Hamaguchi, Y., Fukui, H. and Ishikawa, E. (1975a). Enzyme-linked immunoassay II. A simple method for synthesis of the rabbit antibody-β-D-galactosidase complex and its general applicability. J. Biochem. *78*, 423–425.

Kato, K., Hamaguchi, Y., Fukui, H. and Ishikawa, E. (1975b). Coupling Fab' fragment of rabbit anti-human IgG antibody to β-D-galactosidase and a highly sensitive immunoassay of human IgG. FEBS Lett. *56*, 370–372.

Kato, K., Fukui, H., Hamaguchi, Y. and Ishikawa, E. (1976). Enzyme-linked immunoassay: conjugation of the Fab' fragment of rabbit IgG with β-D-galactosidase from *E. coli* and its use for immunoassay. J. Immunol. *116*, 1554–1560.

Kato, K., Hamaguchi, Y., Okawa, S., Ishikawa, E., Kobayashi, K. and Katunuma, N. (1977). Enzyme immunoassay in rapid progress. Lancet *i*, 40.

Kato, K., Haruyama, Y., Hamaguchi, Y. and Ishikawa, E. (1978). Comparison of three enzyme-linked procedures for the quantitative determination of guinea pig anti-porcine insulin antibody. J. Biochem. *84*, 93–102.

Keilin, D. and Hartree, E.F. (1951). Purification of horse-radish peroxidase and comparison of its properties with those of catalase and methaemoglobin. Biochem. J. *49*, 88–104.

King, T.P., Li, Y. and Kochoumian, L. (1978). Preparation of protein conjugates *via* intermolecular disulfide bond. Biochemistry *17*, 1499–1506.

Kohno, T. and Ishikawa, E. (1987). A novel enzyme immunoassay of anti-insulin IgG in guinea pig serum. Biochem. Biophys. Res. Commun. *147*, 644–649.

Kohno, T. and Ishikawa, E. (1988a). Novel and sensitive enzyme immunoassays for antibodies and their application. J. Miyazaki Med. Assoc. *12*, 177–182.

Kohno, T. and Ishikawa, E. (1988b). Novel enzyme immunoassay (immune complex transfer enzyme immunoassay) for anti-insulin IgG in guinea pig serum. Anal. Lett. *21*, 1019–1031.

Kohno, T., Ishikawa, E., Sugiyama, S. and Nakamura, S. (1988a). Novel enzyme immunoassay of anti-insulin IgG in human serum. J. Clin. Lab. Anal. *2*, 19–24.

Kohno, T., Mitsukawa, T., Matsukura, S. and Ishikawa, E. (1988b). Novel and sensitive enzyme immunoassay for anti-thyroglobulin antibodies in serum using dinitrophenyl thyroglobulin and thyroglobulin-peroxidase conjugate. Anal. Lett. *21*, 2033–2048.

Kohno, T., Mitsukawa, T., Matsukura, S. and Ishikawa, E. (1988c). Novel enzyme immunoassay (immune complex transfer enzyme immunoassay) for anti-thyroglobulin IgG in human serum. J. Clin. Lab. Anal. 2, 209–214.

Kohno, T., Mitsukawa, T., Matsukura, S. and Ishikawa, E. (1988d). Novel and sensitive enzyme immunoassay (immune complex transfer enzyme immunoassay) for anti-thyroglobulin IgG in human serum. Clin. Chem. Enzym. Comms. 1, 89–96.

Kohno, T., Tsunetoshi, Y. and Ishikawa, E. (1988e). Existence of anti-thyroglobulin IgG in healthy subjects. Biochem. Biophys. Res. Commun. 155, 224–229.

Kohno, T., Mitsukawa, T., Matsukura, S., Tsunetoshi, Y. and Ishikawa, E. (1989a). Measurement of anti-thyroglobulin IgG in serum by novel and sensitive immune complex transfer enzyme immunoassay. Clin. Biochem. 22, 277–284.

Kohno, T., Mitsukawa, T., Matsukura, S., Tsunetoshi, Y. and Ishikawa, E. (1989b). More sensitive and simpler immune complex transfer enzyme immunoassay for antithyroglobulin IgG in serum. J. Clin. Lab. Anal. 3, 163–168.

Kohno, T., Mitsukawa, T., Matsukura, S., Tsunetoshi, Y. and Ishikawa, E. (1989c). Anti-thyroglobulin IgG in healthy subjects and patients with thyroid diseases measured by improved immune complex transfer enzyme immunoassay. Clin. Chem. Enzym. Comms. 1, 283–291.

Kohno, H., Kohno, T., Sakoda I. and Ishikawa, E. (1990a). Novel and sensitive enzyme immunoassay (immune complex transfer enzyme immunoassay) for (anti-human T-cell leukemia virus type I) IgG in human serum using recombinant gag-env hybrid protein as antigen. J. Clin. Lab. Anal. 4, 355–362.

Kohno, T., Yamaguchi, K. and Ishikawa, E. (1990b). Immune complex transfer enzyme immunoassays for anti-angiotensin I IgG in serum using angiotensin I conjugates prepared by two different methods. J. Biochem. 108, 741–747.

Kohno, H., Kohno, T., Sakoda, I. and Ishikawa, E. (1991a). Sensitive detection of anti-human T-cell leukemia virus type I IgG in human serum by a novel enzyme immunoassay (immune complex transfer enzyme immunoassay) using recombinant gag-env hybrid protein as antigen. J. Virol. Methods 31, 77–92.

Kohno, T., Hirota, K. and Ishikawa, E. (1991b). Presence of antibodies against β-D-galactosidase from Escherichia coli in serum of healthy subjects examined by immune complex transfer enzyme immunoassay. Clin. Chem. Enzym. Comms. 4, 39–49.

Kohno, T., Katsumaru, H., Nakamoto, H., Yasuda, T., Mitsukawa, T., Matsukura, S., Tsunetoshi, Y. and Ishikawa, E. (1991c). Use of inactive β-D-galactosidase for elimination of interference by anti-β-D-galactosidase antibodies in immune complex transfer enzyme immunoassay for anti-thyroglobulin IgG in serum using β-D-galactosidase from Escherichia coli as label. J. Clin. Lab. Anal. 5, 197–205.

Kohno, T., Sakoda, I. and Ishikawa, E. (1991d). Immune complex transfer enzyme immunoassay for (anti-human T-cell leukemia virus type I) IgG in serum using a synthetic peptide, *env* gp46(188–209), as antigen. J. Clin. Lab. Anal. *5*, 25–37.

Kohno, T., Sakoda, I., Suzuki, M., Izumi, A. and Ishikawa, E. (1991e). Immune complex transfer enzyme immunoassay for (anti-human T-cell leukemia virus type I) IgG in serum using a synthetic peptide, cys-*gag* p19(100–130), as antigen. J. Clin. Lab. Anal. *5*, 307–316.

Kohno, T., Hirota, K., Sakoda, I., Yamasaki, M., Yokoo, Y. and Ishikawa, E. (1992a). Sensitive enzyme immunoassay (immune complex transfer enzyme immunoassay) for (anti-human T-cell leukemia virus type I) IgG in serum using recombinant *gag* p24(14–214) as antigen. J. Clin. Lab. Anal. *6*, 302–310.

Kohno, T., Sakoda, I. and Ishikawa, E. (1992b). Sensitive enzyme immunoassay (immune complex transfer enzyme immunoassay) for (anti-human T-cell leukemia virus type I) IgG in serum using a synthetic peptide, cys-*env* gp46 (188–224), as antigen. J. Clin. Lab. Anal. *6*, 105–112.

Kohno, T., Sakoda, I. and Ishikawa, E. (1992c). Sensitive enzyme immunoassay (immune complex transfer enzyme immunoassay) for (antihuman T-cell leukemia virus type I) immunoglobulin G in serum using a synthetic peptide, ala-cys-*env* gp46(237–262), as antigen. J. Clin. Lab. Anal. *6*, 162–169.

Korn, A.H., Feairheller, S.H. and Filachione, E.M. (1972). Glutaraldehyde: nature of the reagent. J. Mol. Biol. *65*, 525–529.

Lamoyi, E. and Nisonoff, A. (1983). Preparation of $F(ab')_2$ fragments from mouse IgG of various subclasses. J. Iumunol. Methods *56*, 235–243.

LaRochelle, F.T., Jr., North, W.G. and Stern, P. (1980). A new extraction of arginine vasopressin from blood: the use of octadecasilyl-silica. Pflügers Arch. *387*, 79–81.

Mandy, W.J. and Nisonoff, A. (1963). Effect of reduction of several disulfide bonds on the properties and recombination of univalent fragments of rabbit antibody. J. Biol. Chem. *238*, 206–213.

Miles, L.E.M. and Hales, C.N. (1968). Labelled antibodies and immunological assay systems. Nature *219*, 186–189.

Morton, R.K. (1955). Some properties of alkaline phosphatase of cow's milk and calf intestinal mucosa. Biochem. J. *60*, 573–582.

Morton, J.J., Padfield, P.L. and Forsling, M.L. (1975). A radioimmunoassay for plasma arginine-vasopressin in man and dog: application to physiological and pathological states. J. Endocr. *65*, 411–424.

Mukoyama, M., Nakao, K., Yamada, T., Itoh, H., Sugawara, A., Saito, Y., Arai, H., Hosoda, K., Shirakami, G., Morii, N., Shiono, S. and Imura, H. (1988). A monoclonal antibody against N-terminus of α-atrial natriuretic polypeptide

(α-ANP): a useful tool for preferential detection of naturally circulating ANP. Biochem. Biophys. Res. Commun. *151*, 1277–1284.

Nakane, P.K. and Kawaoi, A. (1974). Peroxidase labeled antibody. A new method of conjugation. J. Histochem. Cytochem. *22*, 1084–1091.

Olive, C. and Levy, H.R. (1971). Glucose 6-phosphate dehydrogenase from *Leuconostoc mesenteroides*. J. Biol. Chem. *246*, 2043–2046.

Palmer, J.L. and Nisonoff, A. (1964). Dissociation of rabbit γ-globulin into half molecules after reduction of one labile disulfide bond. Biochemistry *3*, 863–869.

Penefsky, H.S. (1979). A centrifuged-column procedure for the measurement of ligand binding by beef heart F_1. In: Methods in Enzymology (Colowick, S.P. and Kaplan, N.O., eds.), Vol. LVI. Academic Press, New York, pp. 527–530.

Peters, T., Jr. (1975). Serum albumin. In: The Plasma Proteins, Structure, Function and Genetic Control (Putnam, F.W., ed.). Academic Press, New York, pp. 133–181.

Raine, A.E.G., Erne, P., Bürgisser, E., Müller, F.B., Bolli, P., Burkart, F. and Bühler, F.R. (1986). Atrial natriuretic peptide and atrial pressure in patients with congestive heart failure. N. Engl. J. Med. *315*, 533–537.

Robertson, G.L., Klein, L.A., Roth, J. and Gorden, P. (1970). Immunoassay of plasma vasopressin in man. Proc. Natl. Acad. Sci. USA *66*, 1298–1305.

Robertson, G.L., Mahr, E.A., Athar, S. and Sinha, T. (1973). Development and clinical application of a new method for the radioimmunoassay of arginine vasopressin in human plasma. J. Clin. Invest. *52*, 2340–2352.

Ruan, K-h., Hashida, S. and Ishikawa, E. (1984a). A micro-scale preparation of affinity-purified Fab'-enzyme conjugates with high purity for enzyme immunoassay. Anal. Lett. *17*, 2075–2090.

Ruan, K-h., Imagawa, M., Hashida, S. and Ishikawa, E. (1984b). An improved method for the conjugation of Fab' to β-D-galactosidase from *Escherichia coli*. Anal. Lett. *17*, 539–554.

Ruan, K-h., Hashida, S., Yoshitake, S., Ishikawa, E., Wakisaka, O., Yamamoto, Y., Ichioka, T. and Nakajima, K. (1985). A micro-scale affinity-purification of Fab'-horseradish peroxidase conjugates and its use for sandwich enzyme immunoassay of insulin in human serum. Clin. Chim. Acta *147*, 167–172.

Ruan, K-h., Hashida, S., Yoshitake, S., Ishikawa, E., Wakisaka, O., Yamamoto, Y., Ichioka, T. and Nakajima, K. (1986). A more sensitive and less time-consuming sandwich enzyme immunoassay for insulin in human serum with less serum interference. Ann. Clin. Biochem. *23*, 54–58.

Ruan, K.-h., Hashida, S., Tanaka, K., Ishikawa, E., Niitsu, Y., Urushizaki, I. and Ogawa, H. (1987). A small scale sandwich enzyme immunoassay for macromolecular antigens using β-D-galactosidase from *Escherichia coli* and horseradish peroxidase as labels. Anal. Lett. *20*, 587–601.

Scharpé, S., Verkerk, R., Sasmito, E. and Theeuws, M. (1987). Enzyme immunoassay of angiotensin I and renin. Clin. Chem. *33*, 1774–1777.

Stuchbury, T., Shipton, M., Norris, R., Malthouse, J.P.G. and Brocklehurst. K. (1975). A reporter group delivery system with both absolute and selective specificity for thiol groups and an improved fluorescent probe containing the 7-nitrobenzo-2-oxa-1,3-diazole moiety. Biochem. J. *151*, 417–432.

Svasti, J. and Milstein, C. (1972). The disulphide bridges of a mouse immunoglobulin G1 protein. Biochem. J. *126*, 837–850.

Tanaka, K. and Ishikawa, E. (1984). Highly sensitive bioluminescent assay of dehydrogenases using NAD(P)H:FMN oxidoreductase and luciferase from *Photobacterium fischeri*. Anal. Lett. *17*, 2025–2034.

Tanaka, K. and Ishikawa, E. (1986). A highly sensitive bioluminescent assay of β-D-galactosidase from *Escherichia coli* using 2-nitrophenyl-β-D-galactopyranoside as a substrate. Anal. Lett. *19*, 433–444.

Tanaka, K. and Ishikawa, E. (1990). Factors to hamper the detection of one molecule of β-D-galactosidase from *Escherichia coli* by bioluminescent assay coupled with enzymatic cycling. Anal. Lett. *23*, 241–253.

Tanaka, K., Hashida, S., Kohno, T., Yamaguchi, K. and Ishikawa, E. (1989). Novel and sensitive noncompetitive enzyme immunoassay for peptides. Biochem. Biophys. Res. Commun. *160*, 40–45.

Tanaka, K., Hashida, S., Uno, T., Yamaguchi, K. and Ishikawa, E. (1990a). Novel and sensitive noncompetitive enzyme immunoassay for arginine vasopressin. Clin. Chem. Enzym. Comms. *3*, 201–208.

Tanaka, K., Kohno, T., Hashida, S. and Ishikawa, E. (1990b). Novel and sensitive noncompetitive (two-site) enzyme immunoassay for haptens with amino groups. J. Clin. Lab. Anal. *4*, 208–212.

Tijssen, P. (1985). Preparation of enzyme-antibody or other enzyme-maclomolecule conjugates. In: Laboratory Techniques in Biochemistry and Macromolecular Biology. Practice and Theory of Enzyme Immunoassays (Burdon, R.H. and van Knippenberg, P.H., eds.). Elsevier, Amsterdam, New York, Oxford, pp. 221–278.

Udenfriend, S., Stein, S., Böhlen, P. and Dairman, W. (1972). Fluorescamine: a reagent for assay of amino acids, peptides, proteins, and primary amines in the picomole range. Science *178*, 871–872.

Uno, T., Uehara, K., Motomatsu, K., Ishikawa, E. and Kato, K. (1982). Enzyme immunoassay for arginine vasopressin. Experientia *38*, 786–787.

Utsumi, S. and Karush, F. (1965). Peptic fragmentation rabbit γG-immunoglobulin. Biochemistry *4*, 1766–1779.

van Weemen, B.K. and Schuurs, A.H.W.M. (1971). Immunoassay using antigen-enzyme conjugates. FEBS Lett. *15*, 232–236.

Watabe, T., Tanaka, K., Kumagae, M., Itoh, S., Takeda, F., Morio, K., Hasegawa, M., Horiuchi, T., Miyabe, S. and Shimizu, N. (1987). Hormonal responses to insulin-induced hypoglycemia in man. J. Clin. Endocrinol. Metab. *65*, 1187–1191.

Watanabe, H., Wakimasu, M. and Kondo, K. (1989). A sensitive enzyme immunoassay for atrial natriuretic polypeptide. J. Immunol. Methods *124*, 25–28.

Watson, D. (1976). ELISA: a replacement for radioimmunoassays? Lancet *ii*, 570.

Webster, G.C. (1970). Comparison of direct spectrophotometric methods for the measurement of protein concentration. Biochim. Biophys. Acta *207*, 371–373.

Whipple E.B. and Ruta, M. (1974). Structure of aqueous glutaraldehyde. J. Org. Chem. *39*, 1666–1668.

Wilson, M.B. and Nakane, P.K. (1978). Recent developments in the periodate method of conjugating horseradish peroxidase (HRPO) to antibodies. In: Immunofluorescence and Related Staining Techniques (Knapp, W., Holubar, K. and Wick, G. eds.). Elsevier/North-Holland Biomedical Press, Amsterdam, pp. 215–224.

Yamazaki, M., Matsunaga, K., Murayama, S. and Kamoi, K. (1988). Effect of plasma platelet on plasma vasopressin concentration. Med. J. Nagaoka Red Cross Hosp. *1*, 39–44.

Yogi, Y., Hirota, K., Hashida, S., Toshimori, H., Matsukura, S., Setoguchi, T. and Ishikawa, E. (1993a). Improved measurement of anti-thyroglobulin IgG in urine of patients with autoimmune thyroid diseases by sensitive enzyme immunoassay (immune complex transfer enzyme immunoassay). J. Clin. Lab. Anal. *7*, 225–229.

Yogi, Y., Hirota, K., Kohno, T., Toshimori, H., Matsukura, S., Setoguchi, T. and Ishikawa, E. (1993b). Measurement of anti-thyroglobulin IgG in urine of patients with autoimmune thyroid diseases by sensitive enzyme immunoassay (immune complex transfer enzyme immunoassay). J. Clin. Lab. Anal. *7*, 70–79.

Yogi, Y., Kohno, T., Hirota, K., Toshimori, H., Matsukura, S., Setoguchi, T. and Ishikawa, E. (1993c). Immune complex transfer enzyme immunoassay for anti-thyroglobulin IgG using 2,4-dinitrophenyl-thyroglobulin, biotinyl-thyroglobulin and streptavidin-β-D-galactosidase conjugate. Anal. Lett. *26*, 2143–2159.

Yone, K., Hashida, S., Tanaka, K., Ichikawa, Y. and Ishikawa, E. (1990). Specific and sensitive sandwich enzyme immunoassay for human tumor necrosis factor-α. Clin. Chem. Enzym. Comms. *3*, 1–8.

Yoshitake, S., Imagawa, M., Ishikawa, E., Niitsu, Y., Urushizaki, I., Nishiura, M., Kanazawa, R., Kurosaki, H., Tachibana, S., Nakazawa, N. and Ogawa, H. (1982). Mild and efficient conjugation of rabbit Fab′ and horseradish peroxidase using a maleimide compound and its use for enzyme immunoassay. J. Biochem. *92*, 1413–1424.

Subject Index

Printed and bound by CPI Group (UK) Ltd, Croydon, CR0 4YY

08/05/2025

01865005-0001